THE COMMONWEALTH AND INTERNATIONAL LIBRARY

Joint Chairmen of the
Honorary Editorial Advisory Board
SIR ROBERT ROBINSON, O.M., F.R.S., London
and DEAN ATHELSTAN SPILHAUS, Minnesota

Publisher
ROBERT MAXWELL, M.C., M.P.

NAVIGATION AND NAUTICAL COURSES DIVISION

General Editors
CAPT. J. H. CLOUGH SMITH
CAPT. G. E. EARL

Navigation

Navigation

A. C. Gardner and W. G. Creelman

PERGAMON PRESS

OXFORD·LONDON·EDINBURGH·NEW YORK

PARIS·FRANKFURT

PERGAMON PRESS LTD.	Headington Hill Hall, Oxford 4 & 5 Fitzroy Square, London W.1
PERGAMON PRESS (SCOTLAND) LTD.	2 & 3 Teviot Place, Edinburgh 1
PERGAMON PRESS INC.	122 East 55th Street New York 22, N.Y.
PERGAMON PRESS G.m.b.H.	Kaiserstrasse 75, Frankfurt am Main
FEDERAL PUBLICATIONS LTD.	Times House River Valley Road, Singapore
SAMCAX BOOK SERVICES LTD.	Queensway, P.O. Box 2720 Nairobi, Kenya

Set in 11 on 12 pt Bembo
by Santype Ltd. of
Salisbury, Wilts.

Printed in Great Britain by
A. Wheaton & Co. Ltd.
of Exeter, Devon.

Contents

CONTENTS

CONTENTS

and Amplitude of Sun and Star to find the Error and Deviation of the compass—Solution by Spherical Haversine formula and by tables. Verification by scale diagram. The Marc St. Hilaire method of determining a position line.

Introduction

NAVIGATION is a subject that is being increasingly studied by many people who do not intend to become professional navigators. These include yachtsmen and yachtswomen, and boys and girls at school, to whom the subject appeals because of its inherent interest. Moreover, many education authorities have recently introduced navigation into their schools' curricula, because of the subject's broad educational value.

This book, therefore, is intended to cover the basic principles and methods of practical navigation, so that it will be of interest and value to the general reader. It is also designed to cover the syllabuses of the various examining bodies who set General Certificate of Education papers, and Scottish Certificate of Education papers, in Navigation at O-level. It also covers the greater part of the syllabus in Navigation and Knowledge of Principles for the Ministry of Transport's examination for Second Mate.

Chartwork is not included in the book, as this subject is covered by the companion volume *A Course on the Chart* by B. W. Lucke.

A set of ordinary four-figure mathematical tables will

INTRODUCTION

be required to work the examples for exercises that are given in the book. All other tables that are used are contained in the Appendices. For those readers who possess volumes of Nautical Tables, such as those published by Norie, Burton or Inman, answers are also given to five-figure accuracy where required. For the purpose of learning the basic principles and methods of practical navigation, however, the four-figure accuracy of ordinary mathematical tables is considered to be perfectly adequate.

The authors wish to acknowledge their indebtedness to the publishers of Norie's Nautical Tables, Messrs. Imray, Laurie, Norie and Wilson Ltd., for permission to reproduce certain items contained in these publications: namely part of the table of Meridional Parts, the Middle Latitude to Mean Latitude conversion table and some of the Altitude Corrections.

Acknowledgements are also due to the Controller of Her Majesty's Stationery Office for permission to reproduce certain extracts from the 1958 Nautical Almanac and to Her Majesty's Hydrographic Department for permission to reproduce one page from the 1964 European Tide Tables.

Dundee, 1963

A.C.G.
W.G.C.

CHAPTER 1

The terrestrial sphere and its properties

THE earth, or the terrestrial sphere, as it is sometimes called, is not quite a true sphere. The scientists whose work it is to study the exact shape of the earth and whose branch of science is known as geophysics, continue to make fresh discoveries from time to time, but their general conclusions appear to be that the earth is an "oblate spheroid". This means that it is a sphere-shaped body, slightly flattened at the poles, its polar diameter being about 23 miles less than its equatorial diameter.

It will be seen later how this slight irregularity in the shape of the earth affects navigation, with particular reference to the definition of the nautical mile as a unit of distance. But in most problems of navigation the earth is treated as if it were, in fact, a true sphere; and for this reason it is essential that certain basic properties of the sphere should be clearly understood at the outset.

The shape of a true sphere may be defined as that shape which is created by the rotation of a semi-circle about its diameter; or alternatively, a sphere may be defined as a body, every point on the surface of which is equidistant from its centre.

GREAT AND SMALL CIRCLES

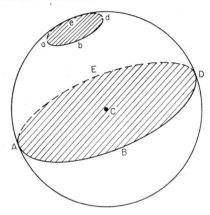

Fig. 1

Circles may be described on the curved surface of a sphere that are similar in appearance to those described on any flat or plane surface. But whereas, on a plane surface, only one kind of circle can be drawn, those drawn on the surface of a sphere can be of two quite different types. These are known as Great Circles and Small Circles respectively.

In Fig. 1, *ABDE* is a great circle and *abde* is a small circle, each drawn on the surface of a sphere of centre *C*. The important point to observe is that, if a knife is used to cut through the sphere along the circumference of the circle *ABDE*, the knife blade will pass through the centre *C* and the sphere will be cut in half. Whereas, if a knife is used to cut through the sphere along the circumference of the circle *abde*, the knife blade will *not* pass through *C*, and the sphere will *not* be cut in half.

A great circle, therefore, is defined as any circle on the surface of a sphere, the plane of which passes through the sphere's centre. And a small circle is any circle on the surface of a sphere the plane of which does not pass through the sphere's centre.

SPHERICAL ANGLES

On a plane or flat surface, an angle is formed by the intersection of two straight lines. On the surface of a sphere, a spherical angle is formed by the intersection of the arcs of two great circles.

SPHERICAL TRIANGLES

On a plane or flat surface, a plane triangle is formed when an area is bounded by three straight lines. On the surface of a sphere a spherical triangle is formed when an area is bounded by the arcs of three great circles.

In Fig. 2, angle A, angle B and angle D are spherical angles because each angle is formed by the intersection of the arcs of two great circles on the surface of the sphere with centre C. Similarly the triangle ABD is a spherical triangle because it is an area on the surface of a sphere bounded by the arcs of three great circles.

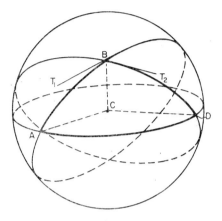

Fig. 2

The dimensions of a spherical angle, i.e. the number of degrees and minutes that it contains, is determined by the tangents to the great circles at their point of intersection. For example, the value of the spherical angle B is determined by the number of degrees and minutes contained between the tangents BT_1 and BT_2 at the point B.

In spherical triangles, the sides, as well as the angles are measured in degrees and minutes. The reason for this is that each side is the arc of a great circle which subtends a certain angle at the centre of the sphere. For example, the side BD is an arc of a great circle that subtends the angle BCD at the centre of the sphere. Similarly AD subtends the angle ACD and AB subtends the angle ACB. So if, in Fig. 2, angle $BCD = 90°$, then side $BD = 90°$. Similarly, if angle $ACB = 90°$, then side $AB = 90°$ and if angle $ACD = 150°$, then side $AD = 150°$.

From this it will be seen, incidentally, that the sum of the three sides of the spherical triangle ABD amounts to $330°$.

Sum of the Sides of a Spherical Triangle

If the size of the spherical triangle ABD is contracted by bringing its sides closer and closer together, the triangle will eventually become so small that it will be a mere dot. The sum of the three sides will then be zero.

If, on the other hand, the size of the triangle *ABD* is expanded, by pushing its sides further and further apart until the area bounded by the arcs of the three great circles is as large as possible, then the enclosed area will become a hemisphere, and the sum of its three sides will be the circumference of the sphere, i.e. 360°.

Therefore, the sum of the sides of a spherical triangle can vary from 0° to 360°, and in calculations, each side must be calculated separately.

Sum of the Angles of a Spherical Triangle

In a plane triangle, the fact that the sum of the three angles amounts to 180° can often be used to assist in calculations; but this is not so in a spherical triangle. If the spherical triangle *ABD* is contracted in size by bringing its sides closer and closer together, a time will come when the triangle occupies a very small area on the surface of the sphere. When this point is reached, the triangle may be considered to be flat or plane, because a small area on a sphere is flat or plane. In other words, the triangle has become a plane triangle, and the sum of its angles is 180°, as in any other plane triangle.

If, on the other hand, the size of the triangle *ABD* is expanded as before, each of the angles *A*, *B* and *D* will eventually become 180°, and the sum of the three angles will amount to 540°.

Therefore, the sum of the angles of a spherical triangle can vary from 180° to 540°, and in calculations, each angle must be calculated separately.

SOME TERRESTRIAL DEFINITIONS

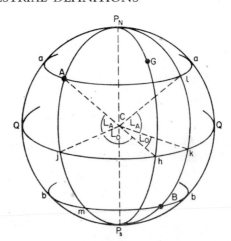

Fig. 3

The Geographical Poles

On the surface of the earth there are two points known as the geographical poles. These are defined as the two points where the axis of rotation of the earth passes through the earth's surface. In Fig. 3, P_N and P_S are the geographical poles.

Meridians

A meridian, or meridian of longitude, is a semi-great circle on the surface of the earth extending from pole to pole. All meridians meet at the North and South Poles. In Fig. 3, $P_N AjmP_S$ and $P_N lkBP_S$ are meridians of longitude passing through the positions A and B respectively.

The Prime Meridian

This is the meridian which passes through Greenwich and all other meridians are numbered with relation to it. It is the meridian of longitude $0°$. In Fig. 3 the point G indicates the position of Greenwich, and $P_N GhP_S$ is therefore the prime meridian, because it passes through Greenwich.

The Equator

The equator is a great circle on the surface of the earth midway between the two poles. Every point on the equator is $90°$ of arc removed from each pole, this measurement being made along the arc of any meridian from equator to pole. In Fig. 3, $QjhkQ$ is the equator and $P_N Aj$, $P_S mj$, $P_N lk$, $P_S Bk$ are all arcs of $90°$.

Parallels of Latitude

A parallel of latitude is a small circle on the surface of the earth parallel to the equator. Parallels of latitude are numbered with relation to the equator, which is in latitude $0°$. In Fig. 3, $aAla$ is the parallel of latitude on which A is situated and $bmBb$ is the parallel of latitude on which B is situated.

Note: At this stage, it should be noted that the area bounded by the arcs $P_N A$, $P_N l$ and Al is not a spherical triangle. $P_N A$ and $P_N l$ are arcs of great circles, but Al is an arc of a small circle. Therefore, by the definition of a spherical triangle, the area bounded by these three arcs, although triangular in appearance, is *not* a spherical triangle. The significance of this point will be appreciated later.

The Latitude of a Place

The latitude of any given place (such as A in Fig. 3) is the arc of any meridian contained between the equator and the given place. It is also the corresponding angle at the centre of the earth. In Fig. 3, the latitude of A is the arc jA or the arc kl. It is also the angle ACj or the angle lCk. Latitudes are measured in degrees and minutes, North or South of the equator. B is in South latitude, and its numerical value is given by the dimensions of the arc jm or the arc kB. The North Pole is in latitude 90° North and the South Pole in latitude 90° South.

The Longitude of a Place

The longitude of any given place (such as A in Fig. 3) is the arc of the equator contained between the prime meridian and the meridian passing through the place. It is also the corresponding angle at the centre of the earth. In Fig. 3 the longitude of A is the arc hj or the angle hCj. Since A lies to the westward of Greenwich, its longitude is expressed as so many degrees and minutes West. The longitude of B is the arc hk or the corresponding angle hCk, and this is expressed in degrees and minutes East of Greenwich. Longitudes, i.e. the numbers attached to the meridians, range from 0° to 180° East and from 0° to 180° West, the 180° meridian being named both East and West.

Difference of Latitude

The difference of latitude, or d.lat, as it is usually called, between two places is the arc of any meridian contained between the parallels of latitude on which the two places are situated. In Fig. 3, the d.lat between A and B is the arc Ajm or the arc Bkl. In numerical calculations it should be apparent that if one place is North of the equator and the other place is South of the equator, i.e. if their latitudes are of "opposite names", the d.lat between the two places is found by adding their latitudes together. If a ship is sailing from A to B the d.lat made good is the sum of the two arcs jA and jm and it is named South, because the ship is sailing in a southerly direction. If a ship is sailing from B to A, the d.lat is named North, because the movement is in a northerly direction. When two places are both North or both South of the equator, i.e. when their latitudes are of the "same name" then the d.lat between them is found by subtracting the lesser latitude from the greater, but it is still named according to the direction of the ship's movement, either North or South.

Difference of Longitude

The difference of longitude, or d.long, as it is usually called, between two places is the lesser arc of equator contained between the meridians passing through the two places. In Fig. 3, the d.long between A and B is the arc jk. If the ship is sailing from A to B, the d.long is named East, but if she is sailing from B to A it is named West, i.e. according to the direction of movement. In numerical calculations it should be apparent that when one place is East of Greenwich and the other place is West, the d.long between them is found by adding their longitudes together. Thus, the d.long between A and B is the sum of the two arcs hj and hk. When the two places are both East or both West of Greenwich, the d.long between them is found by subtracting the lesser longitude from the greater, but the d.long is still named according to the direction of movement.

Crossing the 180° Meridian

When finding the d.long between two places which are on opposite sides of the 180° meridian and each less than 90° of longitude from it, some care must be taken.

For instance, if a ship sails from long 165°E to long 170°W the d.long will be 25° *East*, and if a ship sails from long 150°W to long 160°E then the d.long will be 50° *West*. The reader should reason out for himself why this is so, bearing in mind that the d.long is named according to the direction of the ship's movement. A globe of the earth, with meridians marked on it, may be used to obtain a clearer understanding of these examples.

EXAMPLES 1(a)

1. Find the d.lat and d.long made good when a ship sails from A in lat 40°10′N long 30°15′W to B in lat 30°20′N long 42°30′W.

A	lat 40°10′N		long 30°15′W
B	lat 30°20′N		long 42°30′W
d.lat	9°50′S	d.long	12°15′W
	60		60
or d.lat	= 590′S	or d.long	= 735′W

9

Note that d.lat and d.long are often expressed in minutes of latitude and minutes of longitude, respectively.

2.   Find the d.lat and d.long made good by an aircraft, flying from C in lat 20°10′N long 3°20′W to D in lat 5°20′S long 6°15′E.

C	lat 20°10′N	long	3°20′W
D	lat 5°20′S	long	6°15′E
d.lat	25°30′S	d.long	9°35′E
	60		60
or d.lat	= 1530′S	or d.long	= 575′E

3.   Find the d.lat and d.long made good on a voyage from San Francisco to Sydney. San Francisco is in lat 37°48′N long 122°27′W and Sydney is in lat 33°52′S long 151°13′E.

San Francisco lat 37°48′N	long 122°27′W	180°00′
Sydney lat 33°52′S	long 151°13′E	122°27′
d.lat 71°40′S	273°40′	Diff = 57°33′
60	360 00	180°00′
or d.lat = 4300′S	d.long 86°20′W	151°13′
	60	Diff = 28°47′
	d.long = 5180′W	d.long 86°20′W
		60
		d.long = 5180′W

It is most important that the d.lat and d.long should be "named" correctly, i.e. N or S and E or W respectively.

EXERCISE I(a)

Find the d.lat and d.long made good between the following positions. Assume that, in each case, the ship or aircraft is proceeding from the first position to the second position. The d.lat and d.long must be correctly named.

1. A in lat   33°42′N   long 23°17′W
     B in lat 46°18′N   long 64°56′W.
2. X in lat 47°39′N   long 86°43′W
     Y in lat 18°16′N   long 36°06′W.

3. *M* in lat 18°51′S   long 24°47′E
    N in lat 01°41′S   long 06°39′E.
4. *C* in lat 16°23′S   long 14°17′W
    D in lat 07°18′N   long 22°28′E.
5. *P* in lat 17°19′N   long 162°14′E
    Q in lat 07°49′S   long 153°27′W.
6. *E* in lat 46°24′S   long 140°18′W
    F in lat 32°53′S   long 171°46′E.
7. *K* in lat 29°47′N   long 18°59′W
    L in lat 29°47′S   long 18°59′E.

The Nautical Mile

The nautical mile is the unit of distance used by navigators at sea and in the air. For most practical purposes it is considered to be a length of 6080 ft.

In point of fact, however, the nautical mile varies in length, and how this comes about is explained as follows.

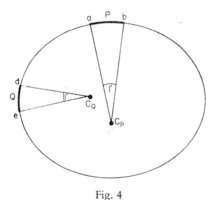

Fig. 4

The earth, as shown in Fig. 4, is an oblate spheroid. It is flattened at the poles. Therefore the curvature of the earth's surface along a meridian at the poles is less than the curvature of the earth's surface along a meridian at the equator. Thus C_P is the centre of curvature of the arc *ab*, near the pole, and C_Q is the centre of curvature of the arc *de*, near the equator.

The length of a nautical mile in any given latitude is defined as "the arc of a meridian subtended by an angle of one minute at the centre of curvature of the meridian for the given latitude".

Thus, in Fig. 4, if the angle at C_Q is 1 min, then the arc *de* is the length of a nautical mile at the equator. Similarly, if the angle at C_P is 1 min, then the arc *ab* is the length of a nautical mile at the pole; *ab* is greater than *de*.

11

The Admiralty Manual of Navigation gives a formula for determining the length of a nautical mile in different latitudes. It is:

Length of nautical mile = $(6077 \cdot 1 - 30 \cdot 7 \cos 2\phi)$ ft, where $\phi =$ the latitude.

At the equator ϕ is $0°$, $\therefore$ 2ϕ is $0°$.

But the cosine of $0° = 1$.

$\therefore$ the length of the n.mile at the equator is

$6077 \cdot 1 - (30 \cdot 7 \times 1) = 6046 \cdot 4$ ft.

At the pole ϕ is $90°$, $\therefore$ $2\phi = 180°$.

But the cosine of $180° = -1$.

$\therefore$ the length of the n.mile at the pole is

$6077 \cdot 1 - (30 \cdot 7 \times -1) = 6077 \cdot 1 + 30 \cdot 7 = 6107 \cdot 8$ ft.

If one uses this formula to calculate the length of the nautical mile in other latitudes, it will be found that the "accepted" figure of 6080 ft is the length of the nautical mile in the latitude of the English Channel.

It will also be observed that in the definition of the nautical mile given above, the expression "arc of the meridian" is used. But the arc of a meridian subtended by an angle of 1 min at the centre of the earth is also 1 min of latitude.

It follows, therefore, that the nautical mile is, in fact, the same unit as 1 min of latitude. Thus, if two places are in the same longitude, the difference of latitude between them, expressed in minutes, is the same as the actual distance between them, expressed in nautical miles.

The Knot

The knot is a unit of speed. One knot means "a speed of one nautical mile per hour". Ten knots means a speed of ten nautical miles per hour and so on. It is therefore manifestly incorrect to say that the distance from one place to another is a hundred knots when, in fact, it is a hundred nautical miles. It would be equally incorrect, of course, to say that a ship's speed was "twelve nautical miles". The correct term here is "twelve knots", unless one adopts a rather unusual and cumbersome mode of expression, and describes the ship's speed as "twelve nautical miles per hour", which is perfectly correct.

The term "knot" is derived from one of the early methods of determining a ship's speed. A small billet of wood, called a "log", was secured to the end of a line, called a "log-line", which was wound on to a reel. Knots were tied in the line at certain specific distances apart, depending on the type of sand glass that was used in conjunction with the line. If the sand glass were a 14 sec glass, the knots on the line would be 23·64 ft apart, and if the glass were a 28 sec glass the knots would be 47·29 ft apart.

The method of use was as follows: the log was lowered over the stern and allowed to trail in the water at the end of a stray length of the log line, the first knot on the line being held firmly by the hand against the taffrail. At a given signal, the sand glass would be turned, and the line released. The log would float astern as the ship went ahead, the line would uncoil from its reel, and the sand would run through the glass. As the last grain of sand left the glass, the number of knots (except the first one) that had passed over the taffrail whilst the sand had been running was noted, and this gave the speed of the ship. The mathematics involved in determining the spacing of the knots on the line is not difficult. If a ship's speed is 1 knot, she will move 6080 ft forward through the water in 3600 sec. Then, in 14 sec, she will move forward $6080 \times 14/3600$ or 23·64 ft.

The Statute Mile

The statute mile, or "land mile", is not generally used in navigation, but navigators may, on occasion, be required to convert nautical miles to statute miles or vice versa.

The statute mile is a unit of distance which was established by statute in the reign of Queen Elizabeth I of England. It is 5280 ft in length. Therefore the relationship it bears to the nautical mile is given by the ratio 5280/6080, which, when reduced to its lowest terms, becomes 66/76. Thus, to convert a given number of statute miles to nautical miles, the given number of statute miles must be multiplied by 66/76. Conversely, to convert a given number of nautical miles to statute miles, the given number of nautical miles must be multiplied by 76/66. When working such conversions, it is useful to remember that, in any given distance, there are more statute miles than there are nautical miles.

The Geographical Mile

From the point of view of the navigator, the "geographical mile" is of little more than academic interest. It may be defined as "the arc of the equator subtended by an angle of one minute at the centre of the earth". It is 6087 ft in length. It will be appreciated that, if the earth were a true sphere, the geographical mile would be exactly the same length as the nautical mile. The oblate shape of the terrestrial spheroid accounts for the difference in the length of a nautical mile at the equator (measured along a meridian) and the length of a geographical mile (measured along the equator).

The Kilometre

Since distances in many European countries are measured in kilometres, the navigator should be able to convert nautical miles (or statute miles) to kilometres and vice versa. The kilometre is defined as 1/10,000 of the distance measured along any meridian from the equator to the pole. It is 3280 ft in length. Therefore the relationship it bears to a nautical mile is given by the ratio 3280/6080, which, reduced to its lowest terms, becomes 41/76. Similarly, the relationship it bears to the statute mile is given by the ratio 3280/5280 or 41/66.

Departure

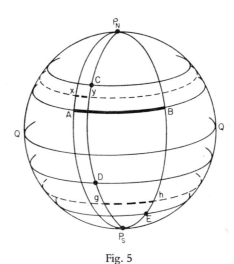

Fig. 5

The "departure" between any two places on the earth's surface is rather difficult to define, because the disposition of the two places with regard to each other affects the definition of the "departure" between them.

In general terms, the departure between two places is the distance in nautical miles between the meridians passing through the two places, measured in an East–West direction, along a certain parallel of latitude.

There are three different concepts of the departure between two places, depending on their relative positions.

Case I. When the two places are on the same parallel of latitude. In Fig. 5, *A* and *B* are two places in the same latitude.

The departure between these two places is the distance in nautical miles between *A* and *B* measured in an East–West direction along their mutual parallel of latitude.

This is the concept of the departure that is used in the navigation problem of "Parallel Sailing" to be described in Chapter 3 of this book.

Case II. A and C are two places on different parallels of latitude; but A and C are so near to each other on the earth that the measurement of distance between them is not appreciably affected if the small part of the earth's surface concerned is regarded as being "plane" or flat. The dotted line *xy* is the parallel of mean latitude between A and C. For example, if A is in lat 30°10′N and C is in lat 32°20′N then the mean latitude between A and C is lat 31°15′N.

In these circumstances, the departure between two places such as A and C is defined as "the distance in nautical miles between the meridians of the two places, measured in an East–West direction along their parallel of mean latitude". In Fig. 5 it is the distance in nautical miles along the parallel of latitude, from *x* to *y*.

This is the concept of the departure that is used in the navigation problem known as "Plane Sailing" or "Traverse Sailing". (See Chapter 3.)

Case III. D and E are two places on different parallels of latitude; but D and E are so far apart that considerable error would arise if the curved surface of the earth were not allowed for when measuring the distance between them; i.e. the earth cannot be considered as plane or flat between two places which are far apart.

The dotted line *gh* in Fig. 5 is the parallel of "middle latitude" between D and E. Because of the spheroidal shape of the earth, the middle latitude is not the same as the mean latitude. The middle latitude is found by applying a certain correction to the mean latitude, as will be explained later.

Thus, the departure between two places such as D and E is defined as "the distance in nautical miles between the meridians of the two places, measured in an East–West direction along their parallel of middle latitude". In Fig. 5, this is the distance in nautical miles along the parallel of latitude, from *g* to *h*.

This is the concept of the departure that is used in the navigation problem of Middle Latitude Sailing. (See Chapter 3.)

The Rhumb Line

The true course of a ship is the angle contained between the direction of the ship's head and the true meridian. Thus, if a ship is to steer a true course from one place to another without changing her heading, she must follow a line which cuts every meridian at the same angle. Such a line is called a "rhumb line" or "loxodrome", the former term being the one usually employed by navigators.

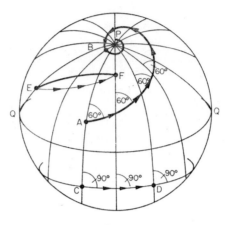

Fig. 6

In Fig. 6, if a ship starts from A and steers a constant true course of 060° (N60°E) she will follow the arrowed line AB, which crosses successive meridians at the same angle of 60°. Such a rhumb line course is a spiral which converges on the nearer pole. Another rhumb line in Fig. 6 is the arrowed line CD, which crosses successive meridians at a constant angle of 90°. This particular rhumb line is also part of a parallel of latitude.

Ships usually steer rhumb line courses from one place to another, because it is convenient and easy to keep the ship heading in a constant direction relative to the meridians that she is crossing.

But there is one most important fact that must be remembered; namely, that the distance measured along the rhumb line from one place to another is *not* the shortest distance between the two places. The shortest possible distance between any two places on the earth is along the arc of a great circle. In Fig. 6 the unmarked line drawn from E to F is the arc of a great circle, because its plane passes through the centre of the earth, and the distance measured along the unmarked line EF is the shortest possible distance from E to F. It will be appreciated however that the unmarked line EF crosses successive meridians at different angles, and if a ship is required to follow such a line in order to go by the shortest possible route, then the course must be altered at frequent intervals as the ship crosses successive meridians. The rhumb line course from E to F is marked with an arrowed line. This crosses successive meridians at the same angle; and another important point that should be noted is that, on the earth, the rhumb line drawn from one place

16

to another is always on the equatorial side of the great circle drawn between the same two places.

EXERCISE I(b)

1. A vessel in lat 18°14′N steams 000° for a certain distance until she is in lat 58°21′N. How far has she steamed?
2. A vessel in lat 06°43′S steams 180° for 1693 miles. What latitude is she then in?
3. A vessel in lat 12°56′N steams 180° for 2135 miles. What latitude is she then in?
4. Convert
    (a) 100 nautical miles to statute miles.
    (b) 100 statute miles to nautical miles.
    (c) 100 nautical miles to kilometres.
    (d) 100 statute miles to kilometres.
    (e) 100 kilometres to statute miles.
    (f) 100 kilometres to nautical miles.
5. A ship's "patent log" is calibrated to record one nautical mile when the ship has run 6080 ft through the water. Find the error in feet in the recorded distance (a) in latitude 10°N (b) in latitude 70°N.

CHAPTER 2

Direction on the earth's surface

For more than 500 years direction on the earth's surface has been determined by some form of magnetic compass. The magnetic needles of a compass acquire their directive force from the earth's magnetic field and it is therefore essential that a navigator should have some understanding of this important phenomenon. Recent research appears to indicate that most, if not all, the planets of the solar system have magnetic fields and the earth is no exception to this rule.

THE EARTH AS A MAGNET. ITS MAGNETIC POLES AND MAGNETIC EQUATOR

The manner in which the earth first acquired its magnetic field, and how that field is constantly maintained, is not clearly understood; but there is no doubt about the fact of its existence, and much is known of its extent and properties. The earth, in fact, appears to be magnetized in such a way that the lines of force of its field flow in a general South to North direction from the South Magnetic Pole to the North Magnetic Pole.

By a well established convention, the North Magnetic Pole of the earth is called the earth's BLUE pole and the South Magnetic Pole is called the earth's RED pole. By a similar convention, the North poles of all other magnets and magnetic needles are called RED and their South poles are called BLUE. In other words, the earth is the only magnet in existence with a BLUE North Pole and a RED South Pole.

A magnetic needle, suspended in the earth's magnetic field, will align itself in the direction of the lines of force of the earth's field. As is generally known, the North or RED end of the needle points towards the North, i.e. towards the earth's BLUE pole. This is in accordance with the First Law of Magnetism which states that opposite poles attract each other, since the RED pole of the needle is attracted towards the BLUE pole of the earth. Similarly, of course, the BLUE pole of the needle (its South Pole) is attracted towards the RED or South Pole of the Earth.

The earth's Magnetic Poles are not coincident with the earth's Geographical Poles. In fact, the North Magnetic Pole is in northern Canada, in approximately lat 71°N long 97°W, which is some 19° of latitude or 1140 n.miles from the North Geographical Pole. The South Magnetic Pole is at a similar distance from the South Geographical Pole. Moreover, neither the North nor the South Magnetic Poles are stationary, as are the Geographical Poles. The North Magnetic Pole, in particular, is moving slowly round the North Geographical Pole in a clockwise direction.

As with the lines of force of all magnetic fields, the lines of force of the earth's magnetic field flow OUT of RED and IN to BLUE. They then, presumably continue to flow through the core of the earth and OUT of RED again, thus completing their circuit.

Figure 7 is a schematic representation of the earth's magnetic field. The points GNP and GSP are the Geographical North and South Poles. The points MNP and MSP are the Magnetic North and South Poles, coloured blue and red respectively. The line joining the two points marked GQ is the Geographical Equator; and the sinuous blue and red line joining the two points marked MQ is the Magnetic Equator.

The lines of force of the earth's field are seen to flow OUT of the RED Magnetic South Pole of the earth and IN to the BLUE Magnetic North Pole of the earth.

Freely suspended magnetic needles, pivoted at their centres, are shown at A and A_1, at B and B_1 and at C and C_1. The horizontal plane through each of these needles is indicated by the dotted line HH, parallel to the earth's surface, at each point.

A freely suspended magnetic needle will align itself, with the direction of the lines of force of the earth's field at any given point on or near the earth's surface. It will be seen that, at A and A_1, the needle is horizontal, because the lines of force of the earth's field are horizontal. At B and B_1 the North or RED end of the needle dips down in line with the direction of the earth's line of force at these two points. At C and C_1 the RED end of the needle is inclined upwards in the direction of the lines of force. If a "dip needle",

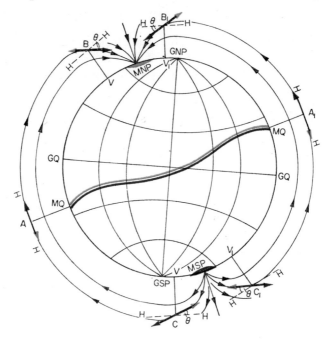

Fig. 7

as such a pivoted magnetic needle is called, is suspended at the North Magnetic Pole, its RED end will point vertically downwards; and at the South Magnetic Pole its RED end will point vertically upwards. The angle (marked θ in Fig. 7) which the dip needle makes with the horizontal plane at any place is called the "Angle of Magnetic Dip" at that place.

From the foregoing it will be apparent that the Magnetic Poles are two points on the earth's surface where the lines of force of the earth's field are entirely vertical and where the angle of Magnetic Dip is $90°$. Similarly the Magnetic Equator is a line joining all places on the earth's surface where the lines of force of the earth's field are horizontal and where the angle of Magnetic Dip is $0°$. As stated before, the Magnetic Equator is a sinuous line which crosses and recrosses the Geographical Equator. It reaches its maximum North latitude in East Africa and its maximum South latitude in Brazil.

The lines of force shown in Fig. 7 represent the lines of total force of the earth's magnetic field, and these are horizontal at the Magnetic Equator but vertical at the Magnetic Poles. At intermediate magnetic latitudes the lines of total force are neither horizontal nor vertical, since they "dip" either up or down at the local angle of dip.

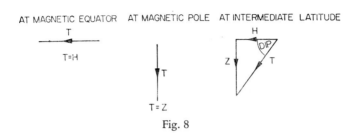

Fig. 8

As shown in Fig. 8, the total force at the Magnetic Equator is entirely horizontal, i.e. total force (T) = horizontal force (H). At the Magnetic Pole the total force is entirely vertical, i.e. total force (T) = vertical force (Z).

At any intermediate latitude, however, the total force is inclined to the horizontal and also to the vertical, so like any other such force, it can be resolved into two components, the horizontal force (H) and the vertical force (Z).

In other words, at any place intermediate between the Magnetic Poles and the Magnetic Equator, there is both a horizontal and a vertical component of the earth's magnetic field. The vertical component (Z) becomes greater as one approaches the Magnetic Poles, whilst the horizontal component (H) becomes less. As will now be seen, this is a matter of great importance as it affects the principle of construction of the magnetic compass.

THE MAGNETIC COMPASS

This consists, basically, of a group of magnetized needles to which is attached a compass card, on which the "points of the compass" are marked. In a ship's standard compass (the most important compass in the ship) there are either four or eight needles, which are suspended by silk threads under the card so that each needle is parallel to a line joining the North and South points of the card. The card is made of rice paper (for extreme lightness) and is stiffened at its circumference by an aluminium ring. The whole arrangement of card and needles is supported in a copper compass bowl by means of a sapphire cap resting on an iridium-tipped pivot. The bowl is made of copper, because copper is a non-magnetic material and will not interfere with the directive force of the magnetized needles. The sapphire cap resting on the iridium-tipped pivot reduces friction to a minimum when the ship alters course. It must be remembered that the magnetized needles of the compass align themselves in a North–South direction and remain aligned in that general direction whatever manoeuvres the ship may make. When the ship alters course, the whole ship turns round the compass card and needles, which are supported on the iridium-tipped pivot. This, of course, turns with the ship, so that it is essential to have the point of contact between the pivot and the cap as free from friction as possible.

The compass bowl, together with the card and needles, are slung in gimbals, so that they remain horizontal when the ship rolls, and the whole is housed in a binnacle. This is usually made of wood, or some other non-magnetic material; the standard compass binnacle is placed on the flying bridge or monkey island, in the centre line of the ship, from which position an almost uninterrupted view of the horizon and of the sky can be obtained to facilitate the taking of compass bearings.

For steering the ship, another magnetic compass is provided. A magnetic steering compass is usually a liquid compass, i.e. the needles are encased in light alloy containers and they and the card are immersed in a mixture of alcohol and water, which has a low freezing point. This has the effect of damping down the oscillations of the card and making it steadier and there-fore easier to steer by when the ship is rolling, since the gimbals are not entirely effective for this purpose. The standard compass, referred to above, is usually a "dry-card" compass, i.e. the needles and card are not immersed in liquid. The dry-card compass is more sensitive than the liquid compass, but is less suitable for steering purposes.

It has been stated that a ship's compass is slung in gimbals so that it remains more or less horizontal when the ship rolls. It is obviously a great advantage to have a horizontal compass card, since navigation is carried out on what at least appears to be the horizontal surface of the earth. It would be most inconvenient if the compass card of a ship's compass were inclined to the horizontal.

Yet this is what would happen if it were not for an important principle that is embodied in the structure of the compass. This principle is that THE POINT OF SUSPENSION OF THE COMPASS NEEDLES IS ABOVE THEIR CENTRE OF GRAVITY.

In Fig. 9(a) N–S is a freely suspended magnetic needle which is pivoted at its centre of gravity. Such a needle is a "dip needle" which has been pre-viously referred to. As shown, it aligns itself with the lines of total force of the earth's magnetic field, so that in the latitude of the British Isles, it "dips" downward at an angle of about 65° to the horizontal. If a compass card were attached to this needle, it would not be very convenient to use.

Figure 9(b) shows, in general principle, how a magnetic compass is con-structed. The pivot fits into the sapphire cap at the point of suspension which is well above the centre of gravity of the needles. The lines of force try to pull the needles into alignment with their own direction, as in Fig. 9(a), but they cannot do so. This is because the weight of each needle (W) acts downwards through G, which, owing to the effect of "dip", is a small distance (GV) to the southward of the vertical through the pivot (vVv_1).

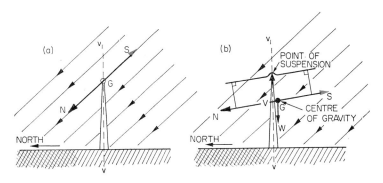

Fig. 9

A mechanical couple of moment $W \times GV$ thus acts in opposition to the turning effect of the lines of force, i.e. the lines of force try to turn the needle anti-clockwise, but the mechanical couple $W \times GV$ tries to turn it clockwise. When these two turning effects reach equilibrium, the needle comes to rest, as shown in Fig. 9(b), with the North end of the needle dipped slightly downwards in the Northern Hemisphere. It is a matter of fact that the North end of any magnetic compass is inclined slightly downwards in the Northern Hemisphere, and slightly upwards in the Southern Hemisphere; but the angle of inclination is slight, and the card is very nearly horizontal in all latitudes. At the Magnetic Equator, of course, the card is exactly horizontal, because the lines of force of the earth's field are horizontal; so G rests naturally on the vertical through the pivot (at V) and the couple $W \times GV$ disappears.

The use of this principle in the construction of the magnetic compass, however, has a most important effect, as follows:

The compass card and needles, as seen above, are mechanically constrained to lie in the horizontal plane in all latitudes.

At the Magnetic Equator this is excellent, because the lines of force of the earth's field are entirely horizontal (horizontal force = total force).

But as a ship carrying a magnetic compass steams Northwards or Southwards from the Magnetic Equator, the lines of force of the earth's field become less and less horizontal and more and more vertical, until, at the Magnetic Poles they are entirely vertical. (See Fig. 8.)

The compass needles, however, are still mechanically constrained to lie in the horizontal plane, and therefore they can only make use of the horizontal component (H) of the earth's field to give them their directive force. This steadily becomes less as the ship goes nearer to either of the Magnetic Poles, until *at* the Magnetic Pole it disappears altogether.

Briefly, therefore, the directive force of the magnetic compass varies directly as the horizontal force of the earth's magnetic field. It is maximum at the Magnetic Equator and zero at the Magnetic Poles. It has been found in practice that a magnetic compass loses its directive force when it is taken to within one or two hundred miles of the North Magnetic Pole. Fortunately, however, ships do not generally navigate in such high latitudes, so the fact that the magnetic compass will not function near the Magnetic Poles does not matter to marine navigators. When aircraft navigate over or near the Magnetic Poles they use a form of gyroscopic compass, or a radio compass, neither of which is dependent on the earth's magnetic field.

Apart from the above important principle of compass construction, there are one or two facts concerning the magnetic needles themselves that should be known. Students of magnetism will be familiar with the formula:

$$t = 2\pi \sqrt{\frac{K}{MH}}$$

where t = time in seconds for one oscillation of a horizontal magnetic
　　　　needle (a compass needle),
　　K = moment of inertia of the needle,
　　M = the magnetic moment of the needle, and
　　H = the horizontal force of the earth's magnetic field.

K, the moment of inertia, is directly proportional to the mass of the needle; and M, the magnetic moment, equals pole strength of needle multiplied by length of needle.

For a compass to be efficient, it must align itself with the horizontal direction of the earth's lines of force as quickly as possible after it has been deflected from this direction. This means that, in the above formula, t must be a small interval of time.

The aim is to make the compass as nearly as possible "aperiodic". This means "without a period of oscillation", when t in the above formula would be NIL. This is impossible in practice; but the aim is achieved to some extent as follows:

(i)　The mass of the needles is kept as small as possible. Therefore K will be small.

(ii)　The pole strength of the needles is made as great as possible, and since long magnets cannot be used, four or eight short ones are used instead. Therefore M will be large.

24

It follows, therefore, that t will be small, and when the compass is deflected it will quickly re-align itself in the direction of the horizontal component of the earth's lines of force.

THE MAGNETIC MERIDIAN. VARIATION

The direction of the horizontal component of the earth's lines of force at any given place is called the Magnetic Meridian. It is usually defined as "the direction that a compass needle will take up when under the influence of the earth's magnetic field only". It is a common misapprehension to suppose that the North end of a compass needle points directly at the North Magnetic Pole of the earth. This is not so, because the lines of force of the earth's field do NOT run symmetrically from Magnetic Pole to Magnetic Pole. Their direction is locally quite variable, and in any given locality their direction is changing slowly all the time. This, of course, is connected with the slow movement of the Magnetic Poles round the Geographical Poles already referred to. The earth's magnetic field, in fact, is slowly changing its direction all the time.

At any given place on the earth's surface the angle that the magnetic meridian makes with the geographical (or "true") meridian is called the "variation" at that place.

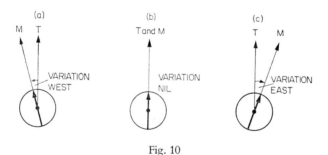

Fig. 10

The variation is named West when the magnetic meridian is inclined to the left of the true meridian, as in Fig. 10(a). Variation is West in the British Isles today.

Variation is NIL when there is no angle between the true and magnetic meridian, as in Fig. 10(b). This is the case in Central America today.

Variation is named East when the magnetic meridian is inclined to the right of the true meridian as in Fig. 10(c). This is the case in the Pacific Ocean to the West of North America.

The variation in any particular locality is given on the Admiralty Chart of

25

the area, usually as a statement in the "compass rose" of the chart. On some charts, however, lines are drawn joining all places on the chart that have a given angle of variation. Such lines are called Isogonals or Isogonic Lines. The line joining all places where the variation is NIL is called the Agonic Line.

Whenever the value of the variation is given on a chart, the year of the given value is stated and the amount by which it is changing annually (called the "secular" change) is also given. For example, on a chart of a sea area near the British Isles there will be a statement like this: "Variation 10°W (1960) decreasing 6' annually." Thus, if a navigator is using this chart in 1965 he will know that he should allow for a variation of 9°30'W.

In addition to the above annual or secular change in variation, there are certain parts of the world, and certain occasions, when abnormal variation is experienced owing to local disturbances in the earth's magnetic field. The navigator has to be on constant guard against this possibility by frequently checking the behaviour of his compass.

THE SHIP AS A MAGNET. DEVIATION OF THE COMPASS

The definition of the magnetic meridian given above specifies that it is the direction taken up by a compass needle when under the influence of the earth's magnetic field ONLY.

If a ship were made entirely of wood or of other non-magnetic material, the compass needles in the ship would align themselves in the magnetic meridian, and the navigator would only have to make allowance for the effect of variation.

Ships, however, are constructed of steel, which, like iron, is a ferrous metal and readily becomes magnetized by induction when placed in a magnetic field, such as the earth's field.

A steel ship, therefore, becomes magnetized; and so, like any other magnet, it has a magnetic field, with lines of force flowing round and across the ship from one point to another. These lines of force deflect the compass needles from the magnetic meridian and give rise to compass deviation.

Compass deviation or, more briefly, deviation is defined as the angle which the compass needle makes with the magnetic meridian. Deviation is called East when the compass needle is deviated to the right of the magnetic meridian, and it is called West when the compass needle is deviated to the left of the magnetic meridian.

Furthermore, and this is of the utmost importance: DEVIATION CHANGES ITS VALUE WHENEVER THERE IS A CHANGE IN THE DIRECTION OF THE SHIP'S HEAD.

These are the main facts of which a brief explanation will now be given.

A ship acquires a considerable part of her magnetic field during the building process.

Figure 11(a) shows a ship that is being built in the Northern hemisphere in a position on the earth corresponding to position B_1 in Fig. 7. The lines of force of the earth's magnetic field flow from South to North in this position and are inclined downwards in the direction shown. The earth forward of the ship and underneath her bows is of BLUE polarity. Therefore, as a result of magnetic induction, the forward and lower part of the ship acquires RED polarity and the aft and upper part of the ship acquires BLUE polarity.

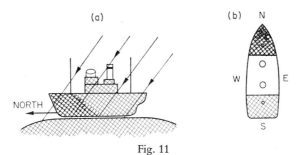

Fig. 11

Figure 11(b) shows the same ship in plan view. The bows of the ship have RED polarity and the stern of the ship has BLUE polarity.

By referring to Fig. 7 it will be appreciated that when a ship is being built anywhere in the world (except at the North or South Magnetic Poles) that part of the ship which is facing North in the building yard will acquire RED polarity and that part of the ship which is facing South in the building yard will acquire BLUE polarity. It should be emphasized, however, that in practice, the magnetic field acquired when building is not so clearly defined as would appear from these diagrams. Similarly, a ship that is built heading East will generally speaking acquire "RED to Port" and "BLUE to Starboard"; a ship built heading South will acquire "RED aft" and "BLUE forward", and so on.

This is a simplified explanation of how a ship acquires her magnetic field. In practice, the magnetic field of a ship is more complicated. Changes of heading and changes of latitude both cause the field to change; but at a given place and on a given heading, the magnetic field of a ship is constant.

Figure 12 shows a ship which has acquired a RED pole in the bow and a BLUE pole in the stern. When this ship puts to sea and heads North, as in Fig. 12(a), the lines of force of the ship's magnetic field are flowing in exactly the opposite direction to the lines of force of the earth's field (H). This will not cause the compass needle to deviate from the magnetic meridian, but it will reduce its directive force, since the ship's field is opposing the earth's field.

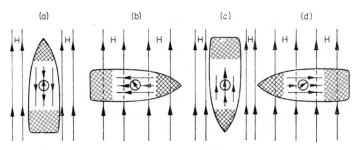

Fig. 12

In Fig. 12(b) the ship is heading East. On this heading the lines of force of the ship's field are flowing at right-angles to the earth's field and will therefore cause maximum westerly deviation (westerly, because the North (RED) pole of the needle is attracted to the BLUE pole of the ship).

In Fig. 12(c) the ship is heading South. On this heading the lines of force of the ship's field and the earth's field are in exactly the same direction. There will be no deviation of the needle from the magnetic meridian but its directive force will be increased by the effect of the ship's field acting in conjunction with H.

Finally, in Fig.12(d), where the ship is heading West, the lines of force of the ship's field are again flowing at right-angles to H, and this will result, in this case, in the maximum easterly deviation of the compass needle from the magnetic meridian.

The changing deviation of a ship as she changes her heading is often shown on a deviation "curve" or graph which is posted up in the chartroom or wheelhouse. The deviation curve of the ship described above would appear as in Fig. 13(a); whilst a ship with a BLUE pole to Starboard, and a RED pole to Port would have a deviation curve like that in Fig. 13(b).

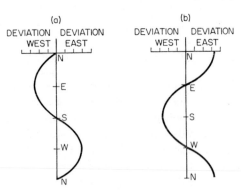

Fig. 13

28

THE MARINER'S COMPASS. POINTS, QUADRANTS AND DEGREES

Having described in some detail how the magnetic compass is constructed and how it works, the different methods of graduating the compass card must now be dealt with.

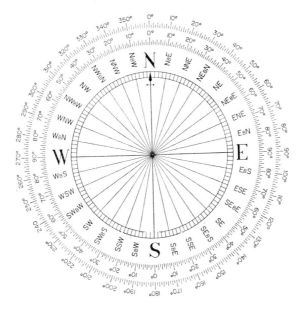

Fig. 14

Figure 14 shows a compass card graduated in points, quadrants and degrees. All three methods of notation must be known, since each method is used, either in navigation or seamanship, for a different purpose, and the competent navigator must be readily able to convert any given course or bearing from one system of notation to another.

The inner ring of Fig. 14 shows the points of the compass of which there are 32. Since there are 360° in a circle, it follows that the spacing between successive points is 11°15′, whilst the spacing between half-points and quarter-points is 5°37½′ and 2°48¾′ respectively.

"Boxing the compass" in points, half-points and quarter-points commences from North and proceeds as follows:

N, N¼E, N½E, N¾E, N by E, N by E¼E, N by E½E, N by E¾E, NNE, NE by N¾N, NE by N½N, NE by N¼N, NE by N, NE¾N, NE½N, NE¼N,

29

NE, NE¼E, and so on round the compass. It will be noted that the points, half-points and quarter-points are always measured from the nearest cardinal point or inter-cardinal point, e.g. from North and North-East in the part of the compass quoted above. There are, for example, no such points of the compass as "NNE½N" or "NNE½E". These should be N by E½E and NE by N½N, respectively.

The outer ring of the compass card shown in Fig. 14 is graduated in the modern and straightforward manner which is known as "360° notation". North = 0°, NE = 045°, East = 090°, SE = 135°, South = 180°, and so on. The ring of the compass card shown between the inner ring and the outer is graduated according to the "quadrantal" system of notation. In this system, the degrees of a course or bearing are measured either from North or South, towards East or West, from 0° to 90°. Thus:

$$NE \text{ (in points)} = 045° \quad (360° \text{ notation}) = N45°E \quad \text{(quadrantal notation)}$$
$$SSE \text{ (in points)} = 157°30' \ (360° \text{ notation}) = S22°30'E \quad \text{(quadrantal notation)}$$
$$WSW \text{ (in points)} = 247°30' \ (360° \text{ notation}) = S67°30'W \ \text{(quadrantal notation)}$$
$$NW \text{ by } N \text{ (in points)} = 326°15' \ (360° \text{ notation}) = N33°45'W \text{(quadrantal notation)}$$

Facility in converting from one to the other of these three systems of notation can only be achieved by practice, and some exercises in such conversions are given in the following exercise.

Exercise II(a)

1. Convert the following into: (a) 360° notation, (b) quadrantal notation.
   (a) NE by E, (b) E by N¼N, (c) E by S, (d) SE by S½S,
   (e) SW by S, (f) W by S½S, (g) WNW, (h) NW by N½N.
2. Convert the following into: (a) points, (b) quadrantal notation.
   (a) 033°45', (b) 073°07½', (c) 123°45', (d) 174°22½',
   (e) 202°30', (f) 230°37½', (g) 298°07½', (h) 348°45'.
3. Convert the following into: (a) points, (b) 360° notation.
   (a) N11°15'E, (b) N73°07½'E, (c) S78°45'E, (d) S22°30'E,
   (e) S33°45'W, (f) S61°52½'W, (g) N50°37½'W, (h) N5°37½'W.

THE CORRECTIONS OF COURSES AND BEARINGS

The correction of courses and bearings, by which is meant the conversion of true courses or bearings to magnetic or compass, and vice versa, is one of the most frequently performed operations in navigation.

It is necessary, however, at this point to define clearly what is meant by "a course" and "a bearing". When a navigator lays off a course or a bearing on a chart, he draws a line on the chart. The correct term for the line is either a "course line" or a "line of bearing", as the case may be. But neither a course, nor a bearing, is itself a line on a chart, or anywhere else. A course is an *angle*, and a bearing is an *angle*. The true course of a ship is the angle contained between the direction of the ship's head and the true meridian.

The magnetic course of a ship is the angle contained between the direction of the ship's head and the magnetic meridian.

The compass course of a ship is the angle contained between the direction of the ship's head and the direction of the compass needle.

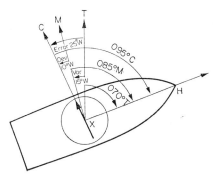

Fig. 15

In Fig. 15 the line *XH* is the direction of the ship's head. It represents the direction in which the navigator wishes his ship to go. His problem is to give the helmsman, at the compass, a compass course to steer, so that the ship will head in the correct direction, and will move along the course line that he has laid off on the chart.

The true meridians are marked on the chart, and therefore the angle *TXH* in Fig. 15 can be measured. This is the true course, which, in this example, is 070°T.

The chart may also state that, in this particular locality, the variation is 15°W. It follows, therefore, that the magnetic course (by definition) is the angle *MXH* and is equal to 085°M.

The navigator then consults the deviation curve for his compass and finds that, on a heading of 085°M, the deviation is 10°W. He applies this to the magnetic course to obtain the compass course which (by definition) is the angle *CXH*, and is equal to 095°C.

The variation and deviation can be combined together by algebraic addition to give the compass error. This is defined as the angle contained between the true meridian and the compass needle, when the ship is on any given heading. In Fig. 15 it is the angle *TXC* and is equal to 25°W. This can be applied directly to the true course to give the compass course, or vice versa.

In Fig. 15, the variation, deviation and error are all West, and navigators often make use of the following "rhyming rules" for correcting courses.

I (a)   True to magnetic and vice versa.   "Variation West,
                                                   Magnetic best."

II (a) Magnetic to compass and vice versa.   "Deviation West,
                                                   Compass best."

III (a) True to compass and vice versa.   "Error West,
                                                   Compass best."

Now let us consider bearings. A bearing, like a course, is an *angle*, and it may be either compass, magnetic or true.

The compass bearing of an object is the angle contained between the compass needle and the line joining the observer to the object.

The magnetic bearing of an object is the angle contained between the magnetic meridian and the line joining the observer to the object.

The true bearing of an object is the angle contained between the true meridian and the line joining the observer to the object.

In practice, the navigator "takes", or observes, the compass bearing of an object, and he then converts that bearing to a true bearing, so that he can lay off the line of bearing on the chart. Or conversely, he may wish to check the compass error. If he knows his position, he can find the true bearing of an object that he can also observe by compass. The difference between the true and compass bearings of the same object is the compass error.

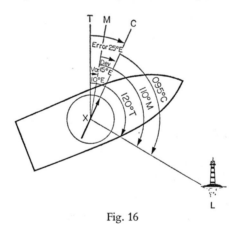

Fig. 16

Figure 16 shows, first of all, that the bearing of an object should not be confused with the course or heading of the ship. *XL* is the line of bearing joining the observer at the ship's compass to the object observed, and it is quite different from the course of the ship. It is only the same as the course if the object observed is right ahead of the ship.

In Fig. 16 the local variation is 10°E and the deviation for the particular heading of the ship (taken from the deviation curve) is 15°E.

32

DIRECTION ON THE EARTH'S SURFACE

The navigator at the compass observes the compass bearing of the lighthouse L to be 095°C. He applies the deviation of 15°E to this and obtains the magnetic bearing of L, which is 110°M. He then applies the variation of 10°E and obtains the true bearing of L which is 120°T, and this is the bearing which he lays off on the chart relative to the true meridian.

The manner in which these corrections are applied should be apparent from the diagram. Alternatively, the variation and deviation may be combined to give compass error and this can be applied directly to the compass bearing to give true. In this example the error is 25°E.

As in the previous example, rhyming rules may be used, which, in this case, are as follows:

I (b)   Compass to magnetic and vice versa.   "Deviation East,
                                                Compass least."

II (b)   Magnetic to true and vice versa.   "Variation East,
                                                Magnetic least."

III (b)   Compass to true and vice versa.   "Error East,
                                                Compass least."

It must be remembered that these rhyming rules can only be used when courses and bearings are expressed in 360° notation. They do not apply to other systems of notation. And it must also be remembered that when the deviation is taken from the deviation curve or graph, the graph must be entered with either the magnetic or compass *heading* (i.e. course) of the ship. This is because the deviation of a compass changes its value *only* with change of *heading*, and does not depend in any way on the bearings that are observed.

EXERCISE II(b)

All answers to be given in 360° notation.

1.   Convert the following compass courses to magnetic courses using the deviation given.
     (a) 045°C dev. 10°W,   (b) 132°C dev. 5°E,   (c) 225°C dev. 6°W,
     (d) 355°C dev. 10°E,   (e) S30°E (C) dev. 5°W,   (f) S30°W (C) dev. 4°E,
     (g) N55°W (C) dev. 7°W,   (h) N5°E (C) dev. 10°W.

2.   Convert the following magnetic courses to compass courses using the deviation given.
     (a) 045°M dev. 10°W,   (b) 132°M dev. 5°E,   (c) 225°M dev. 6°W,
     (d) 355°M dev. 10°W,   (e) S30°E (M) dev. 5°W,   (f) S30°W (M) dev. 4°E,
     (g) N55°W (M) dev. 7°E,   (h) N5°E (M) dev. 10°E.

3.   Convert the following magnetic bearings to true bearings using the variation given.
     (a) 025°M var. 10°W,   (b) 165°M var. 10°E,   (c) 245°M var. 7°W,
     (d) 355°M var. 9°E,   (e) 360°M var. 4°W,   (f) S80°W (M) var. 10°E,
     (g) N50°W (M) var. 8°W,   (h) N7°W (M) var. 10°E.

4.   Convert the following true bearings to magnetic bearings using the variation given.
     (a) 025°T var. 10°W,   (b) 165°T var. 10°E,   (c) 245°T var. 7°W,
     (d) 355°T var. 9°W,   (e) 360°T var. 4°W,   (f) S80°W (T) var. 10°E,
     (g) N50°W (T) var. 8°W,   (h) N7°W (T) var. 10°W.

5. Convert the following true courses to compass courses using the variation and deviation given.
   (a) 045°T var. 10°W dev. 5°W,   (b) 147°T var. 15°E dev. 5°W,
   (c) 247°T var. 10°W dev. 3°W,   (d) 350°T var. 25°W dev. 5°E,
   (e) S33°E (T) var. 7°W dev. 3°W,   (f) N10°E (T) var. 20°E dev. 4°W.
6. Convert the following compass bearings to true bearings using the variation and deviation given.
   (a) 045°C var. 10°W dev. 5°W,   (b) 147°C var. 15°E dev. 5°E,
   (c) 247°C var. 10°W dev. 3°W,   (d) 350°C var. 25°E dev. 5°W,
   (e) S33°E (C) var. 7°W dev. 3°W,   (f) N10°E (C) var. 20°W dev. 4°E.
7. Fill in the blanks in the following tables expressing all courses and bearings in 360° notation.

TABLE A

	Compass course or bearing	Deviation	Magnetic course or bearing	Variation	True course or bearing
1	050		056		036
2		3E	220		225
3		4W	280	18W	
4	003		358		013
5		4W	241	11W	
6	169	3E			184
7		2E		20E	008
8	286	6W		5W	
9	088		091		066
10		4E	205	30W	
11	332		332		014
12	180		178		178

TABLE B

	Compass course or bearing	Variation	Deviation	Error	True course or bearing
1	N46°E	8°W	12°W		
2	S36°W	25°E			S56°W
3			22°E	17°E	S20°W
4	N57°W	16° E	12°W		
5			6°W	4°W	N26°W
6	S20°E	8°W			S40°E

THE GYRO COMPASS

Most modern ships are equipped with at least one gyroscopic compass, in addition to the magnetic compass or compasses that are carried.

The great advantage of the gyro compass, as it is usually called, is that it indicates the true heading of the ship, and therefore requires no correction for variation and deviation. It is a complicated piece of mechanism, however, and if it breaks down at sea it cannot always be repaired. It is for this reason that all merchant ships are required by law to carry a magnetic standard compass in addition to any gyro compasses that may be carried. A magnetic compass rarely, if ever, breaks down.

The principle of the gyro compass is entirely different from that of the magnetic compass, since it in no way depends on the earth's magnetic field for its directive force.

The gyro compass derives its directive force from certain properties of the gyroscope and from two basic natural phenomena, viz: (a) the rotation of the earth and (b) the force of gravity.

A free gyroscope is defined as "a rapidly spinning wheel, called the rotor, so mounted as to have three degrees of freedom".

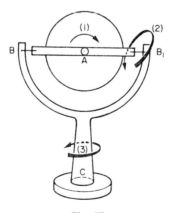

Fig. 17

Figure 17 is a schematic drawing of a free gyroscope and shows what is meant by the term "three degrees of freedom".

The horizontal gyro rotor axis is pivoted into a horizontal circular ring at A (and also at A_1 at the other end of the axis). The horizontal ring is itself pivoted into a semi-circular vertical ring at B and B_1, and the vertical ring is pivoted into C in the base of the instrument.

The gyroscope's "three degrees of freedom", therefore, consist of

(1) freedom to rotate about its axis of rotation (AA_1),
(2) freedom to rotate about a horizontal axis (BB_1), and
(3) freedom to rotate about a vertical axis (through C).

RIGIDITY IN SPACE OR GYROSCOPIC INERTIA

When the wheel, or rotor, of a gyroscope is set spinning, the gyroscope is observed to acquire two important properties, the first of which is called "Rigidity in Space" or "Gyroscopic Inertia".

This means that when the gyro rotor is set spinning with its axis pointing in a certain direction in space, the axis continues to point in that same direction in space, however much the instrument as a whole is moved bodily about from place to place.

This can be readily demonstrated with a small model gyroscope, but a better understanding of this important property will be acquired if it is remembered that the earth itself is a gyroscope. This is so, because, at some time in the far distant past, the earth was set spinning on its axis, like the rotor of a gyroscope. And the axis of the earth at this moment continues to point in a given direction in space, as the earth moves bodily along the orbit round the sun. The exact spot in space at which the northern end of the earth's axis points is called the North Celestial Pole, which is a point in the heavens very close to the Pole Star.

It is for this reason that the Pole Star is the only star that does not appear to move if it is watched for any period of time on a clear night. Observers in the Northern hemisphere will observe that the stars near to the Pole Star appear to move round it in an anti-clockwise direction, whilst the Pole Star itself does not change its position. The Pole Star is at a point in space which is

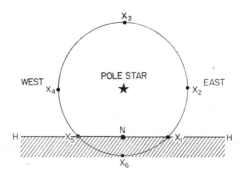

Fig. 18

nearly in line with the earth's axis; but the other stars, near the pole, are not in line with the earth's axis. It is the rotation of the earth that makes these stars *appear* to rotate round the pole. If the earth were not rotating, they would not appear to move at all.

If an observer in Northern latitude faces North on a clear night he may see a star appear to rise above the horizon at X_1 in Fig. 18. If he observes this star for a sufficiently long interval of time, he will see that it reaches the position X_2 after about 5 hr, and X_3 after another 6 hr. If darkness lasted long enough, he would see the star at X_4 after a further 6 hr, and it would sink below the horizon again at X_5 about 5 hr later. It would rise again at X_1, $23^h56^m04^s$ after it had risen there on the previous night. $23^h56^m04^s$ of Mean Time (as kept by ordinary clocks) is the duration of a Sidereal Day, which is defined as "the interval between successive transits of a star over the same meridian".

Now, if the above observer were to set the rotor of a free gyroscope spinning when he first observed the star at X_1, and if he were to point the North end of the rotor axis exactly at the star, he would find that the North end of the axis would follow the apparent path of the star. The North end of the axis would begin to tilt up and drift to the East. After about 5 hr it would continue to tilt up but start to drift to the West—and so on, as it followed the apparent path of the star, and demonstrated its gyroscopic property of *rigidity in space*, or gyroscopic inertia.

Such a free gyroscope would be of little use as a compass, since its axis would be changing direction relative to the meridians all the time. And even if the axis were set to point exactly at the Pole Star, it would continue to point North at that star; but in all latitudes except at the equator, the gyro axis would be tilted either up or down.

As was seen when describing the construction of the magnetic compass, the North–South axis of a compass card must be horizontal, or nearly horizontal, in all latitudes.

The axis of a gyro compass, therefore, must be so adjusted, that it will always remain horizontal and will always point due North along the true meridian. In other words, the North end of the axis must be made to point at N in Fig. 18 since N is on the horizon and also due North of the observer.

To achieve this end, the second property of a free gyroscope, called Precession, is brought into play.

Precession is a property of a free gyroscope, whereby, if an applied force, or torque, is applied to the spinning axis of a free gyroscope, the force will turn 90° in the direction of rotation and then act as a precessed force.

In Fig. 19(a) the rotor of the gyroscope is rotating anti-clockwise as viewed from the South end. AF is an applied force or torque pressing down on the South end. This force turns through 90° in the direction of rotation and then acts as the precessed force *PF* which causes motion about the vertical axis, as shown. In other words a torque applied about the horizontal axis causes movement about the vertical axis.

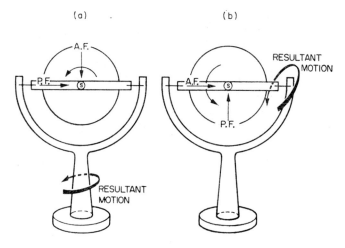

Fig. 19

In Fig. 19(b) the applied force or torque is applied about the vertical axis and the precessed force causes movement about the horizontal axis, as shown.

This property, used in conjunction with the force of gravity, is utilized to provide a "gravity control" and a "damping factor" on the apparent movement of the free gyro axis, and so convert the free gyroscope into a gyro compass.

In one of the best-known gyro compasses the gravity control and damping factors are provided as follows:

Mercury bottles are fixed on brackets at the North and South end of the gyro axis. These mercury bottles are connected from North to South by fine-bore tubes below the level of the axis.

Referring now to Fig. 18, let us suppose that the gyro rotor is set spinning with the North end of its axis pointing at X_1.

The North end immediately begins to tilt up and drift to the East.

As soon as the North end begins to tilt up, however, mercury flows by gravity from the North bottles through the fine bore tubes to the South bottles, and thus produces an excess weight of mercury on the South end of the axis.

This is, in effect, a downward applied force on the South end, which is precessed, and the precessed force pushes the South end to the East, as can be seen in Fig. 19(a).

But by pushing the South end to the East, the North end is pushed to the *West*, and this counteracts the original tendency of the North end to drift away to the East.

The above sequence of events constitutes the gravity control in this type of compass.

Gravity control alone, however, will not convert a free gyro into a gyro compass. A damping factor must also be provided.

In the type of compass described above, the bracket securing the mercury bottles to the rotor casing is attached eccentrically to the casing, in such a manner that the excess weight of mercury on the South end is not applied vertically downwards, but is applied at a point slightly to the eastward of the vertical. In other words, there is a slight eastward applied force on the South end of the axis in addition to the main applied force downwards. It is this eastward applied force that provides the damping factor.

Figure 19(b) shows the effect of an applied force to the eastward on the South end. The force is precessed and pushes the South end up. Consequently it pushes the North end down, thus counteracting the original tendency of the North end to tilt up, and also "damps down" the oscillation of the North end until it settles on the meridian, with the axis horizontal, as is required in a gyro compass.

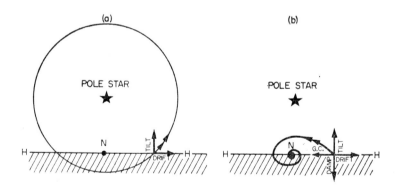

Fig. 20

Figure 20(a), which is similar to Fig. 18, shows the forces that act on the North end of a free gyro axis which is pointing at the Pole Star. They are Tilt (upwards) and Drift (to the East). The resultant path of the North end is shown by the double arrowed line. Figure 20(b) shows the forces that act on the North end of a gyro axis which is no longer a free gyro, but which is gravity controlled and damped. It will be seen that, in addition to tilt and drift, there is the force of gravity control (to the West) and the damping factor (downwards). Again, the resultant path of the North end is indicated by the double arrowed line, which shows that the North end oscillates in a spiral round the northern point of the horizon and finally comes to rest pointing directly at N.

Finally, it should be remembered that whereas a magnetic compass will not function at the North or South Magnetic Poles, a gyro compass will not function at the North or South Geographical Poles. This is because there is no tendency for a free gyroscope axis to tilt when the gyro rotor is set spinning with its axis horizontal at either of these Poles; and since the entire sequence of gravity control and damping described above depends on the original tendency of the rotor axis to tilt, the gyro compass will not function at places where this tendency does not exist.

CHAPTER 3

The "sailings"

PARALLEL SAILING

THE method of finding one's latitude by observing the altitude of the sun when on the observers meridian has been well known to navigators for many centuries, but it was not until 1765 when Harrison designed his marine chronometer that the accurate determination of longitude became possible.

The early navigators then, unable to obtain an accurate longitude, would steer due North or South until they arrived at the desired parallel of latitude and then steer East or West along that parallel to their destination.

This form of navigation was known as parallel sailing, since it consisted of steering along a parallel of latitude. Now the distance along a parallel of latitude is known as departure, so that the distance steamed in parallel sailing is the departure between the two points. If the departure between two points is known, then it should be possible to find the d.long, for it is obvious that there must be a connection between the two, since each measures the distance between two meridians. That connection will now be derived.

41

Figure 21(a) represents the earth viewed from a point opposite the equator, and **Fig.** 21(b) represents the earth viewed from above the North Pole.

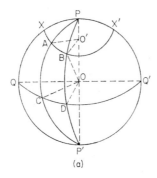

Fig. 21

PP′ The poles   O   The centre of the earth
QQ′ The equator   O′ The centre of parallel XX′
XX′ A parallel of latitude   PACP′ and PBDP′ Two meridians

A and *B* are two places on the parallel *XX′*. By definition, the departure between *A* and *B* is the arc *AB* of the parallel *XX′*, and the d.long between *A* and *B* is the arc *CD* of the equator, *QQ′*.

In Fig. 21(b), angles *O′AB*, *O′BA*, *OCD*, and *ODC* are all 90° since the radius of a circle is at right angles to the circumference.

Also, $\angle AO'B = \angle COD$ (common angle)

∴ triangles *COD* and *AO′B* are similar, so that $AB/CD = O'B/OD$. (1)

In Fig. 21(a),
$O'B = OB \cdot \cos \angle OBO'$ $(BO'O = 90°)$
but $\angle OBO' = \angle BOD$ (alt. angles, *O′B* parallel to *OD*)
also $OB = OD$ (radii of earth)
∴ $O'B = OD \cdot \cos \angle BOD$.
Substitute in (1) for *O′B*,
  $AB/CD = OD \cdot \cos \angle BOD/OD$
  $AB/CD = \cos \angle BOD$.

BOD is the angle subtended at the centre of the earth between the equator and the parallel of latitude passing through *A* and *B*, so that $\angle BOD$ is the latitude of *A* and *B*.

∴ dep./d.long $= \cos$ lat
or dep. $=$ d.long $\times \cos$ lat.

This formula establishes the relationship that exists between dep. and d.long and is known as the parallel sailing formula. Some examples of its use are now given.

EXAMPLE 1

A vessel in lat 43°N, long 52°W, steers a course of 090°(T) for a distance of 496 miles. Find her new position.

d.long = dep.sec lat
     = 496 × sec 43°
d.long = 678·3
     = 11°18·3′E
Original long 52°00′W
    d.long 11°18·3′E

Final long 40°41·7′W

496 log 2·6955
43° log sec 0·1359
————
log 2·8314

Final position: lat 43°N, long 40°41·7′W.

EXAMPLE 2

A vessel in lat 54°23′S, long 16°18′E, steers 270°(T) until she is in long 08°43′W. How far has she steamed?
Original long 16°18′E
Final long 08°43′W

d.long 25°01′W = 1501′W
    dep. = d.long × cos lat
       = 1501 × cos 54°23′
    dep. = 874·2′

1501 log 3·1764
54°23′ log cos 1·7652
————
log 2·9416
Distance steamed: 874·2 miles.

EXAMPLE 3

Two vessels in lat 23°N are 420 miles apart. If both steam due North at the same speed, how far apart will they be after steaming 1927 miles?

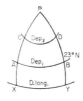

Fig. 22

In the figure, PX and PY are the meridians upon which the two vessels are situated. *A* and *B* are their original positions and *C* and *D* are their final positions.

The d.long between the two vessels will remain constant but the departure will decrease.

$$1 \text{ min of latitude} = 1 \text{ nautical mile.}$$

∴ the distance steamed by the vessels is the d.lat

i.e. d.lat $= 1927' = 32°07'$N.

Original lat	23°00′N
d.lat	32°07′N
Final lat	55°07′N

d.long $=$ dep. $\times$ sec lat
dep.(1) 420 log 2·6232
lat(1) 23° log sec 0·0360

d.long   log 2·6592
d.long   456·2

dep. $=$ d.long $\times$ cos lat
d.long 456·2   log 2·6592
lat(2) 55°07′ log cos 1·7572

dep.(2)   log 2·4165
dep.(2) 261·0

Vessels are 261·0 miles apart.

EXAMPLE 4

Vessel *A* is in lat 28°40′N, long 20°W, and vessel *B* is in lat 39°24′N, long 20°W. *A* leaves at 1200 hr on a certain day, steaming 090°(T) at 12 kt, and *B* leaves at 1800 hr on the same day, also steering 090°(T). At what speed must *B* steam at so that both vessels may be on the same meridian at 1800 hr on the following day?

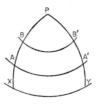

Fig. 23

PX is the meridian of 20°W, and *A* and *B* are the two vessels. *PY* is the meridian that the vessels are on at 1800 hr on the following day.
A has steamed for 30 hr at 12 kt so that her dep. is 360′.
B has steamed for 24 hr at *x* kt so that her dep. is 24*x*.

The d.long covered by each vessel is the same, so that,

44

$$\text{For } A \text{ d.long} = \text{dep}_A \times \text{sec lat } A.$$
$$\text{For } B \text{ d.long} = \text{dep}_B \times \text{sec lat } B.$$
$$\text{dep}_A \times \text{sec lat } A = \text{dep}_B \times \text{sec lat } B$$
$$\text{dep}_B = \text{dep}_A \times \text{sec lat } A \times \text{cos lat } B$$
$$24x = 360 \times \text{sec } 28°40' \times \cos 39°24'$$
$$x = \frac{360 \times \text{sec } 28°40' \times \cos 39°24'}{24}$$

$$x = 13 \cdot 21$$

360 log 2·5563
28°40′ log sec 0·0568
39°24′ log cos $\overline{1}$·8880

_____

2·5011
24 log 1·3802

_____

x log 1·1209
B's speed = 13·21 kt.

EXERCISE III(a)

1. A vessel in lat 48°N steams 090°(T) for a distance of 263 miles. By how much has her longitude changed?
2. A vessel in lat 43°18′N long 24°03′W steams 270°(T) until she arrives in long 32°46′W. How far has she steamed?
3. A vessel in lat 46°30′N long 179°30′E steams 090°(T) for 923 miles. What is her final position?
4. Two vessels are in lat 62°18′N. The longitude of one is 16°42′E and of the other is 04°33′E. How far are the vessels apart?
5. Two vessels are on the equator, one in long 23°18′W, and the other in long 16°41′W. Both steam 000°(T) for 1410 miles. What latitude are they then in, and how far are they apart?
6. Two vessels are in lat 22°N, and are 236 miles apart. Both steam 000°(T) at the same speed until they are in lat 38°14′N. What distance are they then apart and how far have they steamed?
7. Two vessels in lat 14°16′S are 120 miles apart. Both steam 000°(T) at the same speed. What latitude will they be in when they are 96 miles apart?
8. At what speed is the earth revolving,
     (a) at the equator,   (b) in lat 48°N?
9. A vessel in long 40°13′W and on the equator, steams 000°(T) for 1200 miles, 090°(T) for 1200 miles, 180°(T) for 1200 miles, and 270°(T) for 1200 miles. Find her final position.

PLANE AND MIDDLE LATITUDE SAILING

So far we have only considered the distance between two places on the same parallel of latitude. It is now necessary to consider how the rhumb line course and distance between two places on different parallels may be found.

A and B in Fig. 24 are two such places situated on the parallels dd and $d'd'$ respectively, and AB is the rhumb line between them.

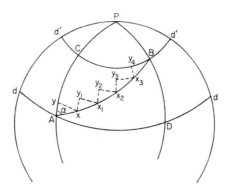

Fig. 24

Since AB is a rhumb line, then its direction is constant, and is equal to the angle CAB which is the rhumb line course between A and B. Similarly, the d.lat is the arc AC or BD.

The departure, however, is not measured along the parallel of A or B, but along some intermediate parallel, which is known as the parallel of true middle altitude. This parallel does not lie exactly midway between A and B, although if the distance is small, say, up to 600 miles, it may be considered to do so without appreciable error, and the departure may be regarded as being measured along the parallel of mean latitude. For greater distances, however, the true middle latitude must be used. This is found by applying a correction to the mean latitude. The value of this correction is given in special tables which are reproduced at the end of the book.

In order to find the course and distance between A and B, let us divide AB into a number of small divisions, AX, XX_1, XX_2, etc.

If we now draw in the meridians and parallels passing through these points we obtain a number of triangles, AYX, XY_1X_1, $X_1Y_2X_2$, etc., and since we have deliberately made the distances small, then these triangles may be considered as right-angled plane triangles.

Consider one of these triangles, AYX.

AY is the d.lat between A and X.
XY is the dep. between A and X.
AX is the distance between A and X.
YAX is the course between A and X.

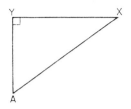

Fig. 25

The dep. XY is strictly the departure measured along the parallel of X, but since the distance between A and X is very small, there is no appreciable change in the departure between A and X, so that XY may be assumed to be the true departure.

Since $\angle AYX = 90°$
then $XY/AY = \tan \angle YAX$
i.e. dep./d.lat $= \tan$ course.
Also $AX = XY \times \operatorname{cosec} \angle YAX$
i.e. distance $=$ dep. $\times \operatorname{cosec}$ course.

This can be done with each of the small triangles in turn and the distances between the various points found as above. The sum of these distances is the total distance between A and B.

Thus, $AB = AX + XX_1 + X_1X_2 + X_2X_3 + X_3B$.

But, $AX = XY \operatorname{cosec} \alpha$, $XX_1 = X_1Y_1 \operatorname{cosec} \alpha$ and so on.

$\therefore AB = XY \operatorname{cosec} \alpha + X_1Y_1.\operatorname{cosec} \alpha + X_2Y_2.\operatorname{cosec} \alpha + X_3Y_3.\operatorname{cosec} \alpha$
$\quad + BY_4 \operatorname{cosec} \alpha = \operatorname{cosec} \alpha(XY + X_1Y_1 + X_2Y_2 + X_3Y_3 + BY_4)$.

The expression in the bracket represents the sum of the departures between the various points along AB and is equal to the true departure between A and B.

Thus distance$_{(A-B)}$ $=$ true dep.$_{(A-B)}$ $\times \operatorname{cosec}$ course.

Also by similar reasoning it can be shown that,

$$\frac{\text{true dep.}_{(A-B)}}{\text{d.lat}_{(A-B)}} = \tan \text{ course.}$$

These two formulae are true for any distance and provide a means of determining the rhumb line course and distance between any two points. Before they can be used, however, it is necessary to know the departure, and herein lies the difference between plane and middle latitude sailing. In the former the mean latitude is used, whereas in the latter the true middle latitude is used.

Thus, for plane sailing,
  dep. = d.long × cos mean lat
and for middle latitude sailing,
  dep. = d.long × cos true mid lat.

Since the use of the mean latitude in determining the departure is only accurate for short distances, it follows that plane sailing may only be used for distances up to about 600 miles. Middle latitude sailing, on the other hand, may be used for any distance.

The following four examples should illustrate the methods of solving both types of sailings. The first two are worked by the plane sailing method, whilst the last two are worked by the middle latitude method. The student should work each of them out by the other method as an exercise and compare the difference in answers.

EXAMPLE 5

Find the course and distance between A in lat 26°47′N long 34°16′W and B in lat 32°38′N long 39°56′W.

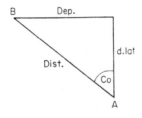

Fig. 26

A lat 26°47′N	long 34°16′W	A lat 26°47′N
B lat 32°38′N	long 39°56′W	B lat 32°38′N
05°51′N	05°40′W	2)59°25′
×60	×60	Mean lat 29°42½′N
d.lat 351′N	d.long 340′W	

dep. = d.long × cos mean lat
  d.long 340   log 2·5315
  mean lat 29°42½′ log cos $\bar{1}$·9388

    dep.   log 2·4703
       dep. 295·3
     distance = dep. × cosec course
       dep. 295·3   log 2·4703
       course 40°05′ log cosec 0·1911

     distance   log 2·6614
      Distance 458·5 miles.

dep./d.lat = tan course
  dep. 295·3 log 2·4703
  d.lat 351 log 2·5453

  course log tan $\bar{1}$·9250
  course N40°05′W

EXAMPLE 6

A vessel in lat 38°46′S long 111°31′E steers a course of 056°(T) for 393 miles. Find her final position.

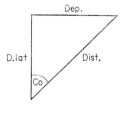

Fig. 27

From the figure
       d.lat = distance × cos course
       dist. 393   log 2·5944
       course 56° log cos $\bar{1}$·7476

       d.lat   log 2·3420
         d.lat 219·8

dep. = distance × sin course
distance 393 log 2·5944
course 56° log sin $\bar{1}$·9186

dep.   log 2·5130
  dep. 325·8

1st lat 38°46′S
½ d.lat 01°49·9′N

mean lat 36°56·1′S

$$d.long = dep. \times sec \ mean \ lat$$

$$\begin{array}{ll} dep. \ 325 \cdot 8 & log \ 2 \cdot 5130 \\ mean \ lat \ 36°56 \cdot 1' & log \ sec \ 0 \cdot 0973 \end{array}$$

$$\begin{array}{ll} d.long & log \ 2 \cdot 6103 \end{array}$$

d.long 407·7

1st lat	38°46′S	long 111°31′E
d.lat	03°39·8′N	d.long 06°47·7′E

Final lat 35°06·2′N	long 118°18·7′E

EXAMPLE 7

Find the course and distance between X in lat 49°58′N long 06°24′W and Y in lat 37°08′N long 34°18′W.

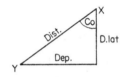

Fig. 28

X lat 49°58′N	long 06°24′W	49°58′
Y lat 37°08′N	long 34°18′W	37°08′
12°50′S	27°54′W	2)87°06′
×60	×60	
		mean lat 43°33′N
d.lat 770′S	d.long 1674′W	corr. +9′
		true mid lat 43°42′N

dep. = d.long × cos mid lat	dep./d.lat = tan course
d.long 1674 log 3·2238	dep. 1211 log 3·0829
mid lat 43°42′ log cos $\overline{1}$·8591	d.lat 770 log 2·8865
dep. log 3·0829	course log tan 0·1964
dep. 1211′	course S57°32′W or 237°32′

$$\text{distance} = \text{dep.} \times \text{cosec co.}$$

dep. 1211   log 3·0829

course 57°33′ log cosec 0·0738

distance   log 3·1567

Distance 1434 miles

EXAMPLE 8

A vessel in lat 38°27′S long 177°18′E steers a course of 118°(T) for 1560 miles. Find her final position.

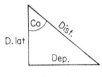

Fig. 29

$$\text{dep.} = \text{distance} \times \text{sin course}$$

distance 1560   log 3·1931

course 62° log sin $\bar{1}$·9459

dep.   log 3·1390

dep. 1377′

$$\text{d.lat} = \text{distance} \times \text{cos course}$$

distance 1560   log 3·1931

course 62° log cos $\bar{1}$·6716

d.lat   log 2·8647

d.lat 732·3′

1st lat 38°27′S

½ d.lat 06°06·2′S

mean lat 44°33·2′S

corr.   +7′

true mid lat 44°40·2′

$$\text{d.long.} = \text{dep.} \times \text{sec mid lat}$$

dep. 1377′   log 3·1390

mid lat 44°40·2′ log sec 0·1480

d.long   log 3·2870

d.long 1936′ = 32°16′E

1st position   lat 38°27′S   long 177°18′E

            d.lat 12°12·3′S   d.long   32°16′E

Final position   lat 50°39·3′S   long 150°26′W

The student should note the way in which the figures in the foregoing examples were drawn, as it is important that these be drawn correctly.

The following four diagrams show how the figures should be drawn for each of the four quadrants.

(i) Course N-E   (ii) Course S-E   (iii) Course S-W   (iv) Course N-W

Fig. 30

EXERCISE III(b)

1. In each of the following, find the course and distance by plane sailing.
    (a) Between *A* in lat 42°56′N long 25°47′W
          and *B* in lat 44°23′N long 23°02′W.
    (b) Between *A* in lat 53°39′S long 135°26′E
          and *B* in lat 57°28′S long 134°01′E.
    (c) Between *A* in lat 16°52′S long 08°51′W
          and *B* in lat 12°46′S long 11°23′W.

2. In each of the following, find the course and distance by middle latitude sailing.
    (a) Between *A* in lat 36°33′N long 58°36′E
          and *B* in lat 40°53′N long 76°53′W.
    (b) Between *A* in lat 39°26′S long 175°32′E
          and *B* in lat 52°09′S long 156°42′W.
    (c) Between *A* in lat 52°46′N long 47°56′E
          and *B* in lat 46°27′N long 15°34′W.

3. A vessel leaves a position in lat 46°18′N long 25°49′E and steers a course of 126°(T) for 352 miles. Find her final position.

4. Find the course and distance between San Francisco in lat 37°48′N long 122°14′W and Honolulu in lat 21°18′N long 157°32′W.

5. A vessel leaves a position in lat 42°56′S long 113°31′E and steers a course of 298°(T) until she arrives in lat 31°42′S. How far has she steamed, and what is her final longitude?

6. A vessel in long 67°30′W steers a south-easterly course for 342 miles and arrives in long 63°17′W. If she changes her latitude by 4°26′S find the course she has steered and the parallels between which she has sailed.

7. A vessel leaves New York (lat 40°42′N long 74°00′W) at 0800 hr G.M.T. on the 1st May for Madeira (lat 32°38′N long 16°55′W). Find the course to steer and the E.T.A. at Madeira if the vessel's speed is 12 kt.

8. A vessel leaves Boston on the 4th August at 1000 hr G.M.T. for Land's End. After steaming for six days, she receives orders to proceed to Gibraltar. Find the position of the vessel when she alters course, the course and distance to steam from the alteration position to Gibraltar, and the E.T.A. at Gibraltar. Assume a speed of 10 kt throughout.

(Boston: lat 42°21′N long 71°03′W
Land's End: lat 50°04′N long 05°45′W
Gibraltar: lat 36°07′N long 05°21′W)

THE TRAVERSE TABLE

This is a table which enables plane right-angled triangles to be solved by inspection rather than by calculation.

The table is designed for the rapid solution of plane sailing problems, and covers all distances up to 600 miles (plane sailing limits). Extracts from the traverse table appear at the end of the book for all distances up to 100 miles, and these extracts will be quite adequate for giving the student practice in the use of the tables and also for solving the problems in the book.

The table is entered with the course angle at the head of the page and the distance in the left hand column. The d.lat and the dep. may then be read off directly in their respective columns. Suppose the course was 155°(T), and the distance 63 miles. The table would be entered with an angle of 25° (180°–155°), and a distance of 63 miles. The d.lat and dep. would be found to be 57·1′S and 26·6′E respectively.

Alternatively, it may be necessary to find the course and distance corresponding to a given d.lat and dep. In this case the table should be searched until the given d.lat and dep. are found together. The corresponding course and distance can then be read off directly. Generally speaking, a certain amount of interpolation is necessary for doing this, and the method is shown in the following example.

It should be noted that when the course angle exceeds 45°, the table is entered with the course angle at the bottom of the page, and that the columns for d.lat and dep. are now reversed.

EXAMPLE 9

Find the course and distance corresponding to a d.lat of 44·8′S and a dep. of 21·3′E.

With a course of S25°E a d.lat of 44·8′ gives dep. 20·9′ and distance 49·6.
With a course of S26°E a d.lat of 44·8′ gives dep. 21·9′ and distance 49·9.

The departure required lies between these two, so that the course must lie between S25°E, and S26°E, and the distance between 49·6 and 49·9 miles.

The true course and distance are then found by interpolation to be S25½°E and 49·7 miles.

CONVERSION OF DEP. INTO D.LONG AND VICE VERSA

This is a necessary operation in plane sailing, and may be done by means of the traverse table as follows.

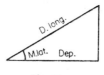

Fig. 31

Figure 31 is the parallel sailing triangle which illustrates the parallel sailing formula.

If the plane sailing triangle is referred to it will be seen that the distance and d.lat form the hypotenuse and the adjacent side of the triangle to the course angle. Similarly, in Fig. 31, the d.long and dep. form the hypotenuse and the adjacent side to the mean lat.

Therefore, if the mean lat, d.long and dep. are substituted in the traverse table for the course, distance, and d.lat, then the departure can be converted into d.long by direct inspection of the table.

For convenience, d.long and dep. are printed in italics above the distance and d.lat columns in the traverse table.

Suppose the mean lat is 54° and the d.long 76′, then by inspection, the dep. is found to be 44′·7.

Example 10

Find the course and distance by means of the traverse table between *A* in lat 36°08N long 76°36′W and *B* in lat 34°56′N long 76°03′W.

A lat	36°08′N	long 76°36′W	36°08′N
B lat	34°56′N	long 76°03′W	34°56′N

	01°12′S	00°33′E	2)71°04′
	× 60	× 60	
			mean lat 35°32′N
d.lat	72′S	d.long 33′E	

From traverse table:
  With d.long 33′ and mean lat 35½°
    dep. 26·9′E

  With d.lat 72′ and dep. 26·9′
    Course   S20½°E or 159½°   Distance 76·5 miles.

54

EXAMPLE 11

A lighthouse in lat 45°26′N long 09°19′W is observed from a ship to bear N64°W, and 16 miles distant. What is the position of the ship?

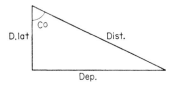

Fig. 32

Since the lighthouse bears N64°W from the ship, it follows that the ship bears S64°E from the lighthouse.

The position of the ship, then, can be found by laying off a course of S64°E and a distance of 16 miles from the lighthouse.

With course S64°E and distance 16 miles

d.lat 7′S   dep. 14·4′E

Lighthouse lat 45°24′N   With mean lat 45°20′N and dep. 14·4′E
½ d.lat   3·5′S   d.long 20·5′E

Mean lat.   45°20·5′N
            Lighthouse lat 45°24′N   long   09°19′W
            d.lat   7′S   d.long   20·5′E

            Ship's lat   45°17′N   long   08°58·5′W.

EXERCISE III(c)
1. Find the d.lat and dep. corresponding to the following courses and distances.
    (a) course N44°E, distance 56 miles,   (b) course 280°, distance 16·5 miles,
    (c) course 160°, distance 92·3 miles,   (d) course SW, distance 67·6 miles,
    (e) course N, distance 49·8 miles,   (f) course 190½°, distance 85·5 miles.
2. Find the courses and distances corresponding to the following d.lats and deps.
    (a) d.lat 46·2′S dep. 21·6′W,   (b) d.lat 84·9′N dep. 16·5′E,
    (c) d.lat 40·3′S dep. 28·9′E,   (d) d.lat 28·9′N dep. 40·3′W,
    (e) d.lat 66·5′N dep. 65·3′W,   (f) d.lat 16·4′S dep. 97·8′W.
3. Find the dep. in each of the following.
    (a) lat 10°30′N d.long 69′W,   (b) lat 20°15′N d.long 18·7′E,
    (c) lat 65°00′N d.long 88·2′E,   (d) lat 69°36′N d.long 25·6′E.
4. Find the d.long in each of the following.
    (a) lat 36°00′N dep. 18·5′E,   (b) lat 20°15′N dep. 29·7′E,
    (c) lat 79°30′S dep. 12·8′W,   (d) lat 45°18′N dep. 64·3′E.
5. Use the traverse table to find the course and distance between A in lat 63°44′N, long 79°36′E, and B in lat 64°22′N, long 79°04′E.
6. A lighthouse in lat 20°43′N long 72°48′E bears 044°(T) distance 14 miles from a ship. What is the position of the ship, and what is the position of another ship 20 miles due East of the lighthouse?

7. A vessel is in lat 24°46′S long 38°42′W. She steams 215°(T) at 12 kt for 4 hr, when she observes a lighthouse bearing 080°(T), distance 10 miles. What is the position of the lighthouse?

8. A vessel in lat 46°18′N long 179°47′E steers 101° (T) for 56 miles. What is her final position?

THE DAY'S WORK

During the course of a day a vessel may steer a number of different courses, and it is necessary to find the average course and distance made good during the day, and also the vessel's dead reckoning (D.R.) position. The D.R. position is the position arrived at after laying off the various courses and distances steamed by the vessel, but making no allowance for the set and drift of the current or tide.

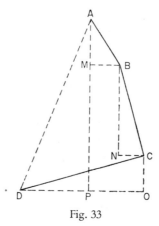

Fig. 33

Suppose *AB*, *BC*, and *CD* are the courses steered by a ship in the course of a day.

The total d.lat made good by the ship during the day (*AP*) is equal to the sum of the individual d.lats made good along each course (*AM*, *BN*, and *CO*).

Similarly, the total dep. made good (*DP*) is equal to the algebraic sum of the individual deps. made good along each course (*BM*, *CN*, and *OD*).

These individual d.lats and deps. can be found by inspection of the traverse table so that the total d.lat and dep. can easily be obtained. From this, the course and distance and the D.R. position can be obtained.

This is what is known as "The Day's Work" and the method of solving the problem is shown in the following examples.

Example 12

A vessel in lat 55°37′N long 45°18′W steers the following courses and distances: 135°(T) for 30 miles, 260°(T) for 54 miles, and 169°(T) for 42 miles. Find the final position of the ship and the course and distance made good, assuming a current to have set the ship 306°(T) for 9 miles during the run.

Course	Distance	d.lat		Departure	
		N	S	E	W
S45°E	30		21·2	21·2	
S80°W	54		9·4		53·2
S11°E	42		41·2	8·0	
N54°W	9	5·3			7·3

5·3N 71·8S 29·2E 60·5W
71·8S   29·2E

d.lat 66·5′S   dep. 31·3′W
Course 205·3°   Distance 73·5 miles.
1st lat 55°37′N   long 45°18′W   mean lat 55°03·7′N
d.lat 01°06·5′S   d.long 54·6′W   d.long 54·6′W

2nd lat 54°30·5′N long 46°12·6′W

The courses should be set out in the form of a table as shown, and the current treated as another course and distance.

Example 13

At noon on the 1st August, a vessel is in lat 44°38′N long 136°18′E. During the next 24 hr she steamed as follows:

1200 set course 032°(C) var. 10°W dev. 2°W log 0
2000 a/c   287°(C) var. 10°W dev. 2°E   log 56
0300 a/c   340°(C) var. 10°W dev. 4°E   log 104
0630 a/c   215°(C) var. 10°W dev. nil   log 129
1200 log 169.

During the day, a current set the ship 270°(T) for 10 miles. Find the vessel's position at noon on the 2nd August and the course and distance made good.

	(1)	(2)	(3)	(C)
	032°(C)	287°(C)	340°(C)	215°(C)
Error	12°W	8°W	6°W	10°W
1st course	020°(T)	2nd course 279°(T)	3rd course 334°(T)	4th course 205°(T)

Course	Distance	d.lat N	d.lat S	Departure E	Departure W
N20°E	56	52·6		19·2	
N81°W	48	7·5			47·4
N26°W	25	22·5			11·0
S25°W	40		36·3		16·9
W	10				10·0

82·6N 36·3S 19·2E 85·3W
36·3S   19·2E

d.lat   46·3′N   dep. 66·1′W
Course N55°W or 305°
Distance 80·7 miles

1st August lat   44°38′N   long   136°18′E   mean lat 45°01·2′N
d.lat   46·3′N   d.long   1°33·5′W   d.long   93·5′W

2nd August lat 45°24·3′N   long   134°44·5′E

N.B. The log indicates the number of miles the vessel has steamed since noon, when the log is set to zero. For instance, at 2000 hr, the log read 56 and the course was altered to 287°(C). Therefore, between 1200 hr and 2000 hr the vessel had steamed for 56 miles on a course of 032°(C).

EXAMPLE 14

At noon on April 5th, a vessel observes a lighthouse in lat 45°34′S long 89°11′E, bearing 291°(T), distance 16 miles. Between then and noon on the 6th her courses are as follows:

1200 course 083°(C) var. 20°E dev. 2°W speed 10 kt
1630 a/c   289°(C) var. 20°E dev. 6°E speed 10 kt
0230 a/c   000°(C) var. 20°E dev. 1°E speed 10 kt
0730 a/c   049°(C) var. 20°E dev. 4°W speed 10 kt.

A current set the ship 169°(T) for 43 miles during the day. Find the ship's position at noon on the 6th April, and the course and distance made good.

In this problem the position of the ship at noon on the 5th must, first of all, be worked out from the position of the lighthouse, as previously explained. The rest of the problem is then as before.

Lighthouse lat 45°34'S   long   89°11'E   Reversed bearing
d.lat   5·7'S   d.long   21·3'E   S69°E—dist 16 miles
                   ———   ———   mean lat 45°37'S
5th April lat   45°39·7'S   long   89°32·3'E   dep. 14·9'E
                                            d.long 21·3'E

	083°(C)	289°(C)	‚000°(C)	049°(C)
Error	18°E	26°E	21°E	16°E

1st		2nd		3rd		4th	
course	101°(T)	course 315°(T)		course 021°(T)		course 065°(T)	

		d.lat		Departure	
Course	Distance	N	S	E	W
S79°E	45		08·6	44·2	
N45°W	100	70·7			70·7
N21°E	50	46·7		17·9	
N65°E	45	19·0		40·8	
S11°E	43		42·2	08·2	

                 136·4'N 50·8'S 111·1'E 70·7'W
                     50·8'S   111·1'E

          d.lat 85·6'N   dep. 40·4'E

Course $025\frac{1}{4}°$(T) or $N25\frac{1}{4}°E$(T)   Distance 94·6 miles.
5th April lat 45°39·7'   d.long 89°32·3'E   mean lat 45°N
d.lat   01°25·6'N   d.long 00°57·1'E   d.long 57·1'E

6th April lat 44°14·1'S   long   90°29·4'E

EXERCISE III(d)

1. In each of the following, find the course and distance made good.
    (a) 080°(T) for 42 miles; 201°(T) for 36 miles; 145°(T) for 27 miles; 045°(T) for 45 miles.
    (b) 180°(T) for 22 miles; 290°(T) for 73 miles; 159°(T) for 68 miles; 270°(T) for 16 miles.
    (c) 125°(T) for 43 miles; 351°(T) for 70 miles; 044°(T) for 68 miles; 190°(T) for 66 miles.

2. At 1200 hr on the 15th August a vessel is in lat 36°15′N long 79°15′W. She then steers as follows:
    1200–1530 co. 135°(C) var. 20°E dev. 4°E dist. 40 miles
    1530–2200 co. 245°(C) var. 20°E dev. 6°W dist. 64 miles
    2200–0030 co. 094°(C) var. 20°E dev. 1°E dist. 28 miles
    0030–0300 co. 208°(C) var. 20°E dev. 2°W dist. 27 miles.
    A current set 340°(T) at 1 kt during the run. Find the vessel's position at 0300 hr on the 16th, and the course and distance made good.

3. At 1200 hr on the 6th September a vessel's position is lat 21°16′N long 138°18′W. During the next 24 hr she steers the following courses:
    1200 set course 105°(C) var. 12°W dev. 7°E log 0
    1600 a/c 051°(C) var. 12°W dev. 3°W log 48
    2015 a/c 018°(C) var. 12°W dev. 6°W log 98
    2315 a/c 319°(C) var. 12°W dev. 1°W log 132
    0315 a/c 225°(C) var. 12°W dev. 2°E log 178
    0745 a/c 355°(C) var. 12°W dev. 3°W log 232
    1200 log 280.
    A current set 205°(T) at 1½ kt throughout the day. Find the vessel's position at noon on the 7th September and the course and distance made good.

4. At noon on the 2nd December a vessel is in lat 64°18′S long 179°42′E. Her courses from then until noon on the 3rd December are as follows:
    1200 set course 301°(C) var. 15°W dev. 4°E speed 10 kt
    1624 a/c 207°(C) var. 15°W dev. 3°W speed 10 kt
    2012 a/c 123°(C) var. 15°W dev. 7°W speed 10 kt
    0600 a/c 199°(C) var. 15°W dev. 4°W speed 10 kt
    1000 a/c 248°(C) var. 15°W dev. 1°E speed 10 kt.
    A current set 305° (M) at ¾ kt throughout the day. Find the vessel's position at noon on the 3rd December and the course and distance made good.

5. At 1200 hr on the 13th April, a vessel observes a lighthouse in lat 20°10′N long 58°19′W, bearing 335°(T), distance 10 miles. Her courses from then until 1200 hr on the following day are as follows:
    1200 set course 207°(C) var. 6°W dev. 4°E log 0
    1710 a/c 248°(C) var. 6°W dev. 7°E log 62
    2320 a/c 343°(C) var. 6°W dev. 2°E log 136
    0500 a/c 047°(C) var. 6°W dev. 5°W log 202
    1200 log 297.
    A current set 170°(T) at ½ kt throughout the day. Find the vessel's position at noon on the 14th, and the course and distance made good.

6. At 1200 hr on the 21st July, a vessel observes a point of land in lat 44°41′N long 119°18′E, bearing 020°(T), distance 16 miles. She then steams as follows until noon on the following day:
    1200 set course 153°(C) var. 10°E dev. 4°W speed, 12 kt
    1830 a/c 051°(C) var. 10°E dev. 3°E speed 12 kt
    0030 a/c 335°(C) var. 10°E dev. 5°E speed 10 kt
    0854 a/c 259°(C) var. 10°E dev. 1°E speed 10 kt.
    A current set the ship 025°(M) at 1 kt throughout the day.
    Find the vessel's position at noon on the 22nd, and the course and distance made good.

7. At noon on the 18th January a vessel sighted a point of land in lat 20°15′S long 18°19′W, bearing 201°(T), distance 10 miles. She then steamed the following courses and distances until noon on the 19th:

1200 set course 130°(C) var. 8°W dev. 3°E log 0
1700 a/c 200°(C) var. 8°W dev. 2°W log 50
2348 a/c 295°(C) var. 8°W dev. 6°W log 118
0748 a/c 351°(C) var. 8°W dev. 3°W log 198
1200 log 240.

Find the D.R. position of the ship at noon on the 19th, and if the observed position at this time was lat 20°21·2′S long 19°42·1′W, find the set and drift of the current.

8. At noon on the 24th August a vessel was in lat 55°17′N long 17°24′W. She then steamed the following courses and distances until noon on the 25th:

1200 set course 006°(C) var. 2°E dev. 2°E speed 12 kt
1800 a/c 147°(C) var. 2°E dev. 5°W speed 12 kt
2230 a/c 117°(C) var. 2°E dev. 3°W speed 12 kt
0330 a/c 180°(C) var. 2°E dev. 2°W speed 12 kt
0510 a/c 220°(C) var. 2°E dev. 3°E speed 12 kt.

A current set the vessel 033°(M) for 27 miles during the day. Find the position at noon on the 25th, and the course and distance made good. Find also the bearing and distance off a lighthouse in lat 54°43′N long 16°23½′W at this time.

THE MERCATOR CHART

The representation of the earth's surface on a plane sheet of paper is not easy as the earth is spherical in shape. The difficulty can easily be realized by cutting an orange in half and removing the pulp. If one of the halves is then placed on to a plane surface and pressed flat, it will be seen that the skin becomes torn in several places.

There are many different methods used for projecting the surface of the earth on to a plane, but only two of these, namely the Mercator and the Gnomonic projections, will be discussed here.

The Mercator projection was first evolved by a Dutch cartographer named Gerard Kramer, the latinized form of whose name is Mercator. He used it in a world map which he published in 1569, but it was not until 1630 that it came into general use in navigation.

The Mercator projection is known to cartographers as a "cylindrical orthomorphic" projection. The word orthomorphic means "correct shape", and its orthomorphic property is one of the advantages of the chart. The main advantage, however, as far as navigation is concerned, is the fact that rhumb lines appear as straight lines. This is of prime importance to the navigator, since it means that all courses steered are represented as straight lines on the chart.

In order that rhumb lines may be represented as straight lines, the meridians must be drawn parallel to each other. This involves a considerable amount of distortion, for the meridians are not parallel to each other but converge towards the poles. The amount of the distortion required is not constant but

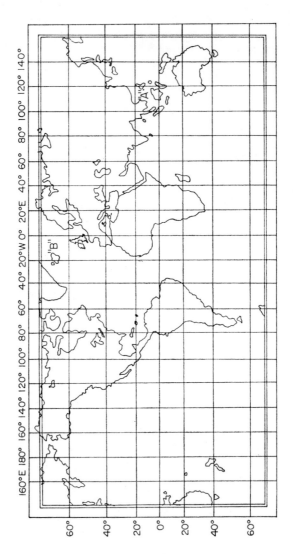

Fig. 34

increases as the poles are approached. Near the equator the meridians are very nearly parallel to each other so that little or no distortion is required; but as the latitude increases, so the convergence of the meridians increases also, and more and more distortion is required. In order that the correct shape of land masses be preserved, it is necessary to increase the distance between successive parallels in the same proportion as the distance between the meridians.

The distortion of the meridians is proportional to the secant of the latitude, so that the distance between successive parallels also varies as the secant of the latitude.

Thus, on a Mercator chart, the meridians appear as parallel straight lines, equal distances apart, while the parallels of latitude appear as straight lines parallel to the equator, but whose distance apart increases as the poles are approached.

Figure 34, is a Mercator chart of the world, and the increased spacing of the parallels can easily be seen. The shapes of the land masses are correctly represented but their relative size is deceptive. Borneo (A), on the equator, appears to be about the same size as Iceland (B), whereas, in actual fact, it is about five and a half times as large. This indicates that, although the shapes of the land masses are correctly shown, their scales vary considerably, due to the increased spacing of the parallels.

The longitude scale is constant in any part of the chart, but the latitude scale, which is also the scale of distance, varies as the secant of the latitude.

Thus

$$\text{lat scale} = \text{long scale} \times \text{sec lat}$$

or,

$$\text{length of } 1' \text{ of lat on chart} = \text{length of } 1' \text{ of long} \times \text{sec lat.}$$

Suppose the scale of longitude is 1 in. to 1 min of longitude, then at the equator, the length of 1 min of latitude will be given by:

$$\begin{aligned}
\text{lat scale} &= 1'' \times \sec 0° \\
&= 1 \times 1\cdot0 \\
&= 1 \text{ in.}
\end{aligned}$$

and at latitude 50°:

$$\begin{aligned}
\text{lat scale} &= 1'' \times \sec 50° \\
&= 1 \times 1\cdot556 \\
&= 1\cdot556 \text{ in.}
\end{aligned}$$

and at the pole:

$$\begin{aligned}
\text{lat scale} &= 1'' \times \sec 90° \\
&= 1 \times \infty \\
&= \infty.
\end{aligned}$$

It can be seen, therefore, that the latitude scale increases with the latitude until the pole is reached when it is so large that it cannot be measured (∞). For this reason, the Polar regions cannot be represented on a Mercator chart, and charts of these regions are produced from Gnomonic projections.

NATURAL SCALE

The natural scale of a chart is given by the ratio:

$$\text{nat. scale} = \frac{\text{chart length}}{\text{earth distance}}.$$

It is normally expressed as the relationship that $1'$ of longitude on the chart bears to the length of $1'$ of longitude on the earth in that latitude.

Suppose that the length of $1'$ of longitude on the chart is 0.34 in., and that the latitude is $47°N$.

Now the length of $1'$ of longitude in any latitude is the departure in that latitude corresponding to a d.long of $1'$.

Therefore, using the formula:
$$\text{dep.} = \text{d.long} \times \cos \text{lat}$$
$$\text{length of } 1' \text{ of long in lat } 47°N = (1 \times \cos 47°) \text{ miles}$$
$$= (1 \times 6080 \times 12 \cos 47°) \text{ in.}$$

$$\text{nat. scale} = \frac{\text{chart length}}{\text{earth distance}} = \frac{0.34}{1 \times 6080 \times \cos 47° \times 12}.$$

$$\text{nat. scale} = \frac{1}{146,350}.$$

CONSTRUCTION OF A CHART

A Mercator chart can be quite easily and accurately constructed from the foregoing if reasonable care is taken.

The following example shows how this may be done.

EXAMPLE 14

Construct a chart on Mercator's principle to cover the area between lat $48°N$ and $52°N$, and between long $0°20'E$ and $6°40'W$, to a natural scale of $1/765,000$ in lat $50°N$.

The first step is to calculate the longitude scale from the natural scale given. If $1°$ of longitude on the chart is x in.

then $\quad x = $ length of 1° of long on earth in 50°N × natural scale

$$x = \frac{60 \times 6080 \times 12 \times \cos 50°}{765,000}$$

$$x = 3 \cdot 678 \text{ in.}$$

The longitude scale then, is 1° = 3·678 in.

Since the chart covers 7° of longitude, then the breadth of the chart is 7 × 3·678 = 25·746 in.

Next the latitude scale must be calculated. Strictly speaking, the length of each minute of latitude should be calculated separately, but this is laborious and unnecessary for it would be impossible to measure the small differences in the lengths with the normal measuring instruments available to a student. It is, then, sufficiently accurate for this chart if the distance apart of each whole degree is calculated separately.

48°N–49°N

$$1° \text{ of lat} = 1° \text{ of long} \times \sec \text{ mean lat}$$
$$= 3 \cdot 678 \times \sec 48°30'$$
$$\text{length on chart} = 5 \cdot 551 \text{ in.}$$

49°N–50°N

$$\text{length on chart} = 3 \cdot 678 \times \sec 49°30'$$
$$= 5 \cdot 663 \text{ in.}$$

50°N–51°N

$$\text{length on chart} = 3 \cdot 678 \times \sec 50°30'$$
$$= 5 \cdot 782 \text{ in.}$$

51°N–52°N

$$\text{length on chart} = 3 \cdot 678 \times \sec 51°30'$$
$$= 5 \cdot 909 \text{ in.}$$

Adding those separate lengths together, the height of the chart is found to be 22·905 in.

The frame of the chart can now be drawn in. Great care must be taken here to ensure that the frame is an exact rectangle.

After completing the frame, the parallels and meridians should be drawn in at one degree intervals and then the lat and long scales subdivided into minutes. The best way of doing this is to divide the degrees into 5 min intervals, either by direct measurement, or by means of a diagonal scale. The minutes should then be inserted freehand. This is quite allowable as the distance between the individual minutes is so very small that no appreciable error will be caused by drawing them in in this manner.

The chart is now completed, except for a compass rose which should be inserted in a suitable position. This is easily done by placing a protractor on the chart and marking off the degrees directly from it.

The chart described above actually covers the area around the English Channel, and the coasts of England and France could be inserted by plotting the position of various points and drawing in the coastline between them. This is a useful exercise and would provide the student with a proper Mercator chart.

MERIDIONAL PARTS

The latitude scale of the chart varies as the secant of the latitude, and increases as the poles are approached. It cannot, therefore, be readily compared with the fixed longitude scale. In order that comparison may be made, the distance apart of the parallels of latitude is expressed in longitude units, or meridional parts, as they are called.

A meridional part, therefore, is the length on the chart of one minute of longitude and the meridional parts for any latitude is the number of longitude units between the equator and the parallel of that latitude.

A table of meridional parts is contained at the end of the book, and if the student will consult these he will see that the meridional parts for lat 56°N is 4054·5. This means that there are 4054·5 long units between the equator and lat 56°.

DIFFERENCE OF MERIDIONAL PARTS (D.M.P.)

This is the difference between the meridional parts for any two latitudes.

For instance, suppose a place A is in lat 50°N and another place B is in lat 40°N. The D.M.P. between the two places would be the difference between the meridional parts of the two places, thus:

$$A \text{ lat } 50°N \text{ M.P.} \quad 3456·5$$
$$B \text{ lat } 40°N \text{ M.P.} \quad 2607·6$$

$$\text{D.M.P.}(A—B) \quad 848·9$$

The rules for finding D.M.P. are the same as for finding d.lat, i.e. same name, subtract: different names, add.

The use of meridional parts provides a ready way of determining the latitude scale in constructing a chart. In the chart illustrated above, the length of 1° of longitude was found to be 3·678 in. By definition, the length of a meridional part is the chart length of 1' of long. Therefore, the length of a mer. part on the chart is 3·678/60 = 0·0613 in.

Taking the section between 49° and 50°,

$$49° \text{ M.P.} \quad 3364\cdot4$$
$$50° \text{ M.P.} \quad 3456\cdot5$$

$$\text{D.M.P.} \quad 92\cdot1$$

Thus, there are 92·1 meridional parts between 49°N and 50°N so that the distance on the chart between these two parallels is $92\cdot1 \times 0\cdot0613 = 5\cdot646$ in.

This differs by 0·017 in. from the result previously obtained and is the more accurate, since it approximates more closely to the methods used by hydrographers.

ADVANTAGES AND DISADVANTAGES

The advantages and disadvantages of the Mercator chart may be summarized as follows:

Advantages

(1) Rhumb lines appear as straight lines.
(2) The latitude scale is also the scale of distance.
Rue (3) ~~Compass~~ bearings may be laid off directly on to the chart.
(4) Shapes of land masses, in the neighbourhood of a point, are correctly shown.

Disadvantages

(1) In high latitudes the distortion of land masses becomes excessive.
(2) Polar regions cannot be shown.
(3) The latitude scale is also the scale of distance, and since this is a variable scale, care must be taken to see that distances are measured on that part of the latitude scale which lies opposite to the area being used.

MERCATOR SAILING

Figure 35 represents part of a Mercator chart, with *A* and *B* two places on it. The rhumb line distance between *A* and *B* is the line *AB* and the course between *A* and *B* is the angle *CAB*. *CB* is the d.long and *AC* the d.lat between *A* and *B*.

AC and *BC* are in different units, so that it cannot be said that the tangent of the course is the ratio *BC/AC*, unless both can be expressed in the same units. This, however, can be done quite easily, for, by means of the table of

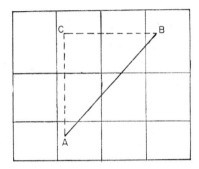

Fig. 35

meridional parts, the d.lat can be expressed in longitude units (D.M.P.). If this is done, then we can say that:

$$\text{tan course} = \frac{\text{d.long}}{\text{D.M.P.}}$$

Thus, in Mercator sailing, the d.lat is expressed in longitude units, whereas in middle latitude and plane sailing the d.long is expressed in nautical miles.

In finding the course and distance by Mercator sailing, two triangles are used: the Mercator sailing triangle (a) for finding the course, and the plane sailing triangle (b) for finding the distance.

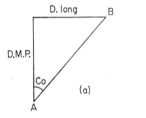
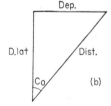

Fig. 36

$$\text{From (a) tan course} = \frac{\text{d.long}}{\text{D.M.P.}}$$

From (b) distance = d.lat × sec course.

EXAMPLE 15

Find the course and distance between A in lat 15°32′N long 12°04′W, and B in lat 45°56′N long 52°36′W.

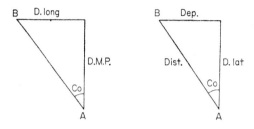

Fig. 37

B lat 45°56′N	long 52°36′W	M.P. 3093
A lat 15°32′N	long 12°04′W	M.P. 937·4
30°24′N	40°32′W	D.M.P. 2155·6
×60	×60	
d.lat 1824′N	d.long 2432′W	

$$\frac{\text{d.long}}{\text{D.M.P.}} = \tan \text{course}$$

d.long 2432 log 3·3860
D.M.P. 2156 log 3·3337

course   log tan 0·0523
    Course N48°26½′W or 311°33½′

distance = d.lat × sec course
d.lat 1824   log 3·2610
course 48°26½′ log sec 0·1782

distance   log 3·4392
    Distance 2749 miles.

EXAMPLE 16

A vessel in lat 25°47′S long 163°48′E steers a course of 038°(T) for 2476 miles. Find her final position.

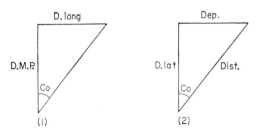

Fig. 38

From (2) d.lat = distance × cos course

$$\text{distance } 2476 \text{ log } 3 \cdot 3938$$
$$\text{course } 38° \text{ log cos } \bar{1} \cdot 8965$$

—

$$\text{d.lat} \qquad \text{log } 3 \cdot 2903$$
$$\text{d.lat} = 1951'\text{N} = 32°31'\text{N.}$$

1st lat   25°47′S   M.P.   1592
d.lat   32°31′N

—

2nd lat   06°44′N   M.P.   402

—

D.M.P.   1994

d.long = D.M.P. × tan course

$$\text{D.M.P. } 1994 \text{ log } 3 \cdot 2997$$
$$\text{course } 38° \quad \text{log tan } \bar{1} \cdot 8928$$

—

$$\text{d.long} \quad \text{log } 3 \cdot 1925$$
$$\text{d.long} = 1558'\text{E} = 25°58'\text{E}$$

1st long 163°48′E
d.long   25°58′E

—

2nd long 170°14′W

Final position: lat 06°44′N   long 170°14′W.

Mercator and middle latitude sailing are both equally accurate, although Mercator sailing is more commonly used as it involves slightly less work. However, middle latitude sailing is more accurate when the course lies nearly East or West, for the following reason.

In Mercator sailing, the secant of the course is used to find the distance. For angles approaching 90°, the secant increases very rapidly, so that very accurate interpolation is necessary in order to obtain an accurate distance. In middle latitude sailing, however, the cosecant of the course is used to find the distance, and for angles approaching 90° the cosecant changes very slowly, so that little or no interpolation is required.

For example, suppose that the d.lat is 600′, and the course 087°. Then, by Mercator sailing,

$$\text{distance} = \text{d.lat} \times \text{sec course}$$
$$= 600 \times \text{sec } 87°$$
$$= 600 \times 19 \cdot 11$$
$$= 11,466 \text{ miles.}$$

Again, using a course of 087°01′:

$$\text{distance} = \text{d.lat} \times \sec 87°01′$$
$$= 600 \times 19{\cdot}21$$
$$= 11{,}526 \text{ miles.}$$

Thus, a change of 1′ in the course causes a change of 60 miles in distance.

Suppose, now, that the departure is 11,000 miles and the course 087°. Then, by middle latitude sailing:

$$\text{distance} = \text{dep.} \times \text{cosec course}$$
$$= 11{,}000 \times \text{cosec } 87°$$
$$= 11{,}000 \times 1{\cdot}0014$$
$$= 11{,}015{\cdot}4 \text{ miles.}$$

Again, using a course of 087°10′:

$$\text{distance} = 11{,}000 \times \text{cosec } 87°10′$$
$$\risingdotseq 11{,}000 \times 1{\cdot}0012$$
$$= 11{,}013{\cdot}2 \text{ miles.}$$

Thus, a change of 10′ causes a change in distance of only 2·2 miles.

The above examples should illustrate quite clearly the advantages of middle latitude sailing for courses around East or West.

EXERCISE III(e)

1. In each of the following, find the course and distance by Mercator sailing:
   (a) From A in lat 23°29′N long 36°18′W
       to B in lat 32°46′N long 09°12′W.
   (b) From X in lat 52°58′S long 79°24′E
       to Y in lat 37°04′S long 58°26′E.
   (c) From L in lat 18°49′N long 172°24′W
       to M in lat 24°16′N long 168°42′E.
2. A vessel in lat 18°16′N long 23°46′W steers a course of 047°(T) for 3590 miles. What is her final position?
3. A vessel in lat 21°04′S long 162°18′E steers a course of 038°(T) for 3980 miles. What is her final position?
4. A vessel in lat 04°16′N long 176°43′ W steers a course of 312°(T) until her longitude is 163°26′E. What is her final latitude, and what distance has she steamed?
5. A vessel leaves a position in lat 26°18′N long 62°43′E and steams for 2342 miles in an easterly direction, when her latitude is then 29°26′N. What is her longitude and what course has she steered?

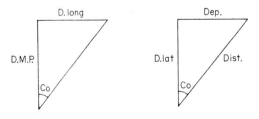

Fig. 39

The above figures are the triangles used in Mercator and middle latitude sailing. Since they are similar triangles, we can say:

$$\frac{\text{D.M.P.}}{\text{d.lat}} = \frac{\text{d.long}}{\text{dep.}} \qquad (1)$$

By the middle latitude formula:

$$\text{d.long} = \text{dep.} \times \sec \text{mid lat.} \qquad (2)$$

Substituting (2) in (1) we get,

$$\frac{\text{D.M.P.}}{\text{d.lat}} = \sec \text{mid lat.} \qquad (3)$$

(3) establishes a useful relationship between D.M.P. and middle latitude and can be used for finding the middle latitude if no correction tables are available.

Problems on the use of the above formula are frequently set in the Ministry of Transport examinations for Second Mate, and the following example is fairly typical. Several exercises on its use are included in the exercise at the end of the chapter.

EXAMPLE 17

The d.lat between two places is 3/5 of the D.M.P. Find the latitudes of the two places assuming that the d.lat is 16°52′.

d.lat   = 3/5 D.M.P.

$$\frac{\text{D.M.P.}}{\text{d.lat}} = \frac{5}{3}$$

$$\text{But,} \ \frac{\text{D.M.P.}}{\text{d.lat}} = \sec \text{mid lat}$$

$$\therefore \ \sec \text{mid lat} = \frac{5}{3}$$

$$\therefore \ \text{mid lat} = 53°08′$$

mid lat	53°08′	mean lat 52°31′	mean lat 52°31′
corr.	−37′	½ d.lat +8°26′	½ d.lat −8°26′
mean lat	52°31′	60°57′	44°05′

Latitudes are 60°57′ and 44°05′N or S.

N.B. The middle latitude is converted to mean latitude and then ½ d.lat is applied each way.

THE GNOMONIC CHART

The gnomonic chart is constructed from what is known as a zenithal projection. In this type of projection, a portion of the earth's surface is projected from the centre of the earth (*O*) on to a plane which is tangential to any convenient point (*K*).

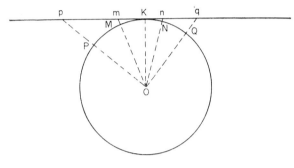

Fig. 40

In Fig. 40, *P* and *Q* represent the pole and the equator, and *M* and *N* are any two points on the central meridian *PKQ*. *p*, *m*, *n*, and *q* represent the projection of these points on the chart.

Now, a great circle is formed by the intersection of a plane passing through the earth's centre with the earth's surface. Also, the intersection of two planes is a straight line. It follows, therefore, that a great circle will be represented on a gnomonic chart by a straight line. It is this property that makes this chart so useful in navigation, for with it the great circle track between any two places can be immediately found by joining the two places with a straight line.

This is the only purpose for which the gnomonic chart is used in navigation, for rhumb lines (other than the equator) do not appear as straight lines, and angles and shapes are distorted, except near the tangent point, so that it cannot be used for measuring courses and distances.

Figure 41 shows a gnomonic chart in which the North Pole is the tangential point. A chart such as this is known as a polar gnomonic chart.

A and *B* represent the positions of New York and Cape St. Vincent, respectively, and the line *AB* is the great circle between them. It is impossible for a vessel to follow the great circle track between two places exactly, as this would involve a constant alteration of course. Instead, a number of points are selected along the great circle and the vessel steers the rhumb line courses between each of these points. The more points there are, the closer will the vessel's track approximate to the true great circle.

73

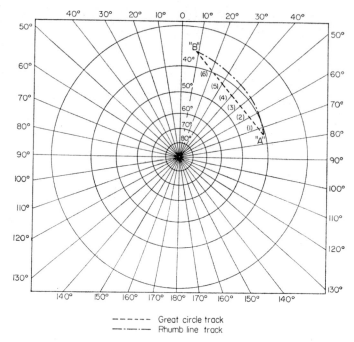

Fig. 41

Suppose that points are to taken every 10° of longitude apart, commencing in 70°W. The positions of these points (1, 2, 3, 4, 5, and 6) are then taken directly from the gnomonic chart and plotted on to the Mercator chart as shown in Fig. 42. The courses and distances can then be laid off directly.

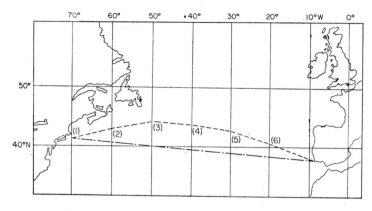

Fig. 42

74

In this way the gnomonic chart can save the navigator considerable time and effort in the calculation of great circle courses.

In the above example, the total distance between New York and Cape St. Vincent, as steered along the various rhumb lines, is 2796 miles, which is only 3 miles more than the true great circle distance of 2793 miles. The rhumb line distance between the two points is 2862 miles.

GREAT CIRCLE SAILING

The shortest distance between two points on the earth's surface is the arc of the great circle contained between these two points. Great circle sailing, then, is the name given to the method of determining the courses and distances along a great circle. Since the course on a great circle is constantly changing, it is necessary to indicate the part of the great circle to which the course applies. Normally, it is the initial course and the final course that is required in problems involving great circle sailing.

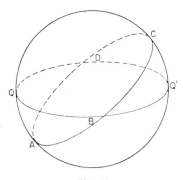

Fig. 43

Before dealing with the actual calculation involved in great circle sailing, let us consider a few points about the great circle itself. In Fig. 43, QQ' is the equator and ABCD any great circle. It will be noted that the great circle always curves towards the pole of the hemisphere in which it is situated so that, on a Mercator chart, the great circle track will always lie to the north of the rhumb line track in the northern hemisphere and to the south of it in the southern hemisphere.

Vertex

This is the point of the great circle nearest to the pole. Every great circle has two vertices, one in the northern and one in the southern hemisphere (C and A in Fig. 43). The course at the vertex is always due East or West.

The great circle shown cuts the equator in two points, B and D. These points are always 180° apart, and the angle between the great circle and the equator at them is equal to the latitude of the vertex. This is obvious, for if the direction of the great circle crossing the equator is 070°, then the plane of it must be inclined to the plane of the equator at an angle of 20° so that its highest point must be situated 20° above and below the equator.

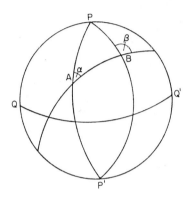

Fig. 44

In Fig. 44, AB is the arc of the great circle passing through A and B. PAP' and PBP' are the meridians passing through A and B. Since PA, PB, and AB are all arcs of great circles, it follows, by definition, that PAB is a spherical triangle.

In triangle PAB, $\angle P$ is the d.long between A and B. PA and PB are the complements of latitudes A and B (co-lat), and α and β are the initial and final courses.

This triangle is solved by use of the spherical haversine formula. This formula is given here without proof, but the full derivation will be found in Appendix I.

To Find a Side (Distance)

To find a side, the angle opposite the side and the other two sides must be known. Thus, in Fig. 44, to find AB, the formula is:

$$\text{Hav } AB = \text{Hav } P \sin PA \sin PB + \text{Hav } (PA \sim PB)$$

To Find an Angle (Course)

To find an angle, the three sides of the triangle must be known. Thus, in Fig. 44, to find $\angle PAB$ (α)

$$\text{Hav } \alpha = \frac{\text{Hav } PB - \text{Hav } (PA \sim AB)}{\sin PA \sin AB}$$

or, as is more common,

$$\text{Hav } \alpha = [\text{Hav } PB - \text{Hav } (PA \sim AB)] \text{ cosec } PA \text{ cosec } AB.$$

The second form makes the solving of the formula simpler as it allows it to be performed in one step.

EXAMPLE 18

Find the distance, the initial and the final courses along the great circle between A in lat 45°36′N long 08°46′W and B in lat 12°18′N long 79°24′W.

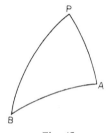

Fig. 45

A lat 45°36′N	B lat 12°18′N	A long 08°46′W	PA 44°24′
90°	90°	B long 79°24′W	PB 77°42′

PA 44°24′	PB 77°42′	$\angle P$ 70°38′	$(PA \sim PB)$ 33°18′

$$\text{Hav } AB = \text{Hav } \angle P \sin PA \sin PB + \text{Hav } (PA \sim PB)$$

$$
\begin{aligned}
P \quad 70°38′ \text{ log Hav } &\bar{1}\cdot5240 \quad \text{(natural Hav } 0\cdot3342) \\
PA \quad 44°24′ \text{ log sin } &\bar{1}\cdot8449 \\
PB \quad 77°42′ \text{ log sin } &\bar{1}\cdot9899 \\
\hline
\text{log } &\bar{1}\cdot3588
\end{aligned}
$$

natural 0·2285

$(PA \sim PB)$ 33°18′ natural Hav 0·0821

AB natural Hav 0·3106

$AB = 67°44′$

Distance = 4064 miles.

77

Hav $\angle A = $ [Hav $PB -$ Hav $(PA \sim AB)$] cosec PA cosec AB.

PB 77°42′ natural Hav 0·3935	PA	44°24′
$(PA \sim AB)$ 23°20′ natural Hav 0·0409	AB	67°44′

natural 0·3526 $(PA \sim AB)$ 23°20′

log $\bar{1}$·5473

PA 44°24′ log cosec 0·1551

AB 67°44′ log cosec 0·0337

A log Hav $\bar{1}$·7361   (natural Hav 0·5446)

$A = 95°07′$

Initial course 264°53′.

Hav $\angle B = $ [Hav $PA -$ Hav $(PB \sim AB)$] cosec PB cosec AB.

PA 44°24′ natural Hav 0·1428	PB	77°42′
$(PB \sim AB)$ 09°58′ natural Hav 0·0076	AB	67°44′

natural 0·1352 $(PB \sim AB)$ 09°58′

log $\bar{1}$·1309

PB 77°42′ log cosec 0·0101

AB 67°44′ log cosec 0·0337

$\angle B$ log Hav $\bar{1}$·1747   (natural Hav 0·1495)

$\angle B = 45°30′$

Final course 225°30′.

EXAMPLE 19

A vessel leaves a position in lat 42°55′S long 48°18′W steering a course of 063°(T). Assuming that she steams along the great circle, find her position after steaming a distance of 2370 miles.

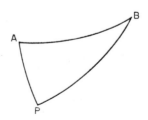

Fig. 46

lat A 42°55' AB 39°30'
     90° PA 47°05'

PA 47°05' $(PA \sim AB)$ 07°35'

Hav PB = Hav A sin PA sin AB + Hav $(PA \sim AB)$
$\angle A$ 117° log Hav $\bar{1}$·8615 (natural Hav 0·7270)
PA 47°05' log sin $\bar{1}$·8647
AB 39°30' log sin $\bar{1}$·8035
---

log $\bar{1}$·5297
---

natural 0·3386
$(PA \sim AB)$ 07°35' natural Hav 0·0044

PB natural Hav 0·3430
PB = 71°42'

                   PB 71°42'
                          90°

                B lat   18°18'S

Hav P = [Hav AB − Hav $(PA \sim PB)$] cosec PA cosec PB
AB 39°30' natural Hav 0·1142 PA 47°05'
$(PA \sim PB)$ 24°37' natural Hav 0·0454 PB 71°42'
---

natural 0·0688 $(PA \sim PB)$ 24°37'
---

log $\bar{2}$·8376
PA 47°05' log cosec 0·1353
PB 71°42' log cosec 0·0225

$\angle P$ log Hav $\bar{2}$·9954 (natural Hav 0·0989)
$\angle P$ = 36°40' A long   48°18'W
                         d.long   36°40'E

                 B long   11°38'W
Final position lat 18°18'S   long 11°38'W.

EXERCISE III(f)

1. Find the initial course and distance between A in lat 43°42'N long 86°17'W, and B in lat 24°16'N long 26°14'W. Find also the course and distance by rhumb line.
2. Find the initial and final courses, and the distance between C. Leeuwin in lat 34°22'S long 115°08'E and C. Guardafui in lat 11°51'S long 51°16'E.

3. Find the initial and final courses, and the distance between Vancouver B.C. in lat 49°18′N long 123°08′W and Sydney N.S.W. in lat 33°52′S long 151°12′E.
4. Two vessels are situated in lat 24°46′S long 18°24′E. Both leave steering 270°, but one follows the great circle track, whilst the other steams along the rhumb line. Find the position of each vessel after steaming 3000 miles.
5. A vessel in lat 34°28′N long 48°14′W steams along the great circle for a distance of 3152 miles, her initial course being 048°. Find her final position.
6. Two vessels leave Capetown (lat 33°56′S long 18°29′E) at 1200 hr G.M.T. on the 8th March, for a voyage to New York (lat 40°42′N long 73°59′W). Both vessels steam at 15 kt but one follows the rhumb line whilst the other follows the great circle. Find the E.T.A. of each vessel at New York.

Exercise III(g)

1. (a) Define and illustrate with a figure, (i) departure, (ii) d.long.
   (b) Prove the formula, dep. =d.long cos lat.
2. (a) Find the latitude in which the dep. is $\frac{2}{3}$ of the d.long.
   (b) Two places A and B in lat 25°N are x miles apart. What is the distance apart of two other places C and D in lat 56°N assuming that the d.long is the same in each case.
3. Explain why "plane sailing" is only suitable for comparatively short distances.
   Find the course and distance between A in lat 32°50′N long 64°32′E and B in lat 25°16′N long 51°20′E. Work by both plane and middle latitude sailing, and explain the difference in answers.
4. Compare Mercator and middle latitude sailing, and describe the principles of each.
   Find the course and distance between X in lat 37°49′N long 72°15′W and Y in lat 39°52′N long 24°25′W. Work by each method and state which answer you consider to be the most accurate, and why?
5. (a) Describe the principles involved in the construction of a Mercator chart.
   (b) What is meant by the natural scale of a chart? Describe how you would construct a chart covering the area between lats 35° and 40°N and longs 10° and 20°W to a natural scale of 1/500,000 in lat 37°30′N. Give the principal dimensions of the chart.
6. Define and explain what is meant by (i) M.P., (ii) D.M.P.
   The d.lat between two places is 3/5 of the D.M.P. If the d.lat between the two places is 13°54′, find the latitudes of the two places.
7. A vessel leaves a position A in long 28°15′W steering 038°. After steaming for 897 miles she arrives at B in long 18°32′W. What is the latitude of A and B.
8. Point A is in lat 54°S. Point B lies due north of A and their distance apart is measured on the chart to be 25 miles. It was found afterwards that the longitude scale had been used instead of the latitude scale. What is true distance apart of the two points.
9. Two vessels in lat 46°N are 28·6 miles apart. If their distance apart on the chart is 6·54 in., what is their d.long and the natural scale of the chart?

CHAPTER 4

Terrestrial position lines

WHAT IS A POSITION LINE?

A POSITION line is, as its name suggests, a line upon which a ship is situated. It does not give any indication of the ship's position other than that it lies somewhere along that line. For instance, if we say that a vessel's latitude is 46°N, then all that we know about that vessel's position is that she lies somewhere along the parallel of 46°N. However, if we also state that her longitude is 35°W then we can obtain her exact position for there is only one position on the parallel of 46°N that lies in longitude 35°W.

Thus, whilst a single position line does not give much indication of a vessel's position, if the vessel can be placed on two separate position lines, then her position will be accurately known.

METHODS OF DETERMINING A POSITION LINE

(1) *Bearing of a Shore Object*

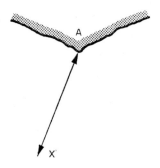

Fig. 47

This is the simplest form of position line and hardly needs any explanation.

In Fig. 47, *A* is a point of land. A ship somewhere to the south of *A* observes the bearing of *A* to be, say, 020°(T). The vessel's position, therefore, lies somewhere on the line *AX*, which is a line of 020°, passing through *A*.

(2) *Distance off by Vertical Angle*

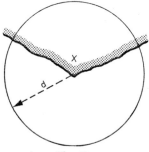

Fig. 48

X is a lighthouse. Supposing the vertical angle subtended by the lighthouse at the ship is measured with a sextant, then the distance of the ship from the lighthouse can be obtained, either from special tables or by plane trigonometry. Suppose the distance so obtained is *d* miles, then the ship is situated somewhere on the circumference of a circle of centre *X*, and radius *d* miles. This is known as a circular position line.

(3) Horizontal Angles

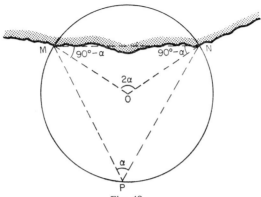

Fig. 49

M and N are two points of land. A vessel observes the horizontal angle between the two points to be, say, $\alpha°$. This puts the vessel somewhere on the arc of a circle having MN as a chord, and such that the angle subtended by MN at the circumference is $\alpha°$.

In order to find the centre of the circle, O, refer to Fig. 49.

$\angle MON = 2\angle MPN = 2\alpha$ (angle at centre = twice angle at the circumference)

$\triangle MON$ is isosceles (OM = ON, radii)

$\therefore \angle OMN = \angle ONM$.

Since the angles of a triangle = 180°

Then $\angle OMN + \angle ONM + 2\alpha = 180°$

$\therefore \angle OMN = \angle ONM = (180° - 2\alpha)/2 = (90° - \alpha)$.

To find O, therefore, join MN and lay off an angle of $(90° - \alpha)$ from each.

The above is true for values of $\alpha < 90°$. For values of $\alpha > 90°$, then the angle of $(\alpha - 90°)$ must be laid off on the opposite side of MN from the ship (Fig. 50).

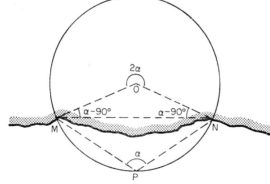

Fig. 50

Fixing the Ship's Position

In order to obtain a position, the ship must be placed on at least two separate position lines. This may be done by combining any two of three methods shown above, as is shown in the following examples.

EXAMPLE 1

A lighthouse *A* is situated in lat 25°36′N long 79°46′W and another lighthouse *B* lies 10 miles due East of it. A ship to the southward observes the bearing of *A* to be 335°(T) and that of *B* to be 049°(T). Find the ship's position.

Scale: I″= 7miles

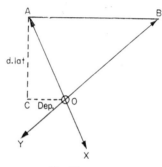

Fig. 51

The problem should be worked on squared paper as shown.

The position of the ship is at *O*, the intersection of the two position lines, *AX* and *BY*.

The latitude and longitude of *O* is found by completing the right-angled triangle *ACO*, and measuring the d.lat and dep. between *A* and *O*.

A lat	25°36′N	long	79°46′W	d.lat 6·2′S dep. 2·9′E
d.lat	6·2′S	d.long	3·2′E	mean lat 25°33′N
B lat	25°29·8′N	long	79°42·8′W	d.long 3·2′E.

EXAMPLE 2

A lighthouse in lat 54°52′S long 78°17′E is observed bearing 213°(T) and at the same instant the vertical sextant angle subtended by the lighthouse was observed to be 0°31′. Find the ship's position. (Height of lighthouse, 360 ft.)

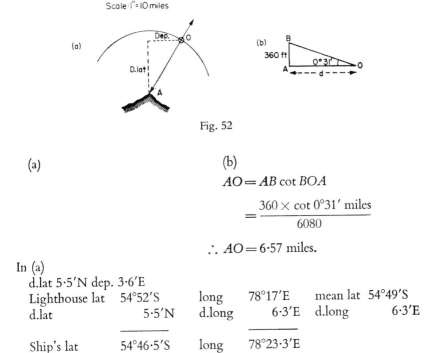

Fig. 52

(a)

(b)

$$AO = AB \cot BOA$$

$$= \frac{360 \times \cot 0°31' \text{ miles}}{6080}$$

$$\therefore AO = 6\cdot57 \text{ miles.}$$

In (a)

d.lat 5·5′N dep. 3·6′E

Lighthouse lat	54°52′S	long	78°17′E	mean lat	54°49′S
d.lat	5·5′N	d.long	6·3′E	d.long	6·3′E
Ship's lat	54°46·5′S	long	78°23·3′E		

N.B. Before solving this problem, the distance off the lighthouse must be calculated by solving the triangle ABO, in which AB is the height of the lighthouse, $\angle BOA$ the angle of elevation, and AO the distance off.

In doing this it is customary to ignore the height of the observer's eye and to assume the observer to be at sea level. The error caused by this assumption is small and tends to make the distance obtained smaller than it actually is, which acts as a safety factor, since it is always a good thing to imagine oneself closer to danger than one actually is.

EXAMPLE 3

HORIZONTAL ANGLES

Three points of land are situated as follows: point A is in lat 20°13′N long 114°24′E. Point B lies 8 miles due West of A, and point C bears 223°, and distant 6 miles from B. A ship to the southward observes the horizontal angle between C and B to be 70°, and the horizontal angle between A and B to be 55°. Find the ship's position.

Scale:1"=5 miles

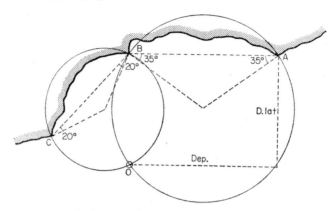

Fig. 53

| *A* lat | 20°13′N | long | 114°24′E | From Fig. d.lat 5·8′S |
| d.lat | 5·8′S | d.long | 8·3′W | dep. 7·8′W |

| Ship's lat | 20°07·2′N | long | 114°15·7′E | mean lat 20°10′N |
| | | | | d.long 8·3′W. |

The horizontal angles are used to obtain the position circles *ABO* and *CBO*; and the position of the ship is fixed at their point of intersection, O.

In questions of this nature the horizontal angles are usually given in the form: *C*70° *B*55° *A*, which indicates that the angle between *C* and *B* is 70°, and between *B* and *A* is 55°.

Exercise IV(a)

1. Position *X* is in lat 45°18′N long 13°47′W and position *Y* bears 115° from *X* and distant 12 miles. A vessel observes the bearing of *X* to be 347°(T) and that of *Y* to be 056°(T). Find the vessel's position.
2. A lighthouse *A* is in lat 54°22′S long 79°42′E. The bearing of *A* from a ship is observed to be 251°(T) and the vertical angle of *A* is 0°58′. Find the vessel's position, assuming the height of the lighthouse to be 550 ft.
3. Two lighthouses, *A* and *B* are situated such that *A* bears 304°(T) distant 8·5 miles from *B*. A vessel to the SW of the lighthouses calculates the distance off by vertical angle to be 6·5 miles from *A* and 8 miles from *B*. What are the true bearings of the two lighthouses from the ship.
4. Position *A* is in lat 35°45′N long 85°16′E. Position *B* lies 5 miles due South of *A* and position *C* lies 6 miles bearing 150°(T) from *B*. A vessel to the eastward observes the horizontal angles between the points to be *A* 40° *B* 55° *C*. Find the vessel's position.
5. Position *X* is in lat 44°38′S long 65°36′E. Position *Y* bears 032°(T) distant 4 miles from *X* and position *Z* bears 256°(T) distant 3 miles from *X*. A vessel to the southward observes *X* and *Y* to be in transit whilst the horizontal angle between *Y* and *Z* is 36°. Find the vessel's position.

6. Position A is in lat 64°32′N long 168°17′W. Position B bears 043°(T) from A and distant 5 miles, and position C bears 075°(T) from B distant 7 miles. A ship to the southward observes the horizontal angles between the points to be A 51° B 100° C. Find the ship's position.

THE TRANSFERRED POSITION LINE

Suppose a vessel takes a bearing of point X which places her somewhere on the position line XY. Her position on XY cannot be determined accurately, so that she could be situated anywhere along XY, say at A, B, or C. Suppose the vessel now steams along her course for a distance of d miles. Had her initial position been at A then her position now would be at A', and similarly,

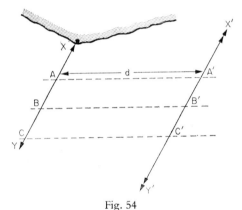

Fig. 54

had her original position been at B or C then her present position would be at B' or C'. Now A', B', and C' are all equidistant from XY, and AA', BB', and CC' are parallel, so that a line drawn through A', B', and C' will be parallel to XY. This line, $X'Y'$, is known as the transferred position line (indicated by a double arrow) and the vessel's position after steaming for d miles will lie somewhere along this line.

The above illustration referred to a straight position line, but it is equally true of a circular one. For instance, suppose that instead of observing the bearing of X, the navigator had observed the vertical sextant angle, and so obtained the distance off, say m miles. This would place the ship somewhere on the circumference of a circle of centre X and radius m miles. If she then steams along her course for a distance of d miles, her position will then be on the circumference of a similar circle of radius m and centre X. The position of X' can be found by laying off the course and distance steamed from X.

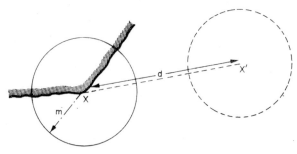

Fig. 55

THE RUNNING FIX

Figure 56 shows how the vessel's position can be obtained from bearings of a single object, using the transferred position line.

A vessel steaming in the direction PQ observes a bearing of X which places her on the position line XY. Suppose the navigator estimates that he is approximately at A, then after steaming a distance of d miles he will be approximately at B and on the transferred position line $X'Y'$. A second bearing of X is now observed which places the vessel on the position line XZ. The vessel is now placed on two position lines simultaneously and must, therefore, lie at their point of intersection, C. The position at the time of the first bearing can now be found by laying back the course and distance steamed from C, which places the vessel originally at D, and not at A.

The method of fixing the ship's position by means of the running fix can be summarized as follows:

(1) Lay off 1st bearing (XY)

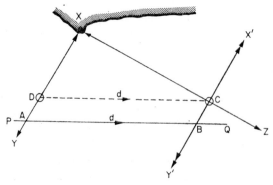

Fig. 56

(2) Selecting any point (A) on XY, lay off the course and distance steamed (AB)
(3) Draw in the transferred position line (X'Y')
(4) Lay off the 2nd bearing (XZ) to cut X'Y' in C
(5) Draw a line back from C, parallel to AB, to cut XY in D, the position at the 1st bearing.

RUNNING FIX, WITH CURRENT

The above illustration takes no account of the effect of tide or current upon the ship. In practice, however, tide or current is nearly always present, and its effect must be allowed for.

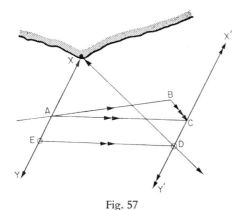

Fig. 57

Figure 57 illustrates the running fix, making due allowance for the estimated set and drift of the tide or current.

A point A on the first position line is selected, and the vessel's course is laid off from there. The distance steamed between the bearings is then laid off along the course line (AB). From B the set and drift of the current or tide experienced between bearings (BC) is laid off. C is the position through which the transferred position line (X'Y') is to be drawn, and AC is the course and distance made good between bearings. X'Y' cuts the 2nd bearing (XZ) in D which is the position of the ship at this time. The position at the 1st bearing is found by laying back a line from D parallel to AC, to cut the 1st position line in (E).

In the following examples some courses and bearings are given as compass and not true. When this occurs, the deviation should be taken from the following deviation curve.

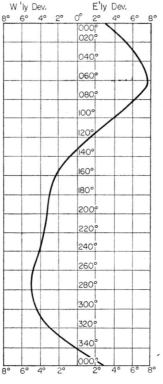

Fig. 58

EXAMPLE 4

From a vessel steering 072°(T) at 15 kt, a lighthouse in lat 54°32′N long 84°36′W is observed bearing 036°(T). One hour later the same lighthouse is again observed bearing 305°(T). Find the position of the vessel at each bearing.

1st bearing

X lat	54°32·0′N	long	84°36·0′W	d.lat	9·7′S
d.lat	9·7′S	d.long	12·0′W	dep.	7·0′W
C lat	54°22·3′N	long	84°48·0′W	d.long	12·0′W

2nd bearing

X lat	54°32·0′N	long	84°36·0′W	d.lat	5·1′E
d.lat	5·1′S	d.long	12·5′W	dep.	7·3′E
D lat	54°26·9′N	long	84°23·5′W	d.long	12·5′E.

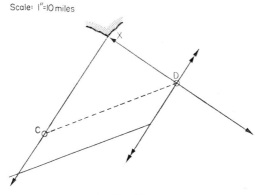

Fig. 59

EXAMPLE 5

A vessel steering 203°(C) at 12 kt observes a lighthouse in lat 20°42′S long 86°52′W bearing 50° on the port bow. One and a half hours later the lighthouse is again observed bearing 20° abaft the port beam. Assuming a current to be setting 126°(M) at 3 kt, find the vessel's position at each bearing (var. 12°E).

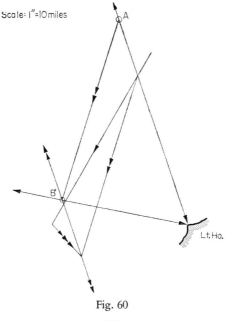

Fig. 60

course	203°(C)	course	211½°(T)	course	211½°(T)
error	8½°E		50°		110°

course	211½°(T)	1st bearing	161½(T)	2nd bearing	101½°(T)
		current	126°(M)		
		var.	12°E		
		current	138°(T)		

1st bearing

Lighthouse lat	20°42·0′S	long	86°52·0′W	d.lat	21·0′N
d.lat	21·0′N	d.long	7·2′W	dep.	6·8′W
Ship's (A) lat	20°21·0′S	long	86°59·2′W	d.long	7·2′W

2nd bearing

Lighthouse lat	20°42·0′S	long	86°52·0′W	d.lat	2·5′N
d.lat	2·5′N	d.long	14·1′W	dep.	13·2′W
Ship's (B) lat	20°39·5′S	long	87°06·1′W	d.long	14·1′W

EXAMPLE 6

From a vessel steering 307°(C) at 10 kt, a lighthouse in lat 54°36′N long 72°18′E is observed bearing 336°(C). After steaming for 2 hr 30 min another lighthouse situated 310°(T) 10 miles from the first is observed bearing 066°(C). Find the ship's position at each bearing, making allowance for a tidal stream setting 208°(T) at 2 kt (var. 7°W).

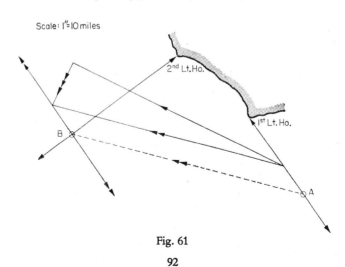

Scale: 1″=10 miles

2nd Lt.Ho.

1st Lt. Ho.

B

A

Fig. 61

92

course	307°(C)	1st bearing	336°(C)	2nd bearing	066°(C)
error	11°W	error	11°W	error	11°W
course	296°(T)	1st bearing	325°(T)	2nd bearing	055°(T)

2nd bearing

Lighthouse lat	54°36·0′N	long	72°18·0′E	d.lat	1·5′S
d.lat	1·5′S	d.long	32·7′W	dep.	19·0′W
Ship's lat (B)	54°34·5′N	long	71°45·3′E	d.long	32·7′W

1st bearing

Lighthouse lat	54°36·0′N	long	72°18·0′E	d.lat	8·2′S
d.lat	8·2′S	d.long	9·8′E	dep.	5·7′E
Ship's lat (A)	54°27·8′N	long	72°27·8′E	d.long	9·8′E

It should be noted that it is not always necessary to use bearings of the same object when working the running fix.

In the following exercise some of the problems, marked with an asterisk (*), may be plotted directly on to the chart given in Chapter 3 which should have been made by the student, and the following positions should now be plotted on the chart for these problems.

(1) A in lat 49°57′N long 05°48′W
(2) B in lat 49°48′N long 05°12′W (Height 230 ft)
(3) C in lat 50°13′N long 03°38′W
(4) D in lat 50°34′N long 01°18′W.

Exercise IV(b)

1. A vessel steering 075°(T) at 15 kt observes a lighthouse in lat 35°18′S long 02°13′E bearing 165°(T). After steaming for 1 hr 40 min the lighthouse is again observed bearing 238°(T). Find the vessel's position at each bearing.

2. From a vessel steering 357°(C) at 12 kt, a lighthouse in lat 45°46′N long 24°02′W is observed bearing 301°(C). Two hours later the same lighthouse bore 248°(C). Find the ship's position at each bearing, assuming that a current set 065°(T) at 3 kt throughout (var. 6°E).

3. At 0830 hr a vessel steering 212°(C) at 12 kt observes a lighthouse in lat 44°32′N long 16°12′W bearing 252°(C). At 1115 hr another lighthouse situated 230°(T) and 29 miles from the first was observed bearing 315°(C). Find the vessel's position at 1000 hr, allowing for a current setting 178°(M) at 2½ kt (var. 10°E).

4.* From a vessel steering 072°(T) at 12 kt, A is observed bearing 042°(T). After steaming for 2 hr 25 min through a current setting 115°(T) at 3 kt, A is again observed bearing 305°(T). Find the position of the ship at each bearing.

5.★ The horizontal angle subtended between A and B is 43°, and at the same time, the vertical angle subtended by B is 00°17′. Find the ship's position. (Vessel is situated to SE of A and B.)

6.★ From a vessel steering 267°(C) at 15 kt, D bears 341°(C). After steaming for 7 hr through a current setting 227°(T) at 2 kt, C is observed bearing 038°(C). Find the position of the ship at each bearing (var. 6°W).

RADIO BEARINGS

Most ships are equipped with radio direction finding apparatus (D/F), by which they are enabled to take bearings of radio signals sent out by certain coastal radio stations and by some lightships. These radio signals travel along the great circle track, so that bearings obtained in this manner are great circle bearings, and cannot, therefore, be laid off directly on a Mercator chart. In order to convert these bearings into Mercatorial bearings, a correction known as the half convergency must be applied.

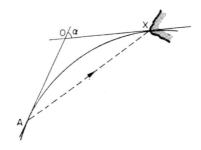

Fig. 62

Suppose a ship situated at A takes a wireless bearing of a radio beacon at X. The curved line AX represents the arc of the great circle between A and X and the straight line AX represents the Mercatorial bearing.

The direction of the great circle at A is given by the tangent to it at that point (AO) and this is the bearing obtained by the ship. Similarly, OX is the direction of the great circle at X. The difference between these two directions (α) is known as the convergency of the great circle between A and X.

Now, since OA and OX are tangents, it follows that AOX is an isosceles triangle so that $\angle OAX = \angle OXA$.

Also: $\alpha = \angle OAX + \angle OXA = 2 \angle OAX$

or, $OAX = \alpha/2$.

$\angle OAX$ is from the figure the difference between the great circle and the Mercatorial bearing and is equal to half of the convergency.

It should be noted that the correction for half convergency is always applied towards the equator, i.e. towards the South in the Northern hemisphere, and towards the North in the Southern hemisphere.

The numerical value of this correction may be obtained from special tables, or from the formula,

$$\tfrac{1}{2} \text{ convergency} = \tfrac{1}{2} \text{ d.long} \times \sin \text{ mid lat.}$$

EXAMPLE 7

From a ship in D.R. lat 36°18′N long 42°17′W the wireless bearing of a radio station in lat 42°24′N long 46°27′W was 333°. What is the Mercatorial bearing of the station?

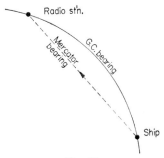

Fig. 63

Radio station's lat	42°24′N	long	46°27′W
Ship's lat	36°18′N	long	42°17′W
	2)78°42′		04°10′W
Mean lat	39°21′N		× 60

d.long   250′W.

$\tfrac{1}{2}$ conv. $= \tfrac{1}{2}$ d.long sin m.lat

$\tfrac{1}{2}$ d.long 125   log 2·0969

mean lat 39°21′ log sin $\bar{1}$·8021

1·8990

$\tfrac{1}{2}$ conv. $= 79\cdot4' =$	01°19′
wireless bearing	333°
$\tfrac{1}{2}$ conv.	−1°19′
Mercator bearing	331°41′

N.B. It is sufficiently accurate to use the mean latitude in this case as the bearing cannot be laid off to any greater accuracy than half a degree.

Sometimes the radio station takes the bearing of the ship, as in the next example.

EXAMPLE 8

A ship in D.R. lat 36°28'S long 107°17'E obtains a bearing from a coast station in lat 43°10'S long 98°24'E of 047°. Find the true bearing to lay off on the chart.

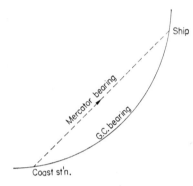

Fig. 64

| Station's lat | 43°10'S | long | 98°24'E |
| Ship's lat | 36°28'S | long | 107°18'E |

| | 2)79°38' | | 8°54'E |
| Mean lat | 39°49'S | | × 60 |

d.long   534'E

½ conv. = ½ d.long × sin m.lat
½ d.long 267'   log 2·4265
mean lat 39°49' log sin Ī·8064

2·2329

½ conv. = 171' = 2°51'
radio bearing   047°
½ conv.   −2°51'

Mercator bearing   044°09' (from station)
Bearing to lay off on chart = 044°09' + 180° = 224°09'.

EXAMPLE 9

A ship in D.R. lat 54°06'N long 06°24'W and steering 056°(T) takes a W/T bearing of a radio station in lat 49°32'N long 01°14'W. The relative bearing obtained with the D/F is 096°. What is the true bearing to lay off on the chart?

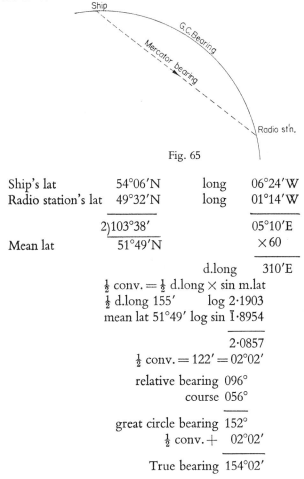

Fig. 65

Ship's lat	54°06′N	long	06°24′W
Radio station's lat	49°32′N	long	01°14′W

$$2)\overline{103°38'} \qquad \overline{05°10'E}$$

Mean lat $\qquad$ 51°49′N $\qquad\qquad$ ×60

$$\overline{\text{d.long} \qquad 310'E}$$

½ conv. = ½ d.long × sin m.lat
½ d.long 155' $\qquad$ log 2·1903
mean lat 51°49′ log sin $\bar{1}$·8954

$$\overline{\qquad\qquad 2·0857}$$

½ conv. = 122′ = 02°02′

relative bearing 096°
course 056°

$$\overline{\text{great circle bearing} \quad 152°}$$
½ conv. + $\quad$ 02°02′

$$\overline{\text{True bearing} \quad 154°02'}$$

Exercise IV(c)

1. From a vessel in D.R. lat 29°56′N long 84°56′W the radio bearing of a coast station in lat 23°14′N long 88°58′W was 209°. Find the Mercatorial bearing.
2. A vessel in D.R. lat 47°18′S long 13°12′E receives a W/T bearing from a radio station in lat 49°12′S long 18°52′E of 295°. Find the true bearing of the radio station to lay off on the chart.
3. A vessel in D.R. lat 49°52′S long 118°16′W is steering 323°(T). The relative bearing of a radio station in lat 52°18′S long 124°17′W is found to be 272°. What is the true bearing of the radio station to lay off on the chart?
4. A vessel in D.R. lat 44°26′N long 18°37′W is steering 016°(T). The relative bearing of a radio station in lat 47°24′N long 13°41′W is found to be 031°. What is the true bearing to lay off on the chart?

CHAPTER 5 **The solar system**

ASTRONOMICAL navigation, with which most of the remainder of this book is concerned, entails some knowledge of astronomy. In particular, an acquaintance with that small part of the universe which is called the Solar System is required.

The sun, which gives light and heat to the earth, is one of the smaller stars in one particular part of the universe. It is not known if other stars have satellites, but the sun has several satellites, or planets, which move in orbits round it. The nearest planet to the sun is Mercury; the second planet outward from it is Venus; and the third planet outward from the sun is the earth. The remaining planets, namely, Mars, Jupiter, Saturn, Uranus, Neptune and Pluto, are, in the order named, at increasingly greater distances from the sun. Mercury and Venus, being nearer to the sun than the earth, are called "inferior" planets, whilst all the other planets, which are further from the sun than the earth, are called "superior" planets.

Several of the planets have satellites of their own which are called "moons".

Some planets have several moons, but the earth only

has one which moves round the earth once a month, in the same direction as the earth's rotation. The approximate radius of the moon's orbit round the earth is 240,000 miles, whilst the approximate radius of the earth's orbit round the sun is 93,000,000 miles. It takes the earth a year to make a complete circuit from a given point in its orbit back to the same point again.

The earth, as it moves along its orbit, also spins on its axis, and makes one revolution in approximately twenty-four hours. The moon, too, spins on its axis as it moves along its orbit round the earth, but it only revolves once on its axis in a month.

The earth is tilted as it moves along its orbit round the sun, the plane of the equator being inclined at an angle of $23\frac{1}{2}°$ to the plane of the orbit. Similarly, the moon is tilted as it moves along its orbit, the plane of its orbit being inclined at an angle of about 5° to the plane of the earth's orbit round the sun.

KEPLER'S LAWS OF PLANETARY MOTION

The German astronomer Kepler, who lived between 1571 and 1630, discovered certain "laws of planetary motion" and proved these laws to be correct by the mathematics of the ellipse.

Kepler's First Law states that the earth, like the other planets, moves in an elliptical orbit round the sun, and that the sun is situated at one of the two foci of the ellipse. Figure 66(a) shows this elliptical orbit of the earth round the sun, the sun being situated, not at the centre of the ellipse, but at F_1, which is one of the two foci with relation to which the ellipse is drawn.

Kepler's Second Law is a little more complicated. It states that "the radius vector of any planet's movement round the sun sweeps out equal areas in equal times".

In Fig. 66(a), the earth is shown as spinning on its axis once a day and also rolling along its orbit. Let us suppose that, at a given instant of time, the earth's centre is at the point A in its orbit. Then F_1A is the radius vector of the earth's movement at that instant. The earth continues to roll its orbit until its centre is at B. Then F_1B is the position of the radius vector at this later instant of time, and the area of the triangle F_1AB is the area that the radius vector has "swept out" whilst the earth has moved from A to B.

Some six months later, the earth will have moved round to C, and later still, it will have moved to D. Then the area of the triangle F_1CD is the area that the radius vector has "swept out" whilst the earth has moved from C to D. Therefore, in accordance with Kepler's Second Law, it follows that, if the area F_1CD is equal to the area F_1AB, then the earth has travelled from C to D in the same time as it travelled from A to B.

This leads to a most important conclusion; namely, that the earth moves faster in its orbit between *A* and *B* than it moves between *C* and *D*. Now, this phenomenon of the varying speed of the earth in its orbit affects, not only navigation, but also everyday life, since it influences our system of measuring the passage of time and also the duration of the seasons.

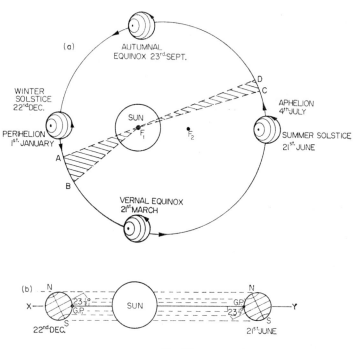

Fig. 66

THE SEASONS

The dates when the earth is in certain positions in its orbit are shown in Fig. 66(a). The earth is said to be in Perihelion when it is nearest to the sun on 1st January, and it is said to be in Aphelion when it is furthest from the sun on 4th July. These two terms *only* refer to the *distance* of the earth from the sun, and are not to be confused with the *Winter* Solstice on 22nd December, and the *Summer* Solstice on 21st June which refer to two entirely different phenomena.

These can probably be better understood by reference to Fig. 66(b), which shows a side view of the earth's orbit, and in which *XY* represents the plane of the orbit.

The point on the earth's surface immediately below any given heavenly body at any instant of time is called the "geographical position" of that body. Figure 66(b) shows that, owing to the $23\frac{1}{2}°$ tilt of the earth's axis, the geographical position of the sun at the Winter Solstice (22nd December) is on the parallel of latitude $23\frac{1}{2}°$S. In other words, as the earth rotates on its axis, the sun is vertically overhead at noon at all places in latitude $23\frac{1}{2}°$S. Also, on this date, the sun's rays skirt over the surface of the earth along the parallel of latitude of $66\frac{1}{2}°$N, which is known as the Arctic Circle. Therefore, on this date, everywhere North of the Arctic Circle is in darkness for the full 24 hr period. Whilst, on the same date, everywhere South of the Antarctic Circle (lat $66\frac{1}{2}°$S) has daylight for 24 hr.

Six months later, on June 21st, the sun's geographical position has moved northward to latitude $23\frac{1}{2}°$N. This is the date of the Summer Solstice, when the sun is vertically overhead at noon along the parallel of $23\frac{1}{2}°$N, the Arctic Circle has 24 hr daylight, and the Antarctic Circle has 24 hr darkness.

As the geographical position of the sun moves northwards it crosses the equator from South to North on 21st March, and this date is known as the Vernal Equinox. The sun is then vertically overhead at noon on the equator, whilst at both poles it is skirting the horizon all day. Again, after the Summer Solstice, the sun's geographical position begins to move southward and it crosses the equator from North to South at the Autumnal Equinox on 23rd September.

The amount of heat received from the sun depends principally on the angle at which the sun's rays strike the earth. During the winter months of the northern hemisphere, the sun's rays strike more directly downwards on to the earth in the southern hemisphere; whilst in the summer months of the northern hemisphere the sun's rays strike more directly downwards in those parts of the world which are North of the equator. If the earth's axis were not tilted, so that the earth's equator were in the same plane as its orbit, there would be no seasons as we understand them. The temperature in any given latitude would be constant, at the same time of day, throughout the year, and would decrease uniformly from equator to poles; and there would be no variation in the duration of daylight and darkness anywhere in the world.

If the dates of the above phenomena are examined, it will be observed that the period from the Vernal Equinox through the Summer Solstice (21st June) to the Autumnal Equinox is 186 days, whilst the period between the Equinoxes measured through the Winter Solstice (22nd December) is 179 days. This means, in effect, that the northern hemisphere has about 7 days more summer than the southern hemisphere, and this is a direct result of the varying speed of the earth in its elliptical orbit as enunciated by Kepler.

It is interesting to note, however, that, owing to the relative nearness of the earth to the sun during the southern hemisphere's Summer, the southern hemisphere does, in fact, receive the same total amount of heat from the sun during a year as that received by the northern hemisphere in a year.

CHAPTER 6

The celestial sphere

To an observer on the earth, the heavens present the aspect of a large, inverted bowl with the earth situated at its centre and the sun, moon, stars and planets situated around its surface, all equidistant from the earth.

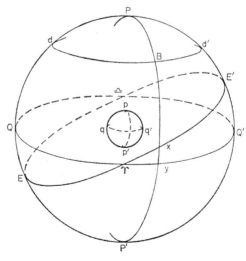

Fig. 67

This concept we know to be untrue, for the earth is not at the centre of the universe and the distance of the other heavenly bodies from the earth varies greatly. However, for the purposes of navigation, we assume that the earth is at the centre of the universe and that all other heavenly bodies are situated on the surface of a large sphere surrounding the earth which we know as the celestial sphere or celestial concave (Fig. 67).

APPARENT MOTION

The sun rises in the East in the morning, moves across the sky during the day, and finally sets in the West in the evening. This is due to the rotation of the earth on its axis, as we well know, but as we are not aware of this rotation, it appears to us that the sun is moving round the earth every 24 hr. Similarly, the other heavenly bodies appear to be doing the same.

This is what is known as the apparent motion of heavenly bodies, and in navigation it is always the apparent motion that is referred to. Therefore, in this, and subsequent chapters, when reference is made to the motion of heavenly bodies, it is their apparent motion that is implied.

Figure 67 represents the celestial sphere with the earth situated at its centre.

Celestial Poles (P and P')

These are the points in the celestial sphere directly above the poles of the earth.

Equinoctial (QQ')

This is the projection of the equator (qq') on the celestial sphere, and is defined as a great circle on the celestial sphere, every point of which is 90° removed from the celestial poles.

Celestial Meridians (PYP')

These are semi-great circles on the celestial sphere whose planes pass through the poles.

Ecliptic (EE')

This is a great circle on the celestial sphere, inclined to the equinoctial at an angle of approximately $23\frac{1}{2}°$. It indicates the annual path of the sun in the celestial sphere.

1st Point of Aries (♈) and 1st Point of Libra (♎)

These are the points on the celestial sphere where the ecliptic cuts the equinoctial. The 1st point of Aries marks the position of the sun at the vernal equinox (21st March) and the 1st point of Libra marks the position of the sun at the autumnal equinox (23rd September). These two points are named after the constellations in which they lie, or, to be more exact, once lay, for they are not stationary points but are moving slowly to the westward, this movement being known as the precession of the equinoxes.

POSITION OF BODIES IN THE CELESTIAL SPHERE

The position of a place on the earth can be defined in terms of its latitude and longitude. In a similar manner the position of a body in the celestial sphere can be defined in terms of its declination and right ascension.

Parallels of declination are defined as small circles on the celestial sphere whose planes are parallel to the equinoctial; *dd'* in Fig. 67 is an example. The declination of a body, therefore, may be defined as the arc of the celestial meridian contained between the equinoctial and the parallel of declination passing through the body. It is measured in degrees, minutes and seconds of arc, and is named North or South according as to whether the body lies to the North or South of the equinoctial. Thus, in Fig. 67, if *B* is some body situated on the parallel of declination *dd'*, then its declination is the arc *YB*, of the meridian *PYP'*.

Right ascension is defined as the arc of the equinoctial contained between the 1st point of Aries and the celestial meridian passing through the body. It may be expressed in either units of arc or time, and is always measured eastward from the 1st point of Aries. Thus, in Fig. 67, the right ascension of *B* is the arc ♈ *Y*.

HOUR ANGLES

Sidereal Hour Angle (S.H.A.)

The sidereal hour angle of a body is defined as the arc of the equinoctial contained between the 1st point of Aries and the celestial meridian passing through the body. It is measured westward from Aries and may be expressed either in units of arc or time. The S.H.A. and right ascension of a body are, therefore, the same thing, except that the former is measured westward from Aries and the latter eastward.

Thus S.H.A. $= 360°$ (24 hr) — right ascension.

In Fig. 67, suppose that the right ascension of *B* was 45° (3 hr), then the S.H.A. of *B* would be

$$\text{S.H.A.} = 360° \ (24 \ hr) - 45° \ (3 \ hr) = 315° \ (21 \ hr).$$

The S.H.A. is measured from the 1st point of Aries which, as previously mentioned, is precessing slowly to the westward. Because of this slow movement of Aries, or the precession of the equinoxes as it is called, the S.H.A. of a body will change slowly during the course of a year. This change, however, is very small, and does not amount to more than 1 min per year for most stars.

Local Hour Angle (L.H.A.) and Greenwich Hour Angle (G.H.A.)

The local hour angle of a body is defined as the arc of the equinoctial contained between the meridian of the observer and the meridian passing through the body. It is measured westward from the observer's meridian in units of arc or time.

The Greenwich hour angle of a body is defined as the arc of the equinoctial contained between the meridian of Greenwich and the meridian passing through the body. It is measured westward from Greenwich in units of arc or time.

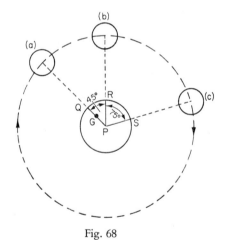

Fig. 68

In Fig. 68, the inner circle represents the earth viewed from above the North Pole, and the outer, dotted circle the daily path of the sun round the earth. *PQ* is the meridian of Greenwich, *PR* the meridian of the observer in long 45°W, and *PS* the meridian of 120°W.

At (a) the sun is on the meridian of Greenwich, so that the G.H.A. is 000°. Three hours later the sun has moved through an angle of 45° and is now on the observer's meridian. The G.H.A. is now 45° (3 hr) and the L.H.A. is 000° (0 hr). After a further five hours, the sun is at (c) on the meridian of 120°W. The G.H.A. is now 120° (8 hr), and the L.H.A. is 75° (5 hr).

From the above, it can be seen that the difference between the G.H.A. and the L.H.A. is the longitude of the observer.

Thus G.H.A. ~ L.H.A. = long.

If the G.H.A. is the greater, then the longitude is West, but if the L.H.A. is the greater, then the longitude is East. This should be fairly obvious by referring to Fig. 68, for if the observer is in West longitude, then the sun will cross the Greenwich meridian before it crosses his, so that the G.H.A. will always be the greater.

The above illustration refers to the sun, but it can be applied equally to any heavenly body.

EXAMPLE 1

The G.H.A. of Aries is 200° and the right ascension of a star is 110°. What will be the L.H.A. of the star to an observer in long 33°E?

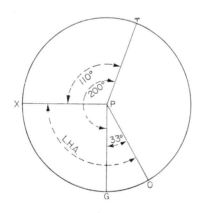

Fig. 69

A figure similar to Fig. 69 should be drawn for problems of this type.

Figure 69 represents the celestial sphere viewed from above the North celestial pole (P). PG, PX, PΥ and PO are the meridians passing through Greenwich, the star, the 1st point of Aries, and the observer, respectively.

From the figure:

$$\text{G.H.A.} \Upsilon = 200°$$
$$\text{S.H.A.} \star = 360° - \text{right ascension} = 360° - 110° = 250°$$
$$\text{G.H.A.} \star = \text{G.H.A.} \Upsilon + \text{S.H.A.} \star$$
$$= 200° + 250°$$
$$= 450°$$

subtracting 360°:

$$\text{G.H.A.} \star = 90°$$
$$\text{L.H.A.} \star = \text{G.H.A.} \star + \text{E. long}$$
$$\therefore \text{L.H.A.} \star = 123°.$$

Example 2

To an observer in long 35°E the sun is on the meridian. Assuming the right ascension of the sun to be 72°, find the G.H.A. of a star whose S.H.A. is 159°.

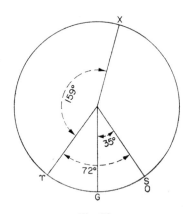

Fig. 70

From the figure:
$$\text{G.H.A.} \Upsilon = \text{L.H.A.} \Upsilon - \text{E. long}$$
$$= 72° - 35°$$
$$= 37°$$
$$\text{G.H.A.} \star = \text{G.H.A.} \Upsilon + \text{S.H.A.}$$
$$= 37° + 159°$$
$$\text{G.H.A.} \star = 196°.$$

EXERCISE VI(a)

1. The G.H.A. of the sun is 315°, and the L.H.A. is 36°. Find the longitude.
2. To an observer in long 164°30′E, the L.H.A. of the sun is 26°15′. What is the G.H.A.?
3. To an observer in long 65°W, the L.H.A. of a star is 48°. If the S.H.A. of the star is 217°, what is the G.H.A. of Aries?
4. The G.H.A. of a star is 49°. If the S.H.A. is 53°, and the right ascension of the sun is 34°, what is the G.H.A. of the sun?
5. A star is observed on the meridian when its G.H.A. is 339°. What is the longitude of the observer?
6. The L.H.A. of the sun is 320°, and the L.H.A. of a star is 36°. If the S.H.A. of the star is 21°, what is the right ascension of the sun?

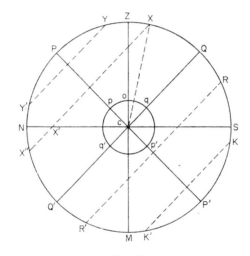

Fig. 71

pp′	The poles of the earth	PP′	The celestial poles
QQ′	The equinoctial	O	The observer
Z	The observer's zenith	X	A star
	NS	The rational horizon	

Figure 71 represents the celestial sphere viewed on the plane of the observer's meridian. The observer is situated at O on the meridian pqp′. The corresponding celestial meridian is PQP′ upon which a star, X, is situated.

Zenith

This is defined as the point in the celestial sphere directly above the observer. In Fig. 71, the observer's zenith is denoted by Z. Great circles on the celestial sphere which pass through the zenith are known as vertical circles. The observer's meridian, PQP', is such a vertical circle.

The point in the celestial sphere directly opposite the zenith is known as the Nadir (M). This point has little significance in navigation.

Rational Horizon

This is defined as a great circle in the celestial sphere, every point on which is 90° removed from the zenith. This is denoted by NS in Fig. 71, and it marks the limits of the observer's view. To an observer at O, all bodies above the rational horizon will be visible, whilst all those below it will be invisible.

Polar Distance

This is defined as the arc of the celestial meridian contained between the body and the pole. It is, therefore, equal to 90° $\pm$ declination, depending upon which pole it is referred to. Normally, however, the polar distance is referred to the observer's elevated pole. Thus, in Fig. 71, the declination of X is the arc QX, and the polar distance is the arc PX.

Zenith Distance

This is defined as the arc of the vertical circle contained between the body and the zenith. In Fig. 71, it is denoted by the arc ZX, or the angle ZCX.

A vertical circle is any great circle in the celestial sphere which passes through the observer's zenith and is therefore perpendicular to the horizon. The Prime Vertical is that vertical circle which passes through the East and West points of the horizon.

True Altitude

This is defined as the arc of the vertical circle contained between the body and the rational horizon. In Fig. 71 it is denoted by the arc XS or the angle XCS.

From the above it will be seen that zenith distance and true altitude are complementary. Thus $ZX = 90° -$ altitude.

In Fig. 71, the daily path of the body, X, is indicated by the line $XX'X''$. The body is on the meridian at X, and then moves along the path XX'', eventually crossing the rational horizon at X'. The body is then below the rational horizon and no longer visible to an observer at O. From the figure, it can be seen that the period when the body is above the horizon is far greater than when it is below it.

Consider now, a star situated on the equinoctial. It will move along the line QQ' and, as can be seen, will be above the horizon for exactly the same time as it is below. Another star of southerly declination, QR, will move along the line RR', and will be above the horizon for a shorter time than it will be below. Yet another star of declination QK, will not be visible at any time during the day, and it should be noted that the polar distance of this star is less than the observer's latitude.

From the above, the following conclusions may be drawn:

(1) Bodies whose declinations have the same name as the observer's latitude will be above the horizon for more than 12 hr, whilst those whose declinations have different names to the observer's latitude will be above the horizon for less than 12 hr.

(2) A body whose declination is of the opposite name to the observer's latitude will only be visible if its polar distance is greater than the observer's latitude.

Circumpolar Bodies

A body is said to be circumpolar when it is visible above the horizon for the full 24 hr.

In Fig. 71, consider a star situated on the parallel of declination YY'. This star is circumpolar to an observer at O, for it can be seen that it is above the rational horizon at all times.

For a body to be circumpolar, two conditions must be satisfied, namely:

(1) The declination of the body must have the same name as the observer's latitude.

(2) The polar distance of the body must be less than the observer's latitude.

The first condition is self-explanatory, but the second needs some explanation.

Suppose, in Fig. 71, a star has a polar distance equal to PN, then it would just touch the horizon at N. If the polar distance were greater than PN, the star would be below the horizon at N, and if the polar distance were less, then it would be above the horizon at N. Since PN is the altitude of the pole, it is therefore equal to the latitude of the observer, so that the body must have a polar distance less than the latitude of the observer if it is to be circumpolar.

GEOGRAPHICAL POSITION OF A HEAVENLY BODY

Since the celestial sphere is a projection of the earth's surface on the heavens, it follows that every body in the heavens has a corresponding position on the earth. This is known as the geographical position of the body and is defined as the point on the earth's surface immediately beneath the body.

The geographical position of a body can be obtained directly from its declination and G.H.A.

By definition declination corresponds exactly with latitude, so that a body having a declination of 20°N would be directly over the parallel of 20°N. Similarly, G.H.A. corresponds with longitude, so that a body having a G.H.A. of 45° would be directly over the meridian of 45°W. G.H.A., however, is always measured westward, whereas longitude may be measured westward or eastward. This means that the G.H.A. will indicate the westerly longitude of the body, so that if the G.H.A. were 315° then the body would lie over the meridian of 315°W or 45°E.

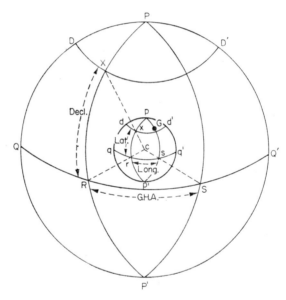

Fig. 72

psp'	The Greenwich meridian
PSP'	The corresponding celestial meridian
PRP'	The celestial meridian passing through the body *X*
prp'	The corresponding meridian on the earth
DD'	The parallel of declination of *X*
dd'	The corresponding parallel of latitude

In Fig. 72 the body is situated at *X*. Its geographical position is at *x*, directly beneath it. The declination of *X* is ∠*XCR*, and this is the same as

112

the latitude of x, which is $\angle xCr$. The G.H.A. of X is $\angle SCR$, and this is equal to the longitude of x, given by $\angle sCr$.

Thus the geographical position of a body is obtained by substituting latitude for declination and longitude for G.H.A.

EXAMPLE 3

To an observer in long 15°E the L.H.A. of the sun is 299°. If the sun's declination is 14°36′S what is the geographical position of the sun?

$$\begin{aligned} \text{G.H.A.} &= \text{L.H.A.} - \text{E. long} \\ &= 299° - 15° \\ &= 284°. \end{aligned}$$

Since the G.H.A. is more than 180°, the longitude of the sun is found by subtracting the G.H.A. from 360°.

Thus long $= 360° - 284° = 76°$E.

Therefore, geographical position $\dfrac{\text{lat } 14°36′S}{\text{long } 76°00′E}$

EXERCISE VI(b)

1. Draw a figure of the celestial sphere, showing the celestial poles, the equinoctial, the ecliptic, the 1st point of Aries and the 1st point of Libra. Show on your sketch the approximate position of the sun on the 1st June and the 1st February, and state what the approximate right ascension of the sun will be in each case. Also, plot the position of a star whose declination is 40°N and right ascension 6 hr.

2. Describe what is meant by the geographical position of a heavenly body.

   To an observer in lat 20°N long 52°W the sun is directly overhead. What is the declination and G.H.A. of the sun?

3. The G.H.A. of the sun is 312°47′ and its declination 12°18′S. What is the geographical position of the sun?

4. A star has a declination of 36°N and an S.H.A. of 246°32′. If the G.H.A. of Aries is 24°14′, what is the geographical position of the star?

5. To an observer in lat 42°N long 75°W a star is directly overhead. What is the G.H.A. of the star and what will be its geographical position in 4 hr?

6. Define, and illustrate by means of a sketch;
   (i) Zenith; (ii) Zenith distance; (iii) Rational horizon.

7. (a) From the list of stars given in the appendix, state which stars will be circumpolar to an observer in (i) 25°N; (ii) 60°N.

   (b) Between what latitudes would it be possible to see both Dubhe (declination 61°58·4′N) and Acrux (declination 62°52·3′S)?

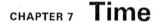

CHAPTER 7 **Time**

THE YEAR AND THE DAY

IN GENERAL terms, a year is the period of time the earth takes to make one complete circuit of its orbit, and a day is the period of time the earth takes to rotate once on its axis.

Methods of measuring intervals of time, such as a year or a day, have, however, always been based on men's observations of the sun and other heavenly bodies, as seen by men on the earth. Modern man is prepared to accept the two astronomical facts that the earth rotates once on its axis in a day and orbits once round the sun in a year; but his system of measuring time is based on what men have always been able to see with their eyes; namely, that the sun in the sky *appears* to rotate once round the earth in a day, and to change its noon position in the sky slowly throughout the year.

During the course of a day, the sun, owing to the rotation of the earth, appears to move along a particular path in the celestial sphere, which, as explained in Chapter 6, is the sun's parallel of declination. Also, during the course of a year, the sun's position, at the same time each day, changes slowly in the celestial sphere, because of the earth's movement in orbit; the sun, therefore, appears to have an additional slow movement round the celestial sphere, which takes a year to complete. The path of this annual movement, also mentioned in Chapter 6, is the ecliptic.

THE APPARENT SOLAR DAY

The sun we see in the sky is called, sensibly enough, the True or Apparent Sun, and since the earth spins on its axis from West to East, the True Sun *appears* to move across the sky from East to West.

An Apparent Solar Day, therefore, is defined as the interval of time which elapses between two successive transits of the True or Apparent Sun over the same meridian.

In discussing the Solar System, however, it was seen that the earth moves round the sun at a varying speed, owing to the eccentricity of its orbit, and also that the earth's equator is inclined at an angle of $23\frac{1}{2}°$ to the plane of the orbit.

As a result of these peculiarities of the earth's true motion round the sun, the apparent motion of the sun round the earth has corresponding peculiarities. One of these is that the interval of time between two successive transits of the Apparent Sun over the same meridian is not of constant duration. This means that, at one time of year, the Apparent Solar Day is of slightly shorter duration than its mean or average duration; whilst, at another time of year, it is slightly longer than its average length.

THE MEAN SOLAR DAY

A Mean Solar Day is the mean, or average, length of a large number of Apparent Solar Days, and is of exactly 24 hr duration.

Alternatively, the Mean Solar Day may be defined in terms of the imaginary movement of the Mean Sun. This is an imaginary body which is conceived to move round the celestial sphere, along the equinoctial, at the mean or average speed of the Apparent Sun in the ecliptic. Using this terminology, the Mean Solar Day is the interval of time that elapses between two successive transits of the Mean Sun over the same meridian, and this is equal to 24 hr of "Mean Time". Mean Time is measured by the imaginary movement of the Mean Sun, in the same way as Apparent Time is measured by the apparent movement of the True or Apparent Sun. Mean Time is the time that is kept by ordinary clocks and watches (when they are good timekeepers), since it is not too difficult to manufacture an instrument, the hands of which go round at a constant rate. It would be extremely difficult to make a clock to keep Apparent Time, since its hands would have to go round at a varying rate.

THE SIDEREAL DAY AND LUNAR DAY

In addition to the Apparent and Mean Solar Days, there are two other "days" to be considered.

The Sidereal Day is the interval of time that elapses between two successive transits of a star over the same meridian and is equal to 23hr 56min 04sec of Mean Time. Astronomers use clocks which keep Sidereal Time, and 24 hr of Sidereal Time, measured by a sidereal clock, is equal to 23hr 56min 04sec measured by an ordinary Mean Time clock.

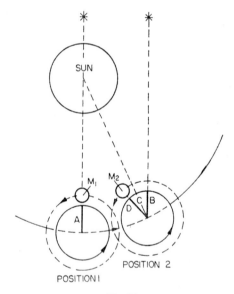

Fig. 73

The Lunar Day is the interval of time that elapses between two successive transits of the moon over the same meridian. Owing to the rather erratic movement of the moon as it orbits round the earth, the Lunar Day is of variable length, but its average duration is 24hr 50min of Mean Time.

Figure 73 shows diagramatically the relationship between a Sidereal Day, an Apparent Solar Day and a Lunar Day. The diagram, which is not drawn to scale, shows a portion of the earth's orbit. At Position 1, a certain meridian is in position A and is directly under the moon, sun, and a distant star at the same instant of time. To an observer on this meridian, the moon, sun and star would all appear to transit his meridian at the same instant of time.

Approximately 24 hr later, the earth will have rotated once on its axis and also moved along its orbit to Position 2. The star is so far away that this relatively slight movement of the earth along its orbit will make no difference to the direction of the rays of light coming from the star. The interval between points A and B in Fig. 73 is, therefore, the period of time it takes the earth to rotate through 360° and is also the interval between two successive transits of a star over the same meridian, i.e. a Sidereal Day, the duration of which is 23hr 56min 04sec of Mean Time.

The meridian in question then continues to move round for a further interval of time, the average length of which is 3min 56sec, until it is at C, when it is again under the sun. The interval between points A and C in Fig. 73 is, therefore, by definition, an Apparent Solar Day, of an average length of 24 hr of Mean Time.

In the meantime, the moon has been moving along its orbit in the same direction as the earth's rotation, and is now at $M2$. The meridian of the earth in question must continue to move round to position D until it can again be under the moon. The interval of time taken for it to move from C to D is approximately 50 min. The interval between points A and D in Fig. 73 is, therefore, a Lunar Day of approximately 24hr 50min duration.

THE YEAR

At the beginning of this chapter it was stated that a year is the period of time the earth takes to make one complete circuit of its orbit. This requires a little more detailed explanation.

The Civil Year, which is the basis of our calendar, is in turn based on the Tropical Year. This is the interval of time that elapses between two coincidences of the sun and the First Point of Aries over the same meridian (the interval between two successive Vernal Equinoxes) and is equal to 365·2422 Mean Solar Days. This was the basis of the Julian calendar, with a leap year every four years, established in the time of Julius Caesar, which continued to be used until 1582, when the present Gregorian calendar was introduced by Pope Gregory XIII. The Gregorian calendar requires that there shall be a leap year every four years, except that three leap years are suppressed in every four centuries. The year 1600 was a leap year. 1700, 1800 and 1900 were not leap years, but the year 2000 will be one. This adjustment of the leap years allows for the fact that the Tropical Year is not exactly 365·25

Mean Solar Days. If this adjustment had not been made, the months would have slowly fallen out of step with the seasons until, eventually, June would have become a winter month.

GREENWICH APPARENT TIME AND LOCAL APPARENT TIME

Apparent Time is the time measured by the apparent movement of the True or Apparent Sun. It is the time recorded by a sun-dial; and it is also of particular interest to the navigator, because it is at 1200 hr Local Apparent Time each day that the True Sun appears to cross every observer's meridian. As will be seen later, this is the time at which an observation of the sun is taken to determine the latitude.

All specific times are hour angles. Thus, Greenwich Apparent Time (G.A.T.) is defined as "the westerly hour angle of the Apparent Sun measured from the anti-meridian of Greenwich". And similarly, Local Apparent Time (L.A.T.) is defined as "the westerly hour angle of the Apparent Sun measured from the anti-meridian of the observer".

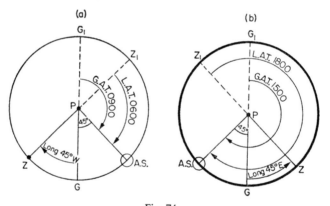

Fig. 74

Figure 74(a) and (b) are views of the celestial sphere looking down on the North Celestial Pole. PG in each diagram, is the celestial meridian of Greenwich and PG_1 is the anti-meridian of Greenwich. Similarly, in each diagram, PZ is the celestial meridian of the observer's zenith (the observer's celestial meridian) and PZ_1 is the anti-meridian of the observer.

In Fig. 74(a) the Apparent Sun is on a meridian 45° East of Greenwich, and the observer is in long 45°W. Therefore, by applying the above definitions of G.A.T. and L.A.T., we see that G.A.T. = 0900 hr and L.A.T. = 0600 hr, since 15° change in longitude is equal to 1 hr change in time.

In Fig. 74(b) the Apparent Sun is on a meridian 45° West of Greenwich and the observer is in long 45°E. Therefore, by applying the above definitions of G.A.T. and L.A.T., we see that G.A.T. = 1500 hr and L.A.T. = 1800 hr.

The relationship between Greenwich Time and Local Time illustrated in these two examples is often remembered by the rhyming rule:

> "Longitude West, Greenwich Time best.
> Longitude East, Greenwich Time least."

GREENWICH MEAN TIME AND LOCAL MEAN TIME

Mean Time is measured by the imaginary movement of the Mean Sun. It is the time recorded by clocks and chronometers which are constructed to keep Mean Time.

Greenwich Mean Time (G.M.T.) is defined as "the westerly hour angle of the Mean Sun from the anti-meridian of Greenwich".

Local Mean Time (L.M.T.) is defined as "the westerly hour angle of the Mean Sun from the anti-meridian of the observer".

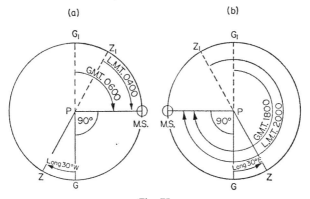

Fig. 75

Figure 75(a) illustrates the relationship between G.M.T. and L.M.T. for an observer in long 30°W. The G.M.T., by definition, equals 0600 hr and the L.M.T., by definition, equals 0400 hr.

Figure 75(b) illustrates the relationship between G.M.T. and L.M.T. for an observer in long 30°E. G.M.T. here equals 1800 hr and L.M.T. equals 2000 hr.

The rhyming rule, referred to above, may also be used to confirm this relationship.

It will be noted that any specific Mean Time or Apparent Time is always measured from the anti-meridian. This is because the day starts at midnight and not at noon.

THE EQUATION OF TIME

The Equation of Time is not really an equation. It is an interval of time, which varies in length from 0 to about 17 min, that has to be applied to Apparent Time to obtain Mean Time and vice-versa.

The Equation of Time is positive, and has a plus sign, when it has to be added to Apparent Time, to give Mean Time; and it is negative, with a minus sign, when it has to be subtracted from Apparent Time, to give Mean Time. It may be thought of in another way, as the correction that has to be applied to the time recorded by a sun-dial to give the time recorded by a clock, when the clock is set to show the Local Mean Time of the meridian on which the sun-dial is situated. A sun-dial on the meridian of Greenwich will record G.A.T. If the Equation of Time is applied to this, it will give G.M.T.

The Equation of Time has two parts which can be called E_1 and E_2. E_1 is caused by the unequal rate of movement of the earth in its orbit according to Kepler's Second Law. This makes the Apparent Sun *appear* to move along the ecliptic at an unequal rate.

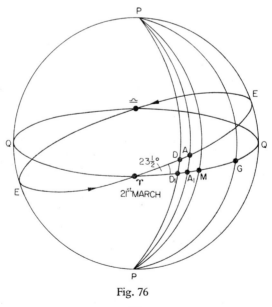

Fig. 76

In order to understand this effect, it is necessary to introduce an imaginary body called the Dynamical Mean Sun which is conceived to move along the ecliptic at a constant rate, equal to the mean rate of the Apparent Sun. This Dynamical Mean Sun must not be confused with the Mean Sun, already referred to, which is conceived to move along the Equinoctial at a constant rate, and by which Mean Time is measured.

Figure 76 shows the celestial sphere with the Apparent Sun (A) in a position that it will occupy between the Vernal Equinox and the Summer Solstice, on about 1st June. At Perihelion the earth travels faster in its orbit than it does at Aphelion, so that in June, the Apparent Sun (A) will be further along the ecliptic than the Dynamical Mean Sun (D).

If the Hour Angles of A and D are measured westwards from the celestial meridian of Greenwich (PGP) then $E_1 = GD_1 - GA_1$ and this will be $+$ because $GD_1 > GA_1$.

Between Aphelion and Perihelion, A will be lagging behind D so that E_1 will be negative. At Perihelion and Aphelion, A and D are together, and E_1 will be NIL.

The second part of the Equation of Time may be called E_2, and this is caused by the fact that the ecliptic is inclined to the Equinoctial at $23\frac{1}{2}°$.

In Fig. 76, M is the Mean Sun, and ΥM measured along the Equinoctial, is equal to ΥD measured along the ecliptic. If the Hour Angles of M and D are now measured westward from the meridian of Greenwich, then $E_2 = GM - GD_1$, and this will be $-$ because $GM < GD_1$. At the Summer Solstice D and M will be on the same meridian $(PEQP)$ and E_2 will be NIL. From Summer Solstice to Autumnal Equinox E_2 will be $+$. It will be $-$ again from Autumnal Equinox to Winter Solstice, when it will again be NIL; and between Winter Solstice and Vernal Equinox it will be $+$ once more.

The maximum value of E_1 is about 7 min and the maximum value of E_2 is about 10 min. The values of E_1 and E_2 may be plotted on a graph as in Fig. 77 where the thin firm line is the graph of E_1 and the pecked line is the graph of E_2. The heavy firm line is the graph of the Equation of Time which is obtained by combining the values of E_1 and E_2 according to usual graphical methods.

From Fig. 77 it may be seen that the Equation of Time is zero on four occasions in the year, approximately on the following dates: April 16th, June 15th, September 1st and December 25th. On these days a sun-dial at Greenwich will show G.M.T. Figure 77 also shows when the Equation of Time reaches its maximum positive and negative values; namely, $+14.5$ min on February 11th, -4 min on May 14th, $+6$ min on July 26th and -16.5 min on November 3rd.

The formal definition of the Equation of Time is: Equation of Time

= Westerly Hour Angle of the Mean Sun — Westerly Hour Angle of the True Sun, and this is usually memorized as

$$\text{Eq. Time} = \text{H.A.M.S.} - \text{H.A.T.S.}$$

It should also be remembered that the Equation of Time is $+$ when H.A.M.S. $>$ H.A.T.S., i.e. when the Mean Sun is further West than the True or Apparent Sun, and when Mean Time is greater than Apparent Time.

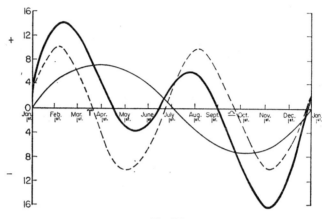

Fig. 77

It is — when H.A.M.S. $<$ H.A.T.S., i.e. when the Mean Sun is to the East of the True or Apparent Sun, and when Mean Time is less than Apparent Time.

The following questions and answers may help to clarify some of the applications of the Equation of Time.

Question. The sun is observed to cross the Greenwich Meridian at noon at 1210 G.M.T. What is the value and sign of the Equation of Time?

Answer. When the Apparent Sun is on an observer's meridian it is always 1200 Local Apparent Time. Therefore, in this case, on the meridian of Greenwich, the time of the sun's meridian passage must be 1200 Greenwich Apparent Time. But G.M.T. $= 1210$.

$$\text{Now, Eq. Time} = \text{G.M.T.} - \text{G.A.T.}$$
$$\therefore \text{Eq. Time} = 1210 - 1200$$
$$= +10 \text{ min.}$$

Question. On board a ship in long 30°W the sun is observed to cross the observer's meridian at noon on February 11th when the Eq. Time is -4 min. What are the L.M.T. and G.M.T. of this occurrence?

Answer.

$$\text{Eq. } T = \text{L.M.T.} - \text{L.A.T.}$$
$$\therefore -4\,\text{min} = \text{L.M.T.} - 1200$$
$$\therefore \text{L.M.T.} = 1200 - 4\,\text{min}$$
$$= 1156$$

Longitude West, Greenwich Time Best $30° = 2$ hr.
$$\therefore \text{G.M.T.} = 1356$$

ZONE TIME AND STANDARD TIME

There are 360 meridians of longitude at 1° intervals round the earth and it would be most confusing if there were a separate Local Mean Time for each meridian.

For this reason the Zone Time and Standard Time systems have been established.

Under the Zone Time system, the earth's surface is divided into Zones each of which is 15° of longitude wide, extending from pole to pole. Zone Zero extends from long $7\frac{1}{2}°$W to long $7\frac{1}{2}°$E, so that the Greenwich Meridian is the mid-meridian of this Zone. Within the boundaries of Zone 0 the Zone Time is G.M.T.

Zone $+1$ extends from $7\frac{1}{2}°$W to $22\frac{1}{2}°$W, its mid-meridian being 15°W. Within the boundaries of this Zone the time kept is 1 hr less than G.M.T., and corresponds to the L.M.T. of long 15°W. This Zone is called Zone $+1$, because an observer on board a ship anywhere in this Zone, keeping the time of Zone $+1$, merely has to *add* 1 hr to his Zone Time to obtain G.M.T.

Zone $+2$ extends from $22\frac{1}{2}°$W to $37\frac{1}{2}°$W, its mid-meridian being 30°W. When keeping this Zone Time, 2 hr must be added to Zone Time to obtain G.M.T.

Zone -1 extends from $7\frac{1}{2}°$E to $22\frac{1}{2}°$E. Zone -2 extends from $22\frac{1}{2}°$E to $37\frac{1}{2}°$E, and so on. When keeping the Zone Time of Zone -1 or Zone -2, one or two hours, as the case may be, must be *subtracted* from Zone Time to obtain G.M.T.

In order to find the Zone in which any place is situated, the quickest method is to change the longitude of the place into time, and the Zone number will be the nearest whole hour. For example, in which Zone is a ship that is reported to be in long 40°W? There are 4 min of time to each degree of arc. Therefore long 40°W is equal to 160 min of time. This equals 2hr 40min. Therefore the ship is in Zone $+3$ and will be keeping a Zone Time which is 3 hr less than G.M.T.

The Zones extend from Zone 0 to Zone $+12$ and Zone -12. Zone $+12$ and Zone -12 cover the same area, namely $172\frac{1}{2}°$W to $172\frac{1}{2}°$E, $7\frac{1}{2}°$ on either side of the 180°Meridian.

STANDARD TIME

Standard Time is a modified type of Zone Time which has been established throughout the world so that, wherever possible, the same time is kept in the same country. Standard Time differs from Zone Time only in the fact that the boundaries of the country or state, and not meridians of longitude, are the boundaries of the Standard Time area.

For example, the Standard Time of the British Isles is G.M.T. (except when Summer Time is in force). The Standard Time of New York State is described as +5, since 5 hr must be added to New York Time to obtain G.M.T. Another way of saying the same thing is to say that New York keeps the L.M.T. of long 75°W. Ceylon, on the other hand, keeps the Standard Time denoted as −5 hr 30 min, which means that 5 hr 30 min must be subtracted from Ceylon Standard Time to obtain G.M.T. Conversely, of course, 5 hr 30 min must be added to G.M.T. to obtain Ceylon Standard Time. In general, it will be noted that Zones and countries in West Longitude are + whilst Zones and countries in East Longitude are −, because the sign indicates how the Zone number must be applied to the Zone or National Time in order to obtain G.M.T.

A list of the Standard Times kept by all the nations and states of the world is given in the Nautical Almanac.

The Date Line corresponds for the greater part of its length with the 180° meridian, and is so called because the date has to be changed when crossing from one side of the line to the other.

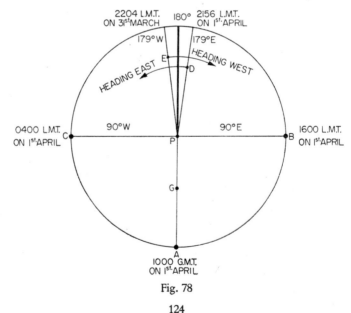

Fig. 78

Figure 78 is a diagram of the earth, looking down on the North Pole. *A* is on the Greenwich Meridian at 1000 hr G.M.T. on 1st April. *B* is an observer in long 90°E. His time will be 1600 hr L.M.T. on 1st April when it is 1000 hr G.M.T. *C* is an observer in long 90°W. His time will be 0400 L.M.T. on 1st April when it is 1000 G.M.T. *D* is an observer in long 179°E. A little calculation will show that his time is 2156 L.M.T. on 1st April when it is 1000 G.M.T. Finally, *E* is an observer in long 179°W and it can readily be shown that his time is 2204 L.M.T. on 31*st March* when it is 1000 G.M.T. on 1st April at Greenwich.

If *D* and *E* were on board ships or aircraft moving East and West respectively, they might both cross the 180° meridian at 2200 hr L.M.T. When *D*, who is heading East, crosses the Date Line, he must retard his calendar by one day. When *E*, who is heading West, crosses the Date Line, he must advance his calendar by one day.

The following worked examples of some time problems may be found useful.

EXAMPLE 1

A ship is in long 50°W at 0400 G.M.T.

What is (a) The S.M.T. (L.M.T.) at ship?

(b) The Zone Time at ship?

long 50° = 3 hr 20 min in time. G.M.T. = 0400   Ship is in Zone

long in Time W — 320   +3

S.M.T. = 0040   ∴ Zone Time is 3 hr less than G.M.T.

= 0100

EXAMPLE 2

A ship is in long 65°E and keeping Zone Time.

(a) In which Zone is she situated?

(b) If it is 0200 hr Zone Time at ship on 2nd June, what are the Greenwich Date and Time?

(c) What is the S.M.T.?

Answers

(a) long 65° = 4 hr 20 min. Therefore the ship is in Zone —4.

(b) Zone Time = June 2nd   02 hr 00 min

—4 hr   4   00

G.M.T. = June 1st   22 hr 00 min (Note change of date)

(c) G.M.T. = June 1st   22 hr 00 min

long in Time + East   4   20

S.M.T. = June 2nd   02 hr 20 min

EXAMPLE 3

A ship sails from Vancouver at 0900 hr Standard Time (Zone + 8), on 1st June, for Sydney, Australia. On what date and at what Local Mean Time will she arrive at a position off Sydney Heads in long 152°30′E if she takes 10 days 6 hr on the passage?

Method 1

Convert all times to G.M.T.
0900 Zone + 8 Time = 1700 hr G.M.T.

∴   Ship sails from Vancouver on June   1 day 17 hr 00 min G.M.T.
    Time on passage   +10   6   00

    Ship arrives off Sydney on June   11   23   00   G.M.T.
    long in Time   +   10   10

                              June   12 day 9 hr 10 min L.M.T.

long 152° = 608 min
      30′ +   2 min
           ─────────
           610 min
long in Time = 10 hr 10 min.

Method 2

Convert to L.M.T. and allow for crossing Date Line.
(This is avoided by Method 1)
The Standard Time of Zone + 8 is the L.M.T. of long 120°W.
∴ Ship (in effect) leaves long 120°W on June 1 day 09 hr 00 min L.M.T.
Time on passage   10   06   00

Ship arrives in long 152°30′E on June   11   15   00 L.M.T.
                                                         of 120°W
d.long in Time (W—)   5   50

d.long 120°W ～ 152°30′E   June   11 day 9 hr 10 min L.M.T.
           = 87°30′W   of 152°30′E
87°   = 348 min
30′   =   2 min   +1 day for crossing Date Line
           ─────────   heading West.
d.long in Time = 350 min   ∴ L.M.T. of arrival in long 152°30′E
           = 5 hr 50 min.   = June 12 day 9 hr 10 min L.M.T.
                              (as before).

THE NAUTICAL ALMANAC

The Nautical Almanac is published annually by Her Majesty's Stationery Office in Britain and the identical American Nautical Almanac is published in the U.S.A.

Extracts from a number of the daily pages of the 1958 Almanac are printed at the back of this book so that they may be used to solve some of the exercises given in later chapters.

In the full Nautical Almanac, some very useful interpolation tables are provided, but since these are bulky and cannot be included here, the following examples of how to extract data from the Almanac without using special tables are now given.

EXAMPLE 4

Extract the Greenwich Hour Angles of:

(1) The sun at 0425 G.M.T. on Friday 19th September 1958.

(2) The Planet Venus at 16 hr 42 min 10 sec G.M.T. on Friday 19th September 1958.

(3) The First Point of Aries at 20 hr 10 min 40 sec G.M.T. on Saturday 20th September 1958.

(1) At 0400 G.M.T. G.H.A. Sun $= 241°29·5'$
  At 0500 G.M.T. G.H.A. Sun $= 256°29·7'$
  Increment in 60 min of Time $= 15°00·2' = 900·2'$ of arc.
  $\therefore$ in 25 min of Time increment will be $900·2 \times 25/60 = 375'$
  $\therefore$ Increment $= 6°15'$
  $\therefore$ G.H.A. Sun at 0425 $= 241°29·5' + 6°15' = 247°44·5'$

(2) At 1600 G.M.T. G.H.A. Venus $= 73°36·7'$
  At 1700 G.M.T. G.H.A. Venus $= 88°36·2'$

  Increment in 3600 sec of Time $= 14°59·5' = 899·5'$ of arc.
  42 min 10 sec $= 2530$ sec.
  $\therefore$ Increment in 2530 sec will be $899·5 \times 2530/3600 = 632·2'$
  $= 10°32·2'$
  $\therefore$ G.H.A. Venus at 16 hr 42 min 10 sec $= 73°36·7' + 10°32·2'$
  $= 84°08·9'$

(3) At 2000 G.M.T. G.H.A. Aries $= 299°12'$
  At 2100 G.M.T. G.H.A. Aries $= 314°14·5'$

  Increment in 3600 sec of Time $= 15°02·5' = 902·5'$ of arc.
  10 min 40 sec $= 640$ sec.
  $\therefore$ Increment in 640 sec will be $902·5 \times 640/3600 = 160·4' = 2°40·4'$
  $\therefore$ G.H.A. Aries at 20 hr 10 min 40 sec $= 299°12' + 2°40·4' = 301°52·4'$

EXAMPLE 5

Extract the Declinations of:

(1) The sun at the time of its Meridian Passage for an observer in long 30°W on 19th September 1958.
(2) The Planet Venus at the time of the Meridian Passage for an observer in long 60°E on 20th September 1958.
(3) The stars Altair, Deneb and Sirius.

(1) The time of Meridian Passage of the sun and of the planets which is given in the Almanac is the L.M.T. of the occurrence, and is at the same L.M.T. throughout the world because of the earth's rotation.
   On 19th September, Meridian Passage of sun =   11 hr 54 min L.M.T.
   Long of observer is 30°W   = + 2 hr 00 min

   ∴. G.M.T. of Meridian Passage   =   13 hr 54 min G.M.T.
   Declination of sun at 13 hr G.M.T. = 1°33·5'N
   Declination of sun at 14 hr G.M.T. = 1°32·5'N

   ∴. in 60 min Declination changes   0°1'
   ∴. in 54 min Declination changes 1' × 54/60 = 0·9'
   ∴. Declination of sun at Meridian Passage (1354 G.M.T.)
                                       = 1°33·5' − 0·9'
                                       = 1°32·6'N

(2) On 20th September, Meridian Passage of Venus =   11 hr 06 min L.M.T.
   Long of observer is 60°E   = − 4 hr 00 min

   ∴. G.M.T. of Meridian Passage   =   7 hr 06 min G.M.T.
   Declination of Venus at 7 hr G.M.T. = 7°48·9'N
   Declination of Venus at 8 hr G.M.T. = 7°47·7'N

   ∴. in 60 min Declination changes   0°1·2'
   ∴. in 6 min Declination changes   1·2 × 6/60 = 0·12'
   ∴. Declination of Venus at Meridian Passage (0706 G.M.T.)
                                       = 7°48·9' − 0·12'
                                       = 7°48·78'N

   It should be noted that when the Declination is increasing, as it often is, the correction must be added.

(3) The Declinations and S.H.A.s of stars only change very slowly owing to the Precession of the Equinoxes. Therefore, the Declinations and S.H.A.s of the principal stars are only given in the Nautical Almanac at three day intervals and no correction is necessary on any given day.

∴ On both 19th and 20th September 1958, the
Declination of Altair is   8°45·8′N
Declination of Deneb is   45°08·3′N
Declination of Sirius is   16°39·4′S

EXAMPLE 6

Find the L.M.T. of Sunrise on 19th September 1958 for an observer in lat 53°N.

The times of Sunrise, Sunset and Twilight are also given at three day intervals in the Almanac, the times given being for the date of the middle day on the page of the full Almanac. In the full Almanac, 20th September is the middle day of the page, and 17th September is the middle day of the previous page. (There are three days to a page.)

On 20th September it can be seen by visual interpolation that, for an observer in lat 53°N, the sun rises at 5 hr 41 min 30 sec L.M.T.

On 17th September the time is given in the full Almanac as 5 hr 36 min 30 sec L.M.T.

There are 5 min difference in three days; therefore, in one day, the difference is 1 min 40 sec.

∴ Sunrise on 19th September = 5 hr 41 min 30 sec − 1 min 40 sec
                         = 5 hr 39 min 50 sec L.M.T.

SIDEREAL TIME

Sidereal Time is the time that is used by astronomers and it is determined by the position of the First Point of Aries in the celestial sphere.

Greenwich Sidereal Time at any instant is defined as the westerly hour angle of the First Point of Aries from the Greenwich Meridian at that instant. It is therefore, by definition, the same value as G.H.A. Aries. For example, if, at a given G.M.T., on a given date, the G.H.A. Aries obtained from the Nautical Almanac is 60°, then the Greenwich Sidereal Time is 4 hr. When the G.H.A. Aries is 310°, then the G.S.T. is 20^h 40^m.

Local Sidereal Time is defined as the westerly hour angle of the First Point of Aries from the observer's meridian. If G.H.A. Aries is 60° and the observer's longitude is 30°W, then L.S.T. is 2 hr. If G.H.A. Aries is 310° and the observer is in longitude 15°E, then L.S.T. is 21^{h}40^m.

It will be noted that, as with Mean Time and Apparent Time, the rules "Longitude East, Greenwich Time Least" and "Longitude West, Greenwich Time Best" apply also to the relationship between G.S.T. and L.S.T.

The most important difference between Sidereal Time and time measured by either the Mean or Apparent Sun is that Sidereal Time is measured from the Greenwich or local *meridian*, whereas Sun Time is measured from the Greenwich or local *anti-meridian*.

Since one Sidereal Day is equal to $23^h56^m04^s$ of Mean Time, it follows that the hands of a sidereal clock take that interval of Mean Time to rotate through 24 hr on the face of the sidereal clock; i.e. one hour of Sidereal Time is of slightly shorter duration than one hour of Mean Time. In fact, 24 hr of Mean Time is 86,400 sec, and 24 hr of Sidereal Time is 86,164 sec of Mean Time.

EXERCISE VII

1. If a certain star appears to cross the Greenwich Meridian at 1800 G.M.T. on 1st January, at what G.M.T. will it cross the Greenwich Meridian on 3rd January?
2. If the moon is seen to rise above the horizon at a certain place at 2000 hr L.M.T. on 1st January, at what approximate L.M.T. will it rise above the horizon on 3rd January?
3. If a certain star and the moon appear to cross an observer's meridian together at a certain instant of time on one day, what will be the approximate interval of time between their transits of the same meridian on the following day?
4. As a result of an observation of the sun, an observer calculates that the sun's celestial meridian was 30°15′W of his own meridian. What was the observer's Local Apparent Time at the time of observation? If the observer was in long 15°15′E, what was the Greenwich Apparent Time of observation?
5. On a certain day, the Nautical Almanac states that the L.M.T. of the sun's Meridian Passage is 1148. What is the value and sign of the Equation of Time?
6. On a certain day the Nautical Almanac states that at 1200 G.M.T. the G.H.A. of the sun is 357°15′. What is the value and sign of the Equation of Time?
7. (a) Given that the Equation of Time is +8 min on a certain date, what is the L.M.T. of the sun's Meridian Passage?
   (b) Given that the Equation of Time is −15 min on a certain date, what is the L.M.T. of the sun's Meridian Passage?
8. At 1200 hr G.M.T. on a certain date when the Equation of Time is −10 min what is the G.H.A. of the sun?
9. A naval vessel is in long 52°10′W. What is the number of the Zone Time that she is keeping? If the chartroom clock aboard shows 1200 hr what is the G.M.T.?
10. If it is 1200 G.M.T. on a certain date, what is the Zone Time on board a naval vessel in long 120°15′E?
11. At Brisbane, Australia (Standard Time Zone −10) the sun was on the meridian at $12^h04^m00^s$ Standard Time and the sun's G.H.A. was 215°00′. Find the Equation of Time and state if its sign is + or −.
12. Find the Local Apparent Time at New York (Standard Time Zone +5) at 1500 Standard Time, when the Equation of Time is +8 min. Long of New York = 74°00′W.
13. A ship leaves Liverpool on 1st April at 2000 hr G.M.T. Find the date and Standard Time of arrival at New York (Standard Time Zone +5) if the ship takes 3 days 4 hr on the passage. Also find the L.M.T. of arrival at New York, which is in long 74°00′W.
14. A ship leaves Sydney, Australia on 1st March at 1000 hr Standard Time and takes 10 days 3 hr steaming time on the passage to Valparaiso. Given that Sydney and

Valparaiso are in the Standard Times of Zones of − 10 and +4 respectively, give the date and Standard Time of the ship's arrival at Valparaiso.

15. A ship leaves Valparaiso on 1st March at 1000 hr Standard Time and takes 10 days 3 hr steaming time on the passage to Sydney. Given the information in the previous question, find the date and Standard Time of arrival at Sydney.

The extracts from the Nautical Almanac printed at the back of this book are to be used for answering questions 16 and 17.

16. Find the Declination and G.H.A. of the sun:
   (a) At 1242 G.M.T. on 19th September 1958.
   (b) At 2320 G.M.T. on 20th September 1958.
   (c) At 1730 G.M.T. on 6th June 1958.
   (d) At 0420 G.M.T. on 26th October 1958.
   (e) At 1732 G.M.T. on 30th December 1958.

17. Find the G.M.T. and Greenwich Date of the sun's Meridian Passage:
   (a) For an observer in long 30°30′W on 19th September 1958.
   (b) For an observer in long 50°15′E on 20th September 1958.
   (c) For an observer in long 100°00′W on 7th June 1958.
   (d) For an observer in long 179°30′E on 27th October 1958.
   (e) For an observer in long 179°45′W on 31st December 1958.

18. (a) G.M.T. $18^h16^m32^s$ L.M.T. $14^h42^m06^s$. Find the longitude.
   (b) G.A.T. $09^h49^m50^s$ L.A.T. $12^h06^m54^s$. Find the longitude.

19. To an observer in long 18°32′E the sun is on the meridian. Find the Greenwich Hour Angle of the sun.

20. To an observer in long 36°15′W the L.A.T. is $15^h04^m12^s$. If the Equation of Time is $+3^m43^s$, what is the G.M.T.?

21. Find:
   (a) The Greenwich Sidereal Time at 0400 G.M.T. on 19th September 1958.
   (b) The Local Sidereal Time at the same instant for an observer in long 25°W.

22. Find:
   (a) The Greenwich Sidereal Time at 1600 G.M.T. on 19th September 1958.
   (b) The Local Sidereal Time at the same instant for an observer in long 80°E.

CHAPTER 8

The sextant and altitudes

THE SEXTANT

THE sextant is an instrument for measuring angles and is extensively used at sea, both for measuring the altitudes of heavenly bodies, and for measuring the horizontal and vertical angles subtended by shore objects.

Basic Principles

The sextant depends on two basic principles of optics:
(1) When a ray of light strikes a plane mirror, the angle of incidence is equal to the angle of reflection.
(2) When a ray of light suffers two successive reflections in the same plane, the angle between the first and last directions of the ray is equal to twice the angle between the mirrors.

The first of these two laws requires no further explanation, but the second will now be fully proved.

A and B, are two plane mirrors inclined to each other at an angle β.

A ray of light from a source S strikes the mirror A at N, making an angle a with the normal XN. The ray is reflected at the same angle and strikes mirror B at O, making an angle of b with the normal OY. The ray is then finally reflected along OP.

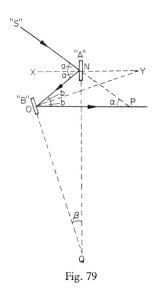

Fig. 79

The angle between the first and last directions of the ray is $\angle NPO = \alpha$, and the angle between the mirrors is $\angle NQO = \beta$.

In $\triangle QON$
$$\angle QNO = (90° - a)$$
$$\angle QON = (90° + b)$$
Since the sum of the angles of a triangle $= 180°$, then
$$(90° + b) + (90 - a) + \beta = 180°.$$
$$\therefore \beta = (a - b) \tag{1}$$

In $\triangle PON$
$$\angle ONP = (180° - 2a)$$
$$\angle PON = 2b$$
$$(180° - 2a) + (2b) + \alpha = 180°$$
$$\therefore \alpha = 2(a - b) \tag{2}$$

Combining (1) and (2)
$$\alpha = 2\beta.$$

Figure 80 shows a typical marine sextant. It consists of a metal frame, at the bottom of which is inscribed a silvered arc, graduated in degrees. On the frame is mounted the index bar which is pivoted to the frame at *A* and is free to move along the arc. A clamp is fitted at the bottom of the index bar and engages on a toothed rack at the back of the arc. By means of the clamp the bar can either be moved freely or clamped in any desired position.

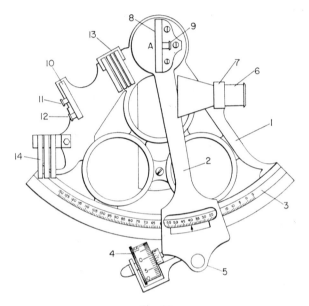

Fig. 80

1. Frame of sextant	2. Index bar
3. Silvered arc	4. Micrometer with vernier
5. Clamp	6. Telescope
7. Telescope collar	8. Index glass
9. 1st adjustment screw	10. Horizon glass
11. 2nd adjustment screw	12. 3rd adjustment screw
13. Index glass shades	14. Horizon glass shades

Fine adjustmens of the bar are made possible by means of a micrometer and vernier attached to a pinion which engages on to the rack. The index glass, which is a plane mirror, is mounted on to the index bar at *A*, and the horizon glass, which is half mirror and half plane glass, is mounted on to the frame. Coloured glass shades are provided for both the index and horizon glasses. Observations are made by means of a telescope which is screwed into a special collar mounted on the frame.

Adjustments of the Sextant

For a sextant to read correctly, it is necessary that:
(1) Both the horizon and index glasses are perpendicular to the plane of the sextant.
(2) When the index bar is set at zero, the horizon and index glasses are parallel to each other.

Before being put into use, the sextant should be checked to ensure that both these conditions are satisfied. This is done by performing what is known as the "three adjustments of the sextant".

1st Adjustment

To place the index bar perpendicular to the plane of the sextant.

To do this, clamp the index bar about one third of the way along the arc (e.g. 40°). Hold the sextant horizontally with the arc away from you and look obliquely into the index glass. An image of the arc will be seen in the index glass and the true arc will be visible at the side of it. If both arcs appear to be in one continuous line, then the glass is perpendicular. If, however, the reflected arc appears above or below the true arc, then the glass is not perpendicular, and error of perpendicularity exists. This may be removed by turning the 1st adjustment screw at the back of the index glass until both images coincide.

2nd Adjustment

To place the horizon glass perpendicular to the plane of the sextant.
(a) *By means of the horizon.* Clamp the index bar at zero, hold the sextant horizontally and observe the horizon. The true horizon will be seen on either side of the horizon glass and a reflection of it will be seen in the mirror part. If the true and reflected horizons appear in one straight line, then the horizon glass is perpendicular, but if they do not, then side error exists, and must be removed by turning the 2nd adjustment screw at the back of the horizon glass.

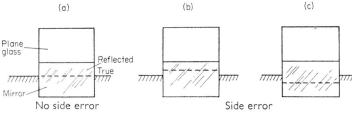

Fig. 81

(b) *By a star.* Clamp the bar at zero and, holding the sextant vertically, observe any bright star. If there is no side error then the true and reflected images of the star will coincide, but if there is side error, then the reflected image will be seen to the side of the true image.

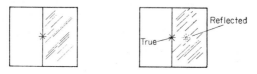

Fig. 82

3rd Adjustment

To place the horizon and index glasses parallel to one another when the index bar is set at zero.

(a) *By the horizon.* Clamp the bar at zero, and holding the sextant vertically, observe the horizon. If the true and reflected images of the horizon, as seen in the horizon glass, appear as one straight line, then the two glasses are parallel, but if they do not, then the glasses are not parallel and index error exists, and must be removed by turning the 3rd adjustment screw at the back of the horizon glass.

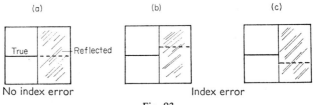

Fig. 83

(b) *By a star.* This is done in exactly the same way as the 2nd adjustment by means of a star, except that if index error exists, the reflected star will appear above or below the true star.

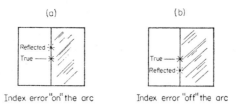

Fig. 84

136

Index error and side error are both corrected by adjustments of the same mirror, so it is quite conceivable that the correction of one may offset the other. It is necessary, therefore, after making the 3rd adjustment, to go back and check the 2nd, and, if necessary, re-adjust it.

Sometimes, the case may arise when it is found impossible to remove both side and index error absolutely. In this case, the side error should be removed, and the value of the index error found and applied to all readings.

The value of the index error may be found by moving the index bar until both images of the horizon or star coincide, and noting the reading on the sextant, which will give the value of the index error. Should the reading be greater than zero, the index error is said to be "on the arc" and its value should be subtracted from all readings. Should, however, the reading be less than zero, then the index error is said to be "off the arc" and its value should be added to all readings.

Determination of Index Error by the Sun

The value of the index error can be determined by observations of the sun, as well as by the horizon or a star, and this is probably the most accurate method of doing it as the accuracy of the results can be checked.

The method of obtaining the index error by the sun is as follows:

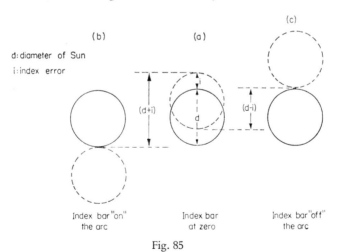

Fig. 85

With the index bar set at zero, the sun is observed. If index error exists then two images of the sun will be seen (Fig. 85(a)), and the amount by which the reflected is above or below the true sun will indicate the value of the index error.

N—F

Suppose that the reflected sun is above the true sun. Move the index bar onto the arc until the reflected sun is below and just touching the true sun (Fig. 85(b)). The upper limb of the reflected sun has moved an amount equal to $(d+i)$ from the zero position and if the reading of the sextant at this point is x, then:

$$(d+i)=x \qquad (1)$$

Now, move the index bar off the arc until the reflected sun is above and just touching the true sun (Fig. 85(c)). The lower limb of the reflected sun has been moved an amount equal to $(d-i)$ from the zero position and if the reading of the sextant at this point is y, then:

$$(d-i)=y \qquad (2)$$

Subtracting (2) from (1),

$$2i=x-y$$

or

$$i=\frac{x-y}{2}.$$

The index error is, therefore, equal to half the difference between the two readings and is named the same as the greater reading (in this case, "on" the arc).

To check the accuracy of these results, the two readings are added and the result divided by four, which gives:

$$\frac{d}{2}=\frac{x+y}{4}.$$

$d/2$ is the value of the sun's semi–diameter and this can be checked against the value tabulated in the Nautical Almanac for the day. If the two values agree then the value of the index error, as found, may be taken as accurate.

A special case arises when the index error is greater than the diameter of the sun.

In Fig. 86(a), the index bar is at zero and the index error is greater than the diameter.

The bar is moved onto the arc until the lower limb of the reflected sun coincides with the upper limb of the true (Fig. 86(b)) and the reading noted. The bar is then moved further onto the arc until the upper limb of the reflected sun coincides with the lower limb of the true (Fig. 86(c)), and the reading noted.

Suppose the reading in (b) was x, and the reading in (c) was y, then:

$$i-d=x$$

and

$$i+d=y$$

Adding $$2i = x + y$$

or, $$i = \frac{x+y}{2}.$$

Similarly, the semi-diameter is given by,

$$\frac{d}{2} = \frac{x \sim y}{4}$$

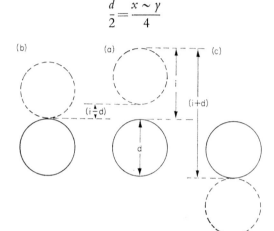

Fig. 86

In this case, the index error is equal to half the sum of the two readings. It should be noted that both the readings will be either "on" or "off" the arc, and the index error is named accordingly.

Error of Collimation

This is an error caused by the telescope not being parallel to the plane of the sextant. To test for this error, the inverting telescope, which is fitted with cross wires, should be used. With the telescope in place, two stars more than 90° apart are brought together on one of the cross wires of the telescope. The sextant is then tilted so that the stars move across onto the other cross wire. If they remain in coincidence whilst doing this then there is no error of collimation, but if they tend to move apart, then error of collimation exists. This may be removed by adjusting two small screws on the telescope collar, but many modern sextants are not fitted with these collimating screws.

Graduation Error

This is caused by faulty graduation of the arc or vernier and cannot be adjusted by the observer. Its presence, however, can be detected by placing a division of the vernier (not the zero or the ten) against a division on the main scale. If no other division coincides, then there is no graduation error. This should be repeated at various points along the scale.

Vernier Error

This is caused by the vernier scale being set too high or too low on the arc. Its presence may be detected by placing the zero of the vernier opposite a division on the main scale. If there is no vernier error, then the only other division coinciding should be the ten. Again, this error cannot be adjusted by the observer.

Shade Error

This is caused by the coloured glass shades being imperfectly ground. If it exists, then either a new shade should be fitted, or the affected shade should not be used.

Centring Error

This is caused by the pivot of the index bar not coinciding with the centre of the circle forming the arc.

The presence of centring error is difficult to determine accurately, except in a properly equipped laboratory. The method of determining it is to obtain a latitude from two stars of equal altitude, one bearing North and the other bearing South. If both latitudes agree, then there is no centring error for that altitude, but if they do not, then the centring error is equal to half the difference between the two latitudes.

In order to obtain the centring error for the whole sextant, the above must be repeated for about every 5° along the arc and a table of errors drawn up.

ALTITUDES

Sensible Horizon

This is a small circle on the celestial sphere whose plane is parallel to the rational horizon, and which passes through the observer's eye.

Visible Horizon

This is a small circle on the surface of the earth representing the observer's field of vision.

The true altitude of a heavenly body is defined as the arc of the vertical circle contained between the body and the rational horizon (*XR*, in Fig. 87) or the angle subtended at the centre of the earth between the body and the rational horizon.

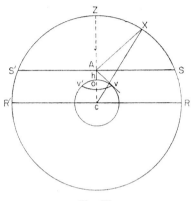

Fig. 87

RCR'	The rational horizon	*SAS'*	The sensible horizon
VV'	The visible horizon	*A*	The observer
h	The observer's height of eye	*c*	The centre of the earth
	X	The body	

In Fig. 87, the true altitude of *X* is the angle *XCR*, but an observer at *A* and of height *h* would not be able to measure this angle. Instead, he would obtain the angle *XAV*, which is the altitude of *X* above the visible horizon (*VV'*). This is known as the sextant altitude and in order to obtain the true altitude from it, the following corrections must be applied:

Index Error

Any index error in the sextant must be applied to the sextant altitude to obtain the observed altitude.

Dip

This is the depression of the visible horizon below the sensible horizon. It varies in amount according to the height of eye and is always subtractive. In Fig. 87, $\angle SAV$ is the angle of dip, and the observed altitude corrected for dip is known as the apparent altitude ($\angle XAS$).

141

Refraction

Light from a body reaching the earth has to pass through the earth's atmosphere, and in doing so becomes refracted towards the earth, so that the body appears to be higher than it actually is.

The density of the atmosphere decreases gradually as the distance from the earth increases, but for simplicity, let us assume that the earth's atmosphere is divided into three definite layers, *A*, *B*, and *C*. Light from a star at *X* would enter the atmosphere at *a*, and being refracted towards the normal, would pass along the path *ab*. On entering layer *B*, it would be refracted along the path *bc*, and again, when entering the layer *C*, it would be refracted along the path *cO*. The observer at *O* would see the body in the direction *Oc*, so that it would appear to be at *X′* and not *X*.

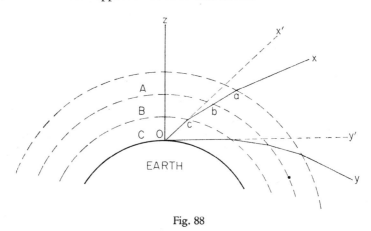

Fig. 88

The amount by which the light is refracted depends upon the angle which the light makes with the normal. In Fig. 88, *Y* is on the horizon and light from it is entering the earth's atmosphere at a more oblique angle than light from *X*, so that it suffers a greater amount of refraction. *Z* is at the observer's zenith and light from it passes along the normal so that there is no refraction.

· Refraction, therefore, varies with altitude, from a maximum when the altitude is 0°, to zero when the altitude is 90°.

The correction for refraction is always subtractive.

Semi-diameter

When observing the altitude of a heavenly body, it is the altitude of the body's centre that is required. This presents no difficulty with stars or planets as they appear as small dots in the heavens, but with the sun and moon it is quite different. These two bodies are quite large and it would be very difficult to measure the altitude of their centres with any accuracy. What is done, then, is to measure the altitude of either the lower or upper limb of the body and then to apply a correction for the body's radius, or semi-diameter, in order to obtain the altitude of the centre.

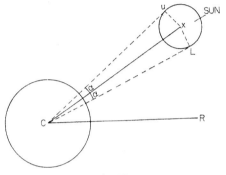

Fig. 89

In Fig. 89 the altitude of the sun's centre above the rational horizon is $\angle XCR$, whereas the altitude actually obtained would be either $\angle LCR$ or $\angle UCR$, depending upon whether the lower or upper limb of the sun is observed. Therefore, in order to obtain the altitude of the sun's centre, the angle α must be either added or subtracted. α is the angle subtended at the centre of the earth by the sun's radius, and its value is tabulated in the Nautical Almanac for each day. The mean value of the semi-diameter for each month is given in the appendix at the back of this book.

The value of the semi-diameter is not constant but varies with the earth's distance from the sun, having its maximum value when the earth is nearest to the sun (December–January) and its minimum value when the earth is farthest away (June–July).

What has been said above about the sun applies equally to the moon, except that the moon's semi-diameter is changing more rapidly since the moon revolves round the earth every 28 days.

Parallax

This is the difference between the altitude of the body above the sensible horizon and the altitude above the rational horizon.

In Fig. 87

$$\text{Parallax} = \angle XCR - \angle XAS.$$

Also,

$$\angle ZAX = \angle AXC + \angle ACX$$
(external angle = sum of internal opposite angles)

or,

$$\angle AXC = \angle ZAX - \angle ACX.$$

But,

$$\angle ZAX = (90° - \angle XAS) \text{ and } \angle ACX = (90° - \angle XCR)$$

$$\therefore \angle AXC = (90° - \angle XAS) - (90° - \angle XCR)$$

$$= \angle XCR - \angle XAS.$$

$$\text{Parallax} = \angle AXC.$$

Thus the parallax is equal to the angle subtended by the earth's radius at the body.

The distance of heavenly bodies from the earth is great in comparison with the earth's radius, so that the correction for parallax is always small, except in the case of the moon which is comparatively near to the earth, where the correction may amount to as much as a degree. For the sun and planets, however, the correction is in the neighbourhood of $0 \cdot 1'$ and for the stars it is too small to be measured.

VARIATION OF PARALLAX WITH ALTITUDE

The correction for parallax varies with the distance of the body from the earth and with the altitude.

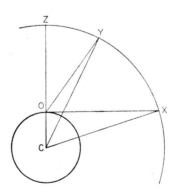

Fig. 90

Suppose that a body is at X, such that the apparent altitude is $0°$, then the angle of parallax will be $\angle OXC$. The body rises in the heavens until it is at Y. The parallax is now $\angle OYC$, and it can be seen from the figure that $\angle OYC < \angle OXC$. The body continues rising until it is at Z, directly overhead. At this point there is no parallax.

From this it is apparent that the parallax varies from a maximum when the altitude is $0°$ to zero when the altitude is $90°$.

This can be proved mathematically as follows:

In $\triangle OXC$,

$$\angle COX = 90°.$$

$$\therefore \ OC = XC \sin \angle OXC. \tag{1}$$

In $\triangle OYC$,

$$\frac{\sin \angle OYC}{OC} = \frac{\sin \angle COY}{CY} \tag{2}$$

Substitute in (2) for OC

$$\frac{\sin \angle OYC}{CX \sin \angle OXC} = \frac{\sin \angle COY}{CY}$$

but

$$CX = CY \ (\text{radii})$$

and

$$\sin \angle COY = \cos \angle YOX$$

$$\therefore \frac{\sin \angle OYC}{\sin \angle OXC} = \cos \angle YOX$$

or

$$\sin \angle OYC = \sin \angle OXC \times \cos \angle YOX.$$

Thus, sin parallax in altitude = sin horizontal parallax × cos altitude.

Therefore, the parallax varies with the cosine of the altitude, and since the cos of $0° = 1$, and the cos of $90° = 0$, it follows that the parallax is maximum at $0°$ and zero at $90°$.

The correction for parallax is always positive.

EXAMPLE 1

On March 2nd, the sextant altitude of the sun's L.L. was observed to be $45°15\cdot2'$, I.E. $2\cdot4'$ off the arc, height of eye, 56 ft. Find the true altitude of the sun.

Sextant altitude	45°15·2′
I.E.	+2·4′
Observed altitude	45°17·6′
Dip (56 ft)	−7·3′
Apparent altitude	45°10·3′
Refraction	−00·9′
	45°09·4′
Semi-diameter	+16·2′
	45°25·6′
Parallax	+00·1′
True altitude	45°25·7′

EXAMPLE 2

On September 18th, the sextant altitude of the sun's U.L. was observed to be 65°29·4′, I.E. 3·6′ on the arc, height of eye, 32 ft. Find the true altitude.

Sextant altitude	65°29·4′
I.E.	−3·6′
Observer's altitude	65°25·8′
Dip (32 ft)	−5·5′
Apparent altitude	65°20·3′
Refraction	−0·4′
	65°19·9′
Semi-diameter	−16·0′
	65°03·9′
Parallax	+0·1′
True altitude	65°04·0′

EXAMPLE 3

The sextant altitude of the star Capella was observed to be 38°15·8′, I.E. 1·6′ on the arc, height of eye, 42 ft. Find the true altitude.

146

| Sextant altitude | 38°15·8′ |
| I.E. | −1·6′ |

| Observer's altitude | 38°14·2′ |
| Dip (42 ft) | −6·4′ |

| Apparent altitude | 38°07·8′ |
| Refraction | −1·2′ |

| True altitude | 38°06·6′ |

Altitude and Zenith Distance

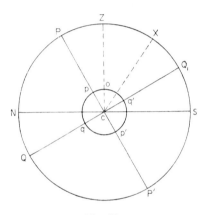

Fig. 91

PP′	The celestial poles	QQ′	The equinoctial
NS	The rational horizon	Z	The observer's zenith
X	The body	O	The observer

C   The centre of the earth

Figure 91 represents the celestial sphere shown on the plane of the observer's meridian.

The true altitude of a body may be defined as the angular height of the body above the rational horizon. Therefore, the true altitude of X is $\angle XCS$.

Similarly, the zenith distance of a body is the angular distance that a body is from the observer's zenith. Therefore, the zenith distance of X is $\angle XCZ$.

From Fig. 91,

$$\angle ZCS = 90°.$$
$$\therefore \angle XCZ = 90° - \angle XCS.$$

147

Thus

$$\text{zenith distance} = 90° - \text{altitude}.$$

The zenith distance of a body is, therefore, the complement of the altitude.

In the three examples worked above, the zenith distance in each case would be:

Example 1   zenith distance $= 90° - 45°25·7' = 44°34·3'$
Example 2   zenith distance $= 90° - 65°04·0' = 24°56·0'$
Example 3   zenith distance $= 90° - 38°06·6' = 51°53·4'.$

EXERCISE VIII

1. (a) State the two optical principles upon which the sextant is based.
   (b) Show that when an angle is measured with a sextant, the angle through which the index bar is moved is only half the angle actually measured.
2. What is the cause of error of perpendicularity, side error and index error? Describe how you would find out if these errors existed and how you would correct them.
3. Explain why it is more satisfactory to use a star for making the 2nd and 3rd adjustments of a sextant, rather than the horizon.
4. Describe, with sketches, how you would determine the index error of a sextant by means of the sun.

   In finding the index error by the sun, the two readings were 36'20" and 27'20", "on" and "off" the arc, respectively. What is the index error, and in what two months could the observations have been made?
5. In order to find the index error of his sextant, an observer measures the vertical angle of a lighthouse, 420 ft high. He first of all moves the index bar until the reflected image of the lighthouse is below and just touching the true image. He then moves the bar off the arc until the reflected image is above and just touching the true image. The reading in the first case was 1°09'40", "on" the arc, and in the second case was 00°03'40", "off" the arc. What was the index error of the sextant, and the distance of the observer from the lighthouse?
6. In each of the following, find the true altitude and zenith distance of the sun:
   (a) March 20th, sextant altitude of sun's L.L. 43°18', I.E. 3·2' off the arc, height of eye, 52 ft.
   (b) October 8th, sextant altitude of sun's U.L. 62°27', I.E. 1·6' on the arc, height of eye, 36 ft.
   (c) January 16th, observed altitude of sun's L.L. 24°52', height of eye, 50 ft.
   (d) April 28th, sextant altitude of sun's U.L. 71°49', I.E. 3·8' on the arc, height of eye, 44 ft.
   (e) May 10th, sextant altitude of sun's L.L. 24°38', I.E. 2·4' off the arc, height of eye, 58 ft.
7. In each of the following, find the true altitude and zenith distance of the star.
   (a) Star Procyon, sextant altitude 36°17', I.E. 2·3' off the arc, height of eye, 65 ft.
   (b) Star Capella, sextant altitude 58°27', I.E. 3·2' off the arc, height of eye, 27 ft.
   (c) Star Canopus, sextant altitude 78°42', I.E. 1·4' on the arc, height of eye, 48 ft.
   (d) Star Sirius, sextant altitude 31°03', I.E. 0·8' on the arc, height of eye, 62 ft.
   (e) Star Vega, sextant altitude 63°43', I.E. 2·6' off the arc, height of eye, 57 ft.

ASTRONOMICAL POSITION CIRCLES

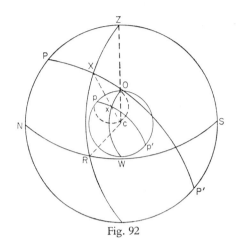

Fig. 92

A body X is situated on the celestial meridian PXP'. The geographical position of the body lies at x on the meridian pxp'. To an observer at O, the true altitude of X is $\angle XCR$, and the zenith distance is $\angle XCZ$.

The zenith distance is represented on the celestial sphere by the arc ZX, and the corresponding arc on the earth is Ox. Now, suppose that the position of x is plotted on a globe and a circle drawn on the globe of centre x and radius Ox, equal to, say $\alpha°$, then the circumference of that circle would represent all the various points on the earth's surface where the zenith distance of X was $\alpha°$.

The observer, then, in observing the altitude of X, places himself somewhere on the circumference of a circle of centre x and radius $\alpha°$. His exact position on the circle is not known, but can be obtained roughly by observing the azimuth of X.

Suppose, in Fig. 93, that x is the geographical position of the body and that the line ox represents the direction of the azimuth of the body, then the observer will be situated on that part of the position circle, aob, which lies in the vicinity of o. He would not necessarily be situated exactly at o, for a distance of a few miles on either side of o would not appreciably change the bearing of X. All that can be said, therefore, about the observer's position is that it lies on the arc of the circle, aob, in the region of o.

Now, for all practical purposes, the arc (rs) can be considered as a straight line, so that it can be said that the observation of a heavenly body will place the observer somewhere on a straight line drawn on the chart at right-angles to the azimuth of the body. This is what is known as an astronomical position line.

149

Suppose that an observation of another body, whose geographical position was x', was made at the same time as the first, then the observer would be placed on a second position line (mn), and his exact position could then be fixed at o, the point of intersection of the two position lines.

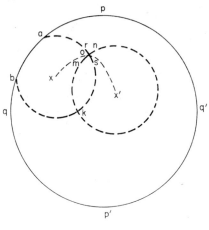

Fig. 93

It will be noted that the two position lines intersect at two points, o and k. These points are, however, widely separated, so there should be no possibility of doubt as to which is the true position. Also the azimuths would be different.

The actual method of obtaining these position lines and of fixing the ship's position are not given here but are fully explained in Chapter 10.

CHAPTER 9

Figure drawing

CHAPTER 10 of this book deals with the calculations involved in astronomical navigation. This chapter deals with the drawing of the necessary figures to accompany these calculations and also with their approximate solution by means of a scale drawing.

There are three main projections used in drawing figures of the celestial sphere. These are the orthographic, stereographic and equidistant projections. Of these three, the equidistant projection is the one that will be used in this book and its construction is described in detail. A brief description of the other two projections is also given, but no details of construction are included.

ORTHOGRAPHIC PROJECTION

In this projection, the eye is assumed to be situated at an infinite distance above the celestial sphere so that all lines projected from the eye onto the sphere will be parallel.

In Fig. 94 the eye is situated above the observer's zenith and the celestial sphere is projected on to the plane

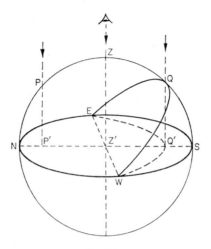

Fig. 94

of the rational horizon NESW. The dotted line $WQ'E$ represents the projection of the equinoctial, and P' the projection of the pole. In this projection, all great circles passing through the zenith appear as straight lines, but all others, such as $WQ'E$, are ellipses, which makes them difficult to draw. Also, there is considerable distortion created in areas removed from the point of projection (Z), so that the representation of a hemisphere on this projection is not practicable.

STEREOGRAPHIC PROJECTION

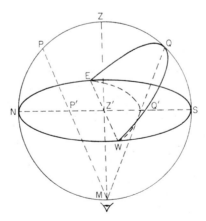

Fig. 95

In this projection, the eye is situated on the circumference of the sphere.

In Fig. 95 the eye is assumed to be at the observer's nadir (M) and all points in the opposite hemisphere are projected onto the plane of the rational horizon from this point. Thus, P' is the projection of the pole and $WQ'E$ the projection of the equinoctial.

The stereographic projection is widely used in navigational figure drawing, for it is accurate and has the advantage that all great circles appear either as straight lines or as the arcs of circles, which makes them easier to draw. The construction of the figure, however, is somewhat laborious, and for the purpose of illustrating a navigational problem, or for the small scale drawings used in this book, the work involved is hardly justified.

EQUIDISTANT PROJECTION

In the equidistant projection, the point of projection is situated at a distance of $1/\sqrt{2}$ times the radius of the sphere beyond the circumference. Thus, in Fig. 96 if the radius of the sphere is R, then the point of projection is situated at K, a distance of $R/\sqrt{2}$ from the circumference of the sphere at M.

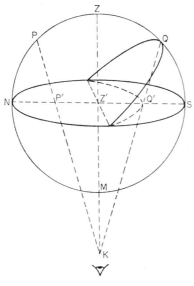

Fig. 96

The advantage of having the point of projection at K is that a constant scale can be used for the projection. In Fig. 96, the latitude of the observer is 45°N. Therefore, the arc ZQ is equal to 45°, and Q lies midway between Z and S. The projection of Q on the rational horizon (Q') is such that Q'

lies midway between Z' and S. Similarly, the projection of the pole (P') lies midway between Z' and N. This is not true with either the stereographic or the orthographic projections and special scales have to be constructed for use with them.

CONSTRUCTION OF A FIGURE ON THE EQUIDISTANT PROJECTION

Before constructing the figure it is necessary to select a suitable scale. The scale to use depends upon the purpose for which the figure is being drawn. If the figure is merely intended to illustrate a problem without deriving any information from it, then a small scale, such as $\frac{1}{10}$ in. $= 10°$, will be quite adequate, but if it is desired to obtain a definite answer from the figure then a larger scale must be used. A suitable scale for this purpose is, 1 cm $= 20°$. This gives a circle of radius 4·5 cm which will fit easily onto the page of a normal exercise book, and with this scale, points can be plotted quite easily to an accuracy of 1°.

The figure may be constructed, either on the plane of the rational horizon, as previously shown in Fig. 96, or on the plane of the observer's meridian. The former is the most common and also the easier to understand.

The method of construction is shown in the following example.

Example 1

Construct a figure of the celestial sphere for an observer in latitude 46°N. On the figure show the position of a star whose declination is 30°N, and whose L.H.A. is 56°.

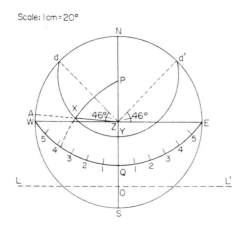

Scale: 1 cm = 20°

Fig. 97

154

(1) Draw a circle of radius 4·5 cm, or whatever scale is chosen. The centre of this circle marks the observer's zenith (Z).

(2) Mark in the four cardinal points (NESW); draw in the observer's meridian (NZS) and the prime vertical (WZE).

(3) To draw in the equinoctial, lay down from Z an amount equal to the latitude, which in this case is 46°. Q, therefore, lies 46° to the South of Z, so that on the scale, $ZQ = 2·3$ cm. Having plotted the position of Q, the equinoctial is drawn in with compasses by locating on NZS the centre of the circle passing through WQE.

(4) Now divide WQ and QE into six equal parts. This is best done by trial and error, using a pair of dividers. Each of these parts represents an arc 15°, or 1 hr on the equinoctial. Thus, a celestial meridian 30° to the West of the observer would cut the equinoctial at (2) on QW, and one 30° to the East of the observer would cut the equinoctial at (2) on QE.

(5) In order that the celestial meridians may be accurately drawn it is necessary to find the locus of their centres. One of the meridians is formed by the arc of the circle passing through WPE and the centre of this meridian lies on NZS. If this point is located (O), then the centres of all the other meridians will lie on a line through O perpendicular to NZS. This line is known as the locus line (LL').

(6) The parallel of declination must now be drawn. First, lay the amount of the declination up from Q, (QY). This establishes the position of the body when on the meridian. To obtain the position when rising and setting, the body's amplitude must be obtained. The amplitudes of a body is the azimuth of the body when rising or setting, measured from East or West. Thus, if a body rises bearing N60°E, then its amplitude would be E30°N. The amplitude may be obtained directly from a special table, such as is contained in Norie's or Burton's Nautical Tables, or it may be calculated from the formula:

$$\text{sin amplitude} = \text{sin declination} \times \text{sec lat.}$$

The derivation of this formula is given in Appendix I, to which the student should refer.

In this example, the latitude is 46°N and the declination is 30°N so that by applying the formula, the amplitude is found to be E46°N for rising and W46°N for setting. It should be noted that the amplitude has the same name as the declination.

The amplitude should now be laid off from Z as shown in the figure and the points d and d' plotted. The circle dYd' may then be drawn in the same manner as the equinoctial.

(7) The figure is now ready for plotting the actual position of the body. The L.H.A. is 56°, which means that the celestial meridian upon which

the body is situated lies 56° to the West of the observer's meridian. To draw in the meridian, mark a point on the equinoctial 56° to the West of Q (this lies between 3 and 4), and by moving the point of the compasses along LL' draw in the meridian. The point where the meridian cuts the parallel of declination is the position of the body.

The azimuth and altitude of the body can now be obtained by joining ZX and producing it to cut the horizon at A.

From the figure

$$\text{Azimuth} = \angle PZX = \text{N}87°\text{W} = 273°$$
$$\text{Altitude } AX = 44°.$$

Figure 97 was drawn on the plane of the rational horizon. The figure may also be drawn on the plane of the observer's meridian, as follows.

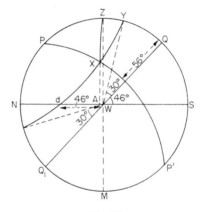

Fig. 98

Figure 98 represents the same example drawn on the plane of the meridian.

The observer's meridian is drawn to the same scale as before. The equinoctial is represented by a straight line inclined to the rational horizon (NWS) at an angle equal to the latitude. The equinoctial and the pole may, therefore, be plotted by laying off angles of 46° from the rational horizon.

To draw in the parallel of declination, mark Y 30° above Q and lay off Wd equal to 46°, the amplitude. Then, with compasses on a straight line through PP' produced, draw in the circle passing through Y and d.

To draw in the meridian passing through the body, lay off from Q an amount equal to the L.H.A. of the body, 56°, and with the compasses on QQ', draw in the meridian PXP'.

Finally, with the compasses along NS, draw in the arc ZX, and produce it to meet NS in A.

FIGURE DRAWING

The figure is now complete and the azimuth of X is given by PZX, and the altitude by the arc AX. The actual measurement of the azimuth and altitude is not so easy in this figure, as PZ and PX are not straight lines, but arcs of circles. In order to measure the azimuth, it is necessary to draw tangents at Z to PZ and ZX and then measure the angle between them which is not very satisfactory. The altitude, AX, being also the arc of a circle, is equally awkward to measure.

EXERCISE IX

1. Determine, by scale drawing, the altitude and azimuth of the sun in each of the following:
   (a) lat 36°N, declination 12°30′N, L.H.A. 3ʰ40ᵐ
   (b) lat 28°S, declination 06°N, L.H.A. 297°42′
   (c) lat 48°N, declination 15°S, L.H.A. 321°18′
   (d) lat 32°S, declination 22°N, L.H.A. 22ʰ20ᵐ.
2. Determine, by scale drawing, the altitude and L.H.A. of the sun in each of the following:
   (a) lat 52°30′N, declination 20°30′S, azimuth 142°
   (b) lat 47°15′S, declination 08°S, azimuth 042°
   (c) lat 29°00′N, declination 22°N, azimuth 282°
   (d) lat 38°30′S, declination 09°30′S, azimuth 332°.
3. Find the G.M.T. when the sun will be on the prime vertical to an observer in lat 56°N, long 24°E, on 7th June 1958.
4. Find the true azimuth and G.M.T. of sunrise on the 20th September 1958, in lat 46°S, long 24°E.
5. From a ship in lat 42°N a star is observed bearing 115°(T) altitude 50°. Find, by scale drawing, the approximate declination and L.H.A. of the star.

Astronomical calculations

In THE last chapter it was shown how the latitude of an observer, and also the altitude, azimuth, and hour angle of a heavenly body can be approximately determined by drawing scale diagrams of the celestial sphere. In this chapter it is intended to show how the exact values of these and certain other quantities may be obtained by calculation.

Any calculation of astronomical navigation, however, is only the mathematical solution of a problem that can be represented by a suitably drawn diagram; and therefore, once the necessary information has been collected, no detailed calculation should be attempted until a diagram, based on the given data, has been drawn.

LATITUDE BY MERIDIAN ALTITUDE OBSERVATION

The simplest calculation of astronomical navigation is that by which an observer determines his latitude as a result of observing the altitude of a heavenly body at the time of meridian passage.

The "meridian altitude" of a heavenly body, for a stationary observer, is the maximum altitude that the body attains when it crosses his meridian at its upper meridian passage.

The meridian altitude may also be the minimum altitude that a circumpolar body attains when it crosses the observer's meridian at an altitude lower than that of the celestial pole, i.e. at its "lower meridian passage". Either the maximum or the minimum altitude that a body attains can be readily determined by means of a marine sextant in the hands of a proficient observer. The upper meridian passage of the sun occurs at 1200 (noon) Local Apparent Time.

EXAMPLE 1

On 7th June 1958, an observer in D.R. long 30°15′W observed the sextant altitude of the sun's lower limb at noon to be 40°12′ bearing South. Index error is −2′, height of eye 60ft. Find the latitude of the observer.

The first part of the work is to correct the altitude and determine the declination of the sun at the time of observation, since the correct latitude can only be obtained by using the correct meridian altitude and the correct declination.

The corrections to the altitude are obtained from the abridged tables at the end of this book (page 235) and are made as follows:

Sextant altitude	40° 12′
Index error	− 2
	40 10
Dip	− 7·6
	40 02·4
Refraction	− 1·1
	40 01·3
SD (L.L.+)	+ 15·8
	40 17·1
Parallax	+ 0·1
True altitude	40° 17·2′

The L.M.T. of the sun's meridian passage on 7th June 1958 is obtained from the extracts from the Nautical Almanac which are given for that date at the end of this book (page 220). This is 11h59m L.M.T. and it must be converted to G.M.T. by applying to it the observer's longitude, expressed in time.

Long of observer 30°15′W   30° hr $=2$hr   15′ $=1$ min

$\therefore$ long in Time $= 2^{h}\ 01^{m}$

L.M.T. of meridian passage $= 11^{h}\ 59^{m}$
Long in Time $=\ 2\ \ 01$

_____

G.M.T. of meridian passage $= 14^{h}\ 00^{m}$ (Longitude West, Greenwich

Time best)

This is the G.M.T. that must be used to extract the correct declination of the sun from the Almanac.

At 1400 G.M.T. on 7th June 1958, the declination of the sun is given in the Nautical Almanac (page 220 of this book) as 22°44·3′N, and this is the value that must be used to calculate the latitude.

All the necessary information is now available, i.e. true altitude of sun on meridian, bearing South $= 40°17·2′$ and declination of sun 22°44·3′N. All that remains to be done is to find the observer's latitude.

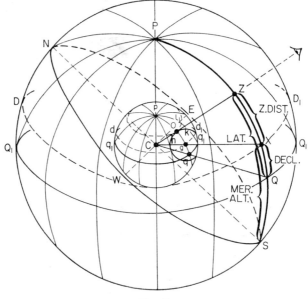

Fig. 99

Figure 99 is an attempt to show the solution of the problem in perspective. It is not suggested that this kind of drawing is necessary for the solution of every such problem, but for the first problem of its type, it is thought that a perspective drawing may lead to a clearer understanding of the principles involved.

In Fig. 99, C is the centre of the earth, O is the observer on the earth, on parallel of latitude ll_1 and Z is the observer's zenith, on his celestial meridian, in the celestial sphere. NEWS is the observer's rational horizon. X is the sun at noon on the observer's celestial meridian, and g is the sun's geographical position. DD_1 is the sun's parallel of declination and dd_1 is the parallel of latitude traced out by the sun's geographical position, g, as the earth rotates on its axis.

At noon, the observer has measured the arc SX with his sextant, and this, when corrected, is the true meridian altitude of the sun. QX is the declination of the sun, obtained from the Almanac.

The latitude of the observer in Fig. 99 is the arc qO on the earth, which is equal to the arc QZ in the celestial sphere.

In order to find QZ, a simple procedure, in this case, is as follows. Subtract the true altitude (SX) from $90°$ to obtain the zenith distance (ZX). To ZX apply QX (the declination) and so obtain QZ, the observer's latitude. The manner in which the declination is applied to the zenith distance depends on the circumstances which can vary (this is why it is necessary to draw a figure of some kind), but in this example it is quite clear that QX must be added to ZX to give QZ, the observer's latitude.

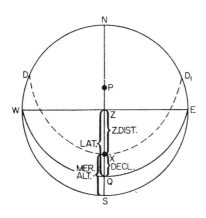

Fig. 100

Figure 100 is the simplified form of diagram that should always be drawn, approximately to scale, in the manner described in the last chapter. This is approximately what an observer would see if his eye were placed outside the celestial sphere in the position of the eye shown in Fig. 99, i.e. vertically above Z, the observer's zenith. The earth is not shown in Fig. 100, but the relationship between Fig. 99 and Fig. 100 should be clearly understood.

As before, it will be seen that QZ, the observer's latitude, is obtained by adding QX (the declination) to ZX (the zenith distance).

Finally, therefore, the observer's latitude, in this particular example, is obtained as follows:

True altitude of Sun	40° 17·2'	(SX)
	90 00	
Zenith distance	49 42·8	(ZX)
Declination	22 44·3	(QX)
Latitude	72° 27·1'	(QZ)

and the latitude is *North* because Z is North of Q.

In the above example, the latitude was found to be of the same name as the declination of the body (both North) and the latitude was greater than the declination.

Example 2

At evening twilight on 20th September 1958, an observer in D.R. latitude 25°10'S observes the star Shaula at meridian passage, to have a sextant altitude of 78°10'. Index error is NIL, height of eye 40ft. Required is the observer's latitude by observation.

As before, the first task is to correct the sextant altitude and to determine the star's declination.

Sextant altitude	78° 10'	
Index error	—	
	78 10	
Dip	— 6·2	
	78 03·8	
Refraction	— 0·2	
True altitude	78 03·6	

Note that, for a star, the only corrections required are for index error, dip and refraction.

The declination of stars changes very little and very slowly. Therefore, the declination which is given in the Nautical Almanac for 19th, 20th and 21st September 1958 needs no correction. Its value for the star Shaula is 37°04·5'S.

A diagram must now be drawn showing the problem that is to be solved. See Fig. 101.

Since the observer's D.R. latitude is 25°10′S and the geographical position of the star is in latitude 37°04·5′S, it follows that X, the position of the star in the diagram, must be South of Z; and Q, the point where the equinoctial

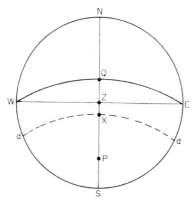

Fig. 101

crosses the observer's meridian, must be 37°04·5′ North of X. This locates Q and X on the diagram relative to Z. Therefore, from diagram:

True altitude	= 78° 03·6′	(SX)
	90 00	
Zenith distance	= 11 56·4	(ZX)
Declination	= 37 04·5	(QX)
∴ Latitude by observation	= 25° 08·1′	(QX)

This latitude is *South* because Z is South of X.

It will be noted that in this last example the latitude and declination was of the same name and that the declination was greater than the latitude.

EXAMPLE 3

An observer on board ship in the North Atlantic in long 30°20′W observes the sun at noon on 26th October 1958 to have a sextant altitude of 28°10′. Index error is −2′, height of eye 45 ft. The sun's upper limb was observed. Find the latitude of the ship.

To correct altitude

Sextant altitude   28°10′

Index error —   2

——————

               28 08

Dip   —   6·6

——————

             28 01·4

Refraction   —   1·8

——————

            27 59·6

SD(U.L.)   —   16·1

——————

            27 43·5

Parallax   +   0·1

——————

True altitude   27 43·6

To correct the declination

L.M.T. of meridian passage $= 11^{h}44^{m}$

Long 30°20′W $+$ 2 $1\frac{1}{2}$

——————

G.M.T. $= 13^{h}45\frac{1}{2}^{m}$

——————

Declination at 13^{h} $= 12°22·7′S$

         at 14^{h} 12 23·6S

——————

Diff for 1^{h} $=$ 0·9

∴ Diff for 45^{m} $=$ 0·7

∴ Declination at $13^{h}45^{m}$ G.M.T.

                      12°23·4′S

The diagram for the solution of this problem is shown in Fig. 102.

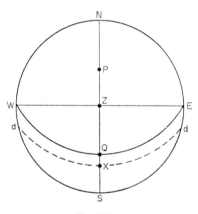

Fig. 102

Since the observer is in the North Atlantic and the sun's geographical position is in lat 12°23·4′S, it follows that X, the sun, is South of Z. The position of X in the diagram is located by measuring SX, the true altitude from S to X.

Also, since the declination is 12°23·4′S, it follows that Q is 12°23·4′ North of X.

Therefore from the diagram:

True altitude $= 27°43·6'$ (SX)

90 00

Zenith distance $= 62\ 16·4$ (ZX)
Declination $= 12\ 23·4$ (QX)

Latitude $= 49\ 53·0$ (QZ)

Again, this latitude is North, since Z is North of Q.

In this last example, the latitude and declination were of opposite names and the latitude was greater than the declination.

EXAMPLE 4

An observer on board ship in the South Pacific observes the star Vega, when it crosses his meridian on 21st September 1958, to have a sextant altitude of 20°10′. Index error $+ 1'$, height of eye 50 ft. Find the latitude.

To correct the altitude

Sextant altitude 20°10′
Index error $+$ 1

20 11   Declination of star Vega
Dip $-$ 6·9   on 21st September 1958
$= 38°45·1'N$
20 04·1
Refraction $-$ 2·6

True altitude 20 01·5

The diagram for the solution of this problem is shown in Fig. 103.

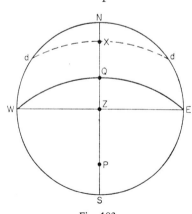

Fig. 103

Since the observer is in the South Pacific and the star's geographical position is on the parallel of latitude of 38°45·1'N, it follows that X in the diagram is North of Z. Its position is determined by making $NX = 20°01·5$ (approximately). But, since the star's declination is 38°45·1'N, it follows that X is 38°45·1' North of Q and Q is 38°45·1' South of X. This determines the position of Q.

From diagram:

$$\text{True altitude} = 20°01·5' \quad (NX)$$
$$90\ 00$$

$$\text{Zenith distance} = 69\ 58·5 \quad (ZX)$$
$$\text{Declination} = 38\ 45·1 \quad (QX)$$

$$\text{Latitude} = 31\ 13·4 \quad (QZ)$$

And this latitude is South, since Z is South of Q. In this example it will be seen that the latitude and declination were of opposite names and the declination was greater than the latitude.

EXAMPLE 5

On board a Polar research vessel off the North Cape in long 25°30'E on 7th June 1958, an observation of the sun's upper limb was made when the sun was on the observer's meridian at lower meridian passage. The sextant altitude was 5°10'. Index error is NIL, height of eye 30 ft. Find the latitude of the ship.

To correct the altitude

Sextant altitude =	5·10·0'
Index error	0
	5 10·0
Dip	− 5·4
	5 04·6
Refraction	−9·6
	4 55·0
SD (U.L.)	−15·8
	4 39·2
Parallax	+ ·1
True altitude	4°39·3'

To find the correct declination

When the sun is on the observer's meridian at *lower* meridian passage it is 0000 hr Local Apparent Time, i.e. it is Local Midnight, and the L.M.T. of lower meridian passage differs by 12 hr from the L.M.T. of upper meridian passage.

On 7th June 1958, L.M.T. of upper
meridian passage of the sun (from
Almanac) $= 11^{\mathrm{h}}59^{\mathrm{m}}$
             $+ 12$

∴ L.M.T. of lower meridian passage $= 23\ 59$
  Long 25°30′E $=\ 1\ 42$

∴ G.M.T. of lower meridian passage $= 22^{\mathrm{h}}17^{\mathrm{m}}$
  Declination of sun at 22^{h} $= 22°46\cdot2′N$
  Declination of sun at 23^{h} $= 22\ 46\cdot5N$

  Diff in 1^{h} $=\ \ \ \ 0\cdot3$

∴ Declination at $22^{\mathrm{h}}17^{\mathrm{m}}$ $= 22°46\cdot3′N$

The polar distance is required in this case, and it is found by subtracting the declination from 90°, i.e. polar distance $= 90°00′ - 22°46\cdot3′$
$$= 67°13\cdot7′$$

Figure 104 is the diagram for the solution of this problem.

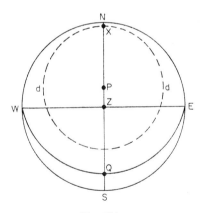

Fig. 104

The observer knows that he is only about 20° South of the North Pole and he therefore knows that the North Celestial Pole will be about 20° North of his zenith. Thus, P must be North of Z. But he also knows that he has observed the sun when it was on his meridian *below* the pole, i.e. nearer to the northern horizon than the pole. Thus, X lies between N and P.

From the diagram, therefore:

$$
\begin{array}{llll}
\text{True altitude} & = & 4°39·3' & (NX) \\
\text{Polar distance} & = & 67°13·7 & (PX) \\
\hline
\text{Latitude} & & = 71°53·0 & (NP)
\end{array}
$$

Why is this so? *Answer*: P is 90° North of Q, and QZ is the latitude of the observer.

Now $QZ + PZ = 90°$
And $NP + PZ = 90°$
$\therefore NP = QZ = $ Latitude.

This result may be stated in words as follows: "The true altitude of the observer's elevated pole (the celestial pole that is above the observer's horizon) is equal to the latitude of the observer." It is this important principle that has been utilized to find the latitude in the above example.

The methods of finding the latitude in the foregoing examples may be summarized into two simple routines, as follows:

(A) To find the latitude from an upper meridian passage observation.

(1) Correct the altitude and name it North or South according to the bearing of the body from the observer.

(2) Subtract the true altitude thus obtained from 90° to obtain the zenith distance, and name this opposite to the altitude.

(3) Apply the declination to the zenith distance to obtain the latitude, using the rule "like" names add, and "unlike" names subtract, naming the latitude according to the greater.

Thus, in Example 1, in which the true altitude is 40°17·2', with the sun bearing South, and the declination of the sun is 22°44·3'N, the routine is as follows:

$$
\begin{array}{lll}
\text{True altitude} & = 40°17·2' & \text{South} \\
& 90\ 00 & \\
\hline
\text{Zenith distance} & = 49\ 42·8 & \text{North} \\
\text{Declination} & = 22\ 44·3 & \text{North} \\
\hline
\text{Latitude} & = 72°27·1' & \text{North}
\end{array}
$$

And in Example 2,

True altitude	= 78°03·6	South
	90 00	
Zenith distance	= 11 56·4	North
Declination	= 37 04·5	South
Latitude	= 25°48·1′	South

(B) To find the latitude from a lower meridian passage observation. This can only be done when the body concerned is circumpolar, and can be observed at its lower meridian passage on the anti-meridian of the observer. The routine in this case is very simple:

(1) Subtract the body's declination from 90° to obtain the polar distance.

(2) Obtain the true altitude, and add this to the polar distance to give the latitude, which must always be named the same as the declination.

Thus, in Example 5, where the declination of the sun is 22°46·3′N, the polar distance = 90° − 22°46·3′ = 67°13·7′. Add to this the true altitude of 4°39·3′ to give the observer's latitude of 71°53′ North.

LATITUDE BY POLE STAR

In explaining the method used in Example 5 above, it was shown that the true altitude of the observer's elevated pole is equal to the observer's latitude.

This is another way of saying that if there were a heavenly body exactly at the North (or South) pole of the heavens, the true altitude of that body would be equal to the latitude of the observer.

There is no heavenly body near the South celestial pole, but it so happens that there is a star, called Polaris, which is very close to the North celestial pole. Its declination is 89°00′N, so that its polar distance is 1°00′, i.e. its geographical position is only 60 n. miles from the earth's North Pole. This star can be located by means of the two "pointers" in the constellation of the Plough.

To enable the latitude to be obtained easily from an observation of the Pole Star, the Nautical Almanac contains a special Pole Star Table, which gives the corrections that must be applied to the true altitude of the Pole Star to obtain the observer's latitude.

EXAMPLE 6

An observer on board a ship in the North Atlantic observes the Pole Star to have a sextant altitude of 55°10′. Index error is NIL, height of eye 40 ft. Sum of corrections from Pole Star table +0°30·2′. Find the observer's latitude.

Sextant altitude	55°10′		True altitude		= 55°03·1′
Index error	0		Sum of corrections		
	———		from Pole Star		
	55 10		Table		+ 0 30·2
Dip	− 6·2				———
	———		Observer's latitude		= 55°33·3′N
	55 03·8				
Refraction	− 0·7				
	———				
True altitude	55°03·1′				

The latitude is North, because the Pole Star is only above the horizon in the northern hemisphere and cannot be seen in any South latitude.

COMPUTING THE SEXTANT MERIDIAN ALTITUDE

Observations of stars are made at morning or evening twilight when using a marine sextant, because, during the twilight period, the brighter stars are visible and the sea horizon can also be clearly seen.

It is therefore a common practice, particularly at evening twilight, to pre-compute the altitude of a star that it is intended to observe.

EXAMPLE 7 (Refer back to Example 2 in the chapter.)

At evening twilight on 20th September 1958, an observer in D.R. latitude 25°10′S wished to pre-compute the sextant altitude that the star Shaula would have when it crossed his meridian. The index error of his sextant was NIL and his height of eye was 40 ft. Find the pre-computed sextant altitude of the star.

Refer now to Fig. 101, which was drawn to find the latitude in Example 2. Redraw the diagram, but mark only N, S, E and W and the observer's zenith at Z.

Then proceed as follows:

The observer's D.R. latitude is 25°10′S, so mark Q, 25°10′ North of Z. The declination of the star Shaula is 37°04·5′S, so mark X 37°04·5′ South of Q.

ZX is the meridian zenith distance of the star and SX is its true meridian altitude.

From diagram:

$$ZX = QX - QZ$$
$$ZX = 37°04·5' - 25°10'$$
$$ZX = 11\ 54·5$$
$$90\ 00$$

$$SX = 78°05·5'$$

This means that the true meridian altitude, as pre-computed for the D.R. latitude of 25°10′S, is 78°05·5′ bearing South, since X is South of Z.

This must be converted to the pre-computed sextant altitude by applying all the usual corrections in reverse.

viz.	True altitude =	78°05·5′
	Refraction	+ 0·2
		78 05·7
	Dip	+ 6·2
		78°11·9
	Index error	NIL

∴ Pre-computed sextant altitude = 78°11·9′ bearing South.

In the event, the actual sextant altitude, when the star became visible, was found to be 78°10′ (see Example 2) simply because the correct latitude of the observer was 1·9′ different from his D.R. latitude.

EXERCISE X(a)

Use the extracts from the Nautical Almanac given in this book for solving questions 1–10.

1. On 19th September 1958, the sextant altitude of the sun's lower limb at noon was observed to be 40°10′ bearing South. Index error was 2′ off the arc, height of eye 40 ft. The observer's D.R. longitude was 35°15′W. Find his latitude.
2. On 20th September 1958, in D.R. lat 31°30′S the star Sirius was observed to have a sextant altitude of 75°10′ when on the observer's meridian. Index error was 3′ on the arc, height of eye 50 ft. Find the observer's latitude by observation.
3. On 21st September 1958, in D.R. lat 39°00′S the sun's upper limb at noon was observed to have a sextant altitude of 50°10′. Index error was +2′, height of eye 55 ft. The observer's D.R. longitude was 175°15′E. Find his latitude.
4. On 20th September 1958, the star Sirius was observed to have a sextant altitude of 75°10′ when on the observer's meridian bearing South. Index error was 3′ on the arc, height of eye 50 ft. Find the observer's latitude.
5. On 7th June 1958, the lower limb of the sun at noon was observed to have a sextant altitude of 72°10′ bearing North. Index error was NIL, height of eye 45 ft. The observer's D.R. longitude was 170°30′W. Find his latitude.

NAVIGATION

6. On 20th September 1958 the star Dubhe was observed to have a sextant altitude of 10°15′ when on the observer's meridian at lower meridian passage. Index error was +1′, height of eye 35 ft. Find the observer's latitude.

7. On 26th October 1958, on board a vessel sailing from Auckland to the Fiji Isles in D.R. long 179°30′E, at noon, the sextant altitude of the sun's lower limb was observed to be 72°15′ bearing North. Index error was NIL, height of eye 42 ft. Find the latitude.

8. On 19th September 1958 on board a ship in D.R. lat 21°40′N the sextant altitude of the star Rigel was observed to be 60°10′ when on the observer's meridian. Index error was −2′, height of eye 40 ft. Find the latitude by observation.

9. On 31st December 1958 on board a vessel in the Antarctic Ocean in D.R. long 179°15′W, an observation of the sun's lower limb was taken at local midnight, when the sun was on the observer's meridian below the pole. The sextant altitude was 3°05′. Index error was NIL, height of eye 30 ft. Find the observer's latitude.

10. On 20th September 1958 an observer in D.R. lat 50°10′N intended to take a meridian altitude of the star Pollux. Given that the index error of his sextant was +2′ and his height of eye was 40 ft, find the altitude that he should have set on his sextant in readiness to make the observation. Also state the bearing of Pollux at the time of observation.

In each of the following questions (11–20) find the latitude from the information given.

11. Sextant altitude of sun's lower limb 39°36·5′ bearing North. Index error was +2·2′, height of eye 23 ft, s. diameter 15·8′, declination 23°00·3′N.

12. Sextant altitude of sun's upper limb 74°28·8′, D.R. lat 6°10′S. Index error was +3′, height of eye 30 ft, s. diameter 16·3′, declination 21°57·3′S.

13. Sextant altitude of star Spica 29°00′ bearing South. Index error was −3·2′, height of eye 21 ft, declination 10°56·8′S.

14. Sextant altitude of star Castor 47°36′, D.R. lat 10°30′S. Index error was +2·3′, height of eye 25 ft, declination 31°58·7′N.

15. Sextant altitude of star Capella 18°20·2′ when on observer's meridian at lower meridian passage. Index error was −1·6′, height of eye 29 ft, declination 45°57·2′N.

16. Sextant altitude of star Achenar 24°16·1′ when on observer's meridian below the Pole. Index error was −1·5′, height of eye 38 ft, declination 57°27·3′S.

17. Sextant altitude of star Mirfak 17°56·1′ when on observer's meridian below the Pole. Index error was +0·1′, height of eye 34 ft, declination 49°42·8′N.

18. Sextant altitude of Pole Star 26°11·2′. Index error was −2·2′, height of eye 18 ft, sum of corrections from Pole Star table = +0°11·2′.

19. Sextant altitude of Pole Star 40°30·3′. Index error was +1·8′, height of eye 15 ft, sum of corrections from Pole Star table = −0°46·3′.

20. Sextant altitude of Pole Star 26°40·2′. Index error was +0·2′, height of eye 21 ft, sum of corrections from Pole Star table = +0°06·5′.

In the following questions (21–25) find the pre-computed sextant altitude and bearing of the body observed from the information given.

21. 13th September 1958, D.R. lat was 48°10′N, declination of sun 3°51′N. Height of eye was 17 ft, index error 2′ on the arc. Find the sextant altitude of the sun's lower limb at upper meridian passage.

22. 19th June 1958, D.R. lat was 56°10′N, declination of star Capella 45°57·3′N.

172

Height of eye was 24 ft, index error 1·5′ off the arc. Find the sextant altitude of the star at lower meridian passage.

23. 28th December 1958, D.R. lat was 9°45′S, declination of sun 23°16·2′S. Height of eye was 31 ft, index error 2·1′ off the arc. Find the sextant altitude of the sun's upper limb at upper meridian passage.

24. 15th July 1958, D.R. lat was 31°30′S, declination of star Canopus 52°40·4′S. Height of eye was 42 ft, index error 1·6′ on the arc. Find the sextant altitude of the star at upper meridian passage.

25. 8th October 1958, D.R. lat was 35°00′N, declination of star Dubhe 61°58·3′N. Height of eye was 21 ft, index error 2·3′ off the arc. Find the sextant altitude of the star at lower meridian passage.

THE AZIMUTH OF A HEAVENLY BODY. ITS USE TO DETERMINE COMPASS ERROR AND DEVIATION

The azimuth of a heavenly body is the angle at the observer's zenith contained between the observer's meridian and the vertical circle passing through the body. It is the true bearing of a heavenly body from the observer, and when the observer's position is known, the azimuth or true bearing of a given heavenly body can be calculated, either by spherical trigonometry, or by the use of special "Azimuth Tables".

If the compass bearing of a given heavenly body is observed at the instant of time for which its true bearing is calculated, then the error of the compass can be ascertained, since the compass error is the difference between the true bearing and the compass bearing of any object. When the local variation is known, the deviation of the compass can also be found.

In Chapter 9 the method of finding the approximate azimuth of a heavenly body by scale drawing was demonstrated. In this chapter it is proposed to show how the exact azimuth may be calculated; but, as in the case of the latitude calculation, a diagram must first be drawn, approximately to scale, before the main part of the calculation is attempted. The method is best demonstrated by a worked example.

Example 8

On 20th September 1958 an observer on board ship in D.R. position 50°20′N 25°15′W observed the sun to bear 130° by compass. The G.M.T. by the ship's chronometer was 11ʰ10ᵐ00ˢ. The local variation was 24°W. Find the error and deviation of the ship's compass.

Before a diagram can be drawn, certain necessary items of information must be collected, which, in this instance, are: (1) Latitude of observer, (2) Declination of sun and (3) Local Hour Angle of sun at the time of observation.

The latitude of the observer is known (50°20′N), but the declination and L.H.A. must be found from the Nautical Almanac.

On 20th September 1958, the declination of the sun at 1110 G.M.T. is found by interpolation to be 1°12′·0N.

Now, at 1100 G.M.T. G.H.A. sun = 346°36·3′
and   at 1200 G.M.T. G.H.A. sun = 361 36·5

∴ in 60 min G.H.A. changes   15°00′·2
∴ in 10 min G.H.A. changes   2°30′
∴ at 1210 G.M.T. G.H.A. sun   = 349°06·3′.

This means, that, at the time of observation, the sun was 349°06·3′ West of the Greenwich Meridian. The observer was in longitude 25°15′W, and therefore the sun was 349°06·3′—25°15′ West of the observer's meridian, i.e. L.H.A. sun = 323°51·3′W or 36°08·7′E. This is illustrated in Fig. 105(a).

The necessary information has now been collected, and the essential diagram (Fig. 105(b)) can now be drawn.

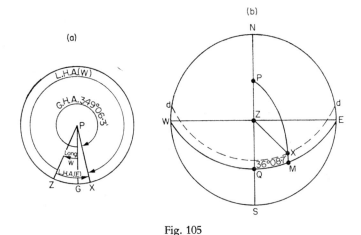

Fig. 105

In Fig. 105(b) QZ is the latitude, ∴ PZ = 90°—lat
MX is the declination, ∴ PX = 90°—declination
Angle P = Arc QM = L.H.A. of the sun.

Thus, in the spherical triangle PZX of Fig. 105(b), the side PZ, the side PX and the angle P are known. From this information the azimuth of the sun, angle PZX, can be calculated by the use of the Spherical Haversine Formula, the derivation of which is given in Appendix I of this book.

Two steps are necessary in this solution, as follows:

(1)   First find the side ZX.

By the Spherical Haversine Formula:

$$\text{Hav } P = \frac{\text{Hav } ZX - \text{Hav}(PZ \sim PX)}{\sin PZ \sin PX}$$

whence $\text{Hav } ZX = \text{Hav } P \sin PZ \sin PX + \text{Hav}(PZ \sim PX)$

In this example, angle $P = 36°08\cdot7'$ $PZ = (90° - 50°20')$
$$= 39°40'$$

and $PX = (90° - 1°12') = 88°48'$ and $(PZ \sim PX) = 49°08'$.

The values of the Haversines required can be obtained from the Table of Natural Haversines printed at the end of this book. The other logarithms and log ratios required can be obtained from any ordinary set of four figure mathematical tables. The working is as follows:

$$\text{Angle } P, 36°08\cdot7' \text{ natural Hav} = 0\cdot0963 \text{ log} = \bar{2}\cdot9836$$
$$PZ, 39°40' \text{ log sin} = \bar{1}\cdot8050$$
$$PX, 88°48' \text{ log sin} = \bar{1}\cdot9999$$

$$\overline{\bar{2}\cdot7885}$$
$$\text{antilog} = 0\cdot0614$$
$$(PZ \sim PX), 49°08' \text{ natural Hav} = 0\cdot1729$$

$$\therefore ZX, \text{ natural Hav} = 0\cdot2343$$
$$\therefore ZX = 57°54'$$

(2)   In the spherical triangle PZX, the three sides, PZ, PX and ZX are now known. The Spherical Haversine Formula can now be used again to find the azimuth (angle PZX) which is required.

$$\text{Hav } Z = \frac{\text{Hav } PX - \text{Hav}(PZ \sim ZX)}{\sin PZ \sin ZX}$$

For ease of working, this formula is written:

$\text{Hav } Z = \{\text{Hav } PX - \text{Hav}(PZ \sim ZX)\} \text{ cosec } PZ \text{ cosec } ZX.$

In this example, $PX = 88°48'$, $PZ = 39°40'$, $ZX = 57°54'$ and $(PZ \sim ZX) = 18°14'$.

The working is as follows:

PX, 88°48′ natural Hav $\quad = 0\cdot4896$
$(PZ \sim ZX)$, 18°14′ natural Hav $= 0\cdot0251$

$\qquad\qquad\qquad 0\cdot4645 \log = \bar{1}\cdot6670$
PZ, 39°40′ log cosec $\quad = 0\cdot1950$
ZX, 57°54′ log cosec $\quad = 0\cdot0721$

$\qquad$ log Haversine $Z \qquad = \bar{1}\cdot9341$
$\qquad$ antilog (natural Hav Z) $= 0\cdot8592$
$\qquad \therefore$ Angle $Z \qquad\qquad = 135°55′$
Whence: True bearing of sun $\quad = 135°55′$ T
$\qquad$ Compass bearing of sun $\quad = 130°00′$ C

$\qquad \therefore$ Compass error $\quad = \quad 5°55′$ East
$\qquad\qquad$ Variation $\qquad = \ 24°00′$ West

$\qquad \therefore$ Deviation $\qquad = \ 29°55′$ East

For those readers who have access to five-figure Nautical Tables the working, using such tables, is given below.

To find ZX	To find angle Z
P, 36°08·7′ log Hav $= 8\cdot98334$	PX, 88°48′ natural Hav $\quad = 0\cdot48953$
PZ, 39°40′ $\quad$ log sin $= 9\cdot80504$	$(PZ \sim ZX)$, 18°13·8′
PX, 88°48′ $\quad$ log sin $= 9\cdot99991$	$\qquad$ natural Hav $\quad = 0\cdot02509$
$\qquad\qquad$ log $= 8\cdot78829$	$\qquad$ natural Hav $= 0\cdot46444$
$\qquad\qquad$ natural $= 0\cdot06142$	$\qquad\qquad$ log Hav $= 9\cdot66693$
$(PZ \sim PX)$ 49°08′	PZ, 39°40′ log cosec $\quad = 10\cdot19496$
$\qquad$ natural Hav $= 0\cdot17285$	ZX, 57°53·8′ log cosec $\quad = 10\cdot07207$
ZX natural Hav $\quad = 0\cdot23427$	Z log Hav $\qquad\qquad = 9\cdot93396$
$ZX = 57°53′\cdot8$	Angle $Z = 135°53′$

AZIMUTH TABLES

By the above method, the error and deviation of the compass have been found to a high degree of accuracy.

In practical navigation such extreme accuracy is unnecessary. A ship can only be steered to an accuracy of about one degree, and a compass bearing can only be read to an accuracy of about half a degree. Therefore, for purposes of practical navigation, a method of obtaining the true azimuth of a heavenly body which is accurate to one quarter of a degree, is generally considered to be sufficiently accurate.

This standard of accuracy is obtained, without too much interpolation, by the use of "Azimuth Tables" of one kind or another. Probably the most commonly used azimuth tables are the A.B.C. Tables, contained in most sets of Nautical Tables, to which some readers of this book may have access.

These tables solve the PZX spherical triangle rapidly and accurately enough for practical purposes, but the same information has to be collected as that which is required for solution by the Haversine Formula.

In the above example, the information with which to enter the A.B.C. Tables is—lat 50°20′N, declination 1°12′N, L.H.A. 36°08′E.

Table A, entered with lat 50°20′N, H.A. 36°08′, gives $A = 1 \cdot 65$S

Table B, entered with declination 1°12′N, H.A. 36°08′, gives $B = 0 \cdot 04$N

Whence $C = 1 \cdot 61$S

Now enter Table C with lat 50°20′N and C 1·61 S.

This gives azimuth S44·2°E

∴ True azimuth $= 135 \cdot 8°$

$= 135°48′$

EXAMPLE 9

An observer on board ship in D.R. position 40°20′S, 70°15′E, on 20th September 1958, takes a compass bearing of the star Menkar at 01ʰ20ᵐ00ˢ G.M.T. The bearing by compass was 327° and the local variation was 30° West. Find the error and deviation of the compass.

The information required to draw the necessary diagrams is as follows: Lat 40°20′S, thus PZ (where P is the South Celestial Pole) is 49°40′. Referring to the extracts from the Nautical Almanac given at the end of this book, it is found that the declination of Menkar on 20th September 1958 was 3°55·8′N. Therefore, PX (measured from the South Celestial Pole because the observer is in South latitude) $= 93°55·8′$. Also from the Nautical Almanac:

G.H.A. Aries at 0100 hr G.M.T. $= 13°25·2′$
and at   0200 hr G.M.T. $= 28\ 27·6$

Diff for 60 min $= 15\ 02·4$
∴ Increment for 20 min $=\ \ 5\ 00·8$

∴ G.H.A. Aries at 01^h20^m00 G.M.T. $= 18°26'$
    S.H.A. of star Menkar $= 314\ 57\cdot9$

∴ G.H.A. of star $= 333\ 23\cdot9W$
    Long of observer $= \ 70\ 15\ \ E(+)$

L.H.A. star $= 403\ 38\cdot9W$
                               $- \ 360\ \ 00$

∴ L.H.A. star $= \ \ 43\ 38\cdot9W$

The necessary diagrams can now be drawn as in Fig. 106(a) and (b).

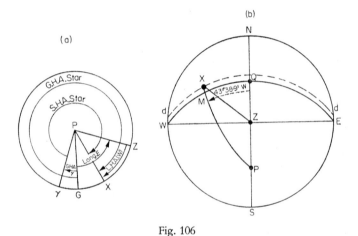

Fig. 106

It should be noted that the L.H.A. of Menkar can be verified directly from Fig. 106(a).

$$\text{Arc } GX = 360° - 333°23\cdot9' = 26°36\cdot1'.$$
$$\text{But L.H.A. of star} = \text{arc } ZX = \text{arc } GZ - \text{arc } GX.$$
$$\therefore \text{ L.H.A. star} = 70°15' - 26°36\cdot1' = 43°38\cdot9'W.$$

Thus, in the spherical triangle PZX, we have:

$PZ = 49°40'$, $PX = 93°55\cdot8'$ and angle $P = 43°38\cdot9'$
Hav $ZX = $ Hav P sin PZ sin $PX + $ Hav $(PZ \sim PX)$
P, $43°38\cdot9'$ natural Hav $= 0\cdot1382$ log $= \bar{1}\cdot1405$
PZ, $49°40'$ log sin $= \bar{1}\cdot8821$
PX, $93°55\cdot8'$ log sin $= \bar{1}\cdot9990$

log	$= \bar{1}\cdot0216$
antilog	$= 0\cdot1051$
$(PZ \sim PX)$, 44°15·8′ natural Hav	$= 0\cdot1419$
ZX natural Hav	$= 0\cdot2470$
$\therefore ZX = 59°36′$	

Again in the spherical triangle PZX, we now have:

$PZ = 49°40′$, $PX = 93°55\cdot8′$ and $ZX = 59°36′$
Hav $Z = \{$Hav $PX -$ Hav $(PZ \sim ZX)\}$ cosec PZ cosec ZX

PX, 93°55·8′ natural Hav	$= 0\cdot5343$
$(PZ \sim ZX)$ 9°56′ natural Hav	$= 0\cdot0075$
Natural	$= 0\cdot5268$

Log	$= \bar{1}\cdot7217$
PZ, 49°40′ log cosec	$= 0\cdot1179$
ZX, 59°36′ log cosec	$= 0\cdot0642$
log Hav Z	$= \bar{1}\cdot9038$
antilog	$= 0\cdot8013$ (natural Hav Z)
$\therefore Z = 127°03′$	

From Fig. 106(b) it will be seen that this angle is 127°03′ West of South. Therefore, the true azimuth of the star $= 180° + 127°03′$.

$\therefore$ True bearing of star	$= 307°03′$	T
Compass bearing of star	$= 327\ 00$	C
$\therefore$ Compass error	$=\ \ 19\ 57$	West
Variation	$=\ \ 30\ 00$	West
$\therefore$ Deviation	$=\ \ 10°03′$	East

By five-figure Nautical Tables

To find ZX

P, 43°38·9′ log Hav	$= 9\cdot14053$
PZ, 49°40′ log sin	$= 9\cdot88212$
PX, 93°55·8′ log sin	$= 9\cdot99898$

179

log	$= 9\cdot02163$

natural	$= 0\cdot10510$
$(PZ \sim PX)$ 44°15·8′ natural Hav	$= 0\cdot14193$

ZX, natural Hav	$= 0\cdot24703$

$\therefore ZX = 59°36\cdot3'$

To find Z

PX, 93°55·8′ natural Hav	$= 0\cdot53428$
$(PZ \sim ZX)$ 9°56·3′ natural Hav	$= 0\cdot00751$

natural	$= 0\cdot52677$

log	$= 9\cdot72162$
PZ, 49°40′ log cosec	$= 10\cdot11788$
ZX, 59°36·3′ log cosec	$= 10\cdot06421$

Z log Hav	$= 9\cdot90371$

$\therefore Z = 127°02'$

By A.B.C. Tables

Given lat 40°20′S; declination 3°55·8′N; L.H.A. 43°38·9′W

Table A $= 0\cdot89$N

Table B $= 0\cdot10$N

C $= 0\cdot99$N

From Table C Azimuth $=$ N53°W

$= 307°$

THE AMPLITUDE OF A HEAVENLY BODY. ERROR AND DEVIATION BY AMPLITUDE

The amplitude of a heavenly body is the arc of the horizon contained between the East or West points of the horizon, and the position of the body when rising or setting. Alternatively, it is the angle at the observer's zenith contained between the Prime Vertical and the vertical circle on which the body is situated when its true altitude is zero.

In Fig. 107, X_1 is a heavenly body which is just rising above the eastern horizon. X_1X_2 is the body's parallel of declination which is North of the equinoctial. The arc EX_1 or the angle EZX_1 is the amplitude of the body,

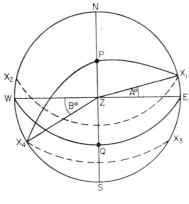

Fig. 107

and is named $EA°N$. Similarly X_4 is a heavenly body which is just setting below the western horizon. This body has South declination, and its amplitude is $WB°S$.

Amplitudes, therefore, are always given as angles or arcs measured from the East or West points of the horizon, towards the North, if the body's declination is North, and towards the South if the body's declination is South.

The true amplitude of a heavenly body may be easily calculated by the use of the formula for amplitude, the derivation of which is given in Appendix I of the book. That is,

$$\text{sin Amplitude} = \text{sin Declination} \times \text{sec latitude}.$$

An amplitude may be readily changed into a bearing or azimuth in 360° notation. That is, $E20°N = 070°$ and $W20°S = 250°$, and it may then be compared with a compass bearing of the given heavenly body in order to obtain the compass error and deviation.

The sun is usually observed for amplitude when it is rising or setting, but it must be observed at "theoretical sunrise" or at "theoretical sunset" when its true altitude is zero, since the above formula depends on the zenith distance being 90°. For an observer at sea level, therefore, the bearing of the sun must be taken when its lower limb is a semi-diameter above the visible horizon. That is when the observed altitude of the sun's lower limb is 0°16',

whence	Observed altitude of L.L.	$= 0°16'$
	S.D.	$+16'$
		$0°32'$
	Refraction for $0°$	$-32'$

$\therefore$ True altitude of sun's centre $= 0°00'$

There are two special cases of amplitude to be noted:

(1) When the declination of a heavenly body is zero its amplitude is NIL. That is, the body rises bearing East (T) and sets bearing West (T).

(2) When an observer is on the equator, the true amplitude is the same value as the body's declination. For example, for an observer on the equator on 21st June, when the sun's declination is 23°27'N, the true amplitude of the sun is E23°27'N at sunrise and W23°27'N at sunset. This should be verified by drawing a diagram of the celestial sphere for an observer on the equator.

EXAMPLE 10

On 19th September 1958, in lat 50°10'N, long 20°15'W, the sun was observed at theoretical sunrise to bear 080° by compass. If the local variation was 10°20'W, find the error and deviation of the compass.

The working is as follows:

Ascertain the declination of the sun at sunrise. To do this, enter the Nautical Almanac Sunrise Table for lat 50°N. This gives the Local Mean Time of Sunrise on 19th September 1958, as 5h42m. Longitude of observer = 20°15'W = 1h21m. Therefore, G.M.T. of Sunrise = 5h42m + 1h21m = 7h03m G.M.T. Use this G.M.T. to extract the declination of the sun, which for this date and G.M.T. is 1°39·3'N.

Sin amplitude = sin declination × sec latitude.

Declination 1°39·3' log sin	$= \bar{2}·4606$
Lat 50°10' log sec	$= 0·1934$
Amplitude log sin	$= \bar{2}·6540$
$\therefore$ Amplitude angle	$= 2°35'$
$\therefore$ True amplitude	$= E2°35'N$
$\therefore$ True bearing	$= 087°25'(T)$
Compass bearing	$= 080\ 00(C)$
Compass error	$=\ \ \ 7\ 25\ E$
Variation	$=\ \ 10\ 20\ W$
Deviation	$=\ \ 17°45'E$

Using five-figure Nautical Tables

$$1°39\cdot3' \text{ log sin} \qquad = 8\cdot46060$$
$$50°10' \text{ log sec} \qquad = 10\cdot19344$$

$$\text{Amplitude log sin} \qquad = 8\cdot65404$$
$$\therefore \text{ Amplitude angle} = 2°35' \text{ as above.}$$

EXERCISE 10(b)

Use the extracts from the Nautical Almanac printed in this book to answer questions 1–5 of this exercise.

1. On 21st September 1958 an observer in D.R. position 54°10′N 29°15′W observed the sun to bear 230° by compass. The G.M.T. by the ship's chronometer was 17^{h}20^{m}00^s. The local variation was 27°W. Find the error and deviation of the ship's compass.

2. On 19th September 1958 an observer on board ship in lat 38°40′S long 60°10′E took a compass bearing of the star Aldebaran at 01^{h}42^{m}00^s G.M.T. The bearing by compass was 010°. If the local variation was 37°20′W, find the error and deviation of the compass.

3. On 6th June 1958, an observer on board ship in D.R. position 39°40′N 160°10′W took a compass bearing of the sun at 20^{h}32^{m}00^s G.M.T. The bearing by compass was 090°00′. If the local variation was 15°00′E, find the error and deviation of the compass.

4. On 20th September 1958 an observer on board ship in D.R. position 35°15′N 44°40′W took a compass bearing of the star Alphard at 08^{h}24^{m}00^s G.M.T. The bearing by compass was 130°00′. If the local variation was 22°30′W, find the error and deviation of the compass.

5. On 30th December 1958 on board ship in D.R. position 47°10′S 155°30′E an observer took a compass bearing of the sun at 04^{h}20^m G.M.T. and found it to be 290° by compass. If the local variation was 17°30′E find the error and deviation of the compass.

In the following questions (6–10) find the error of the compass from the information given.

6. Star Vega observed to bear 120° by compass. D.R. position was 57°35′N 04°35′W, G.H.A. Aries 246°01·6′, S.H.A. star 81°06·5, declination of star 38°44·7′N.

7. Sun observed to bear 075° by compass. D.R. position was 47°05′N, 179°55′W, G.H.A. sun 104°56′, declination of sun 23°16·8′N.

8. Star Hadar observed to bear 135° by compass. D.R. position was 50°30′S 90°00′E, G.H.A. Aries 19°23·9′, S.H.A. star 149°46·9′, declination of star 60°10·5′S.

9. Sun observed to bear 040° by compass. D.R. position was 47°50′S 82°22′E, G.H.A. sun 247°02·9′, declination of sun 20°34·8′N.

10. Star Rasalhague observed to bear 075° by compass. D.R. position was 33°33′N 179°50′W, G.H.A. Aries 358°50·7′, S.H.A. star 96°45·4′, declination of star 12°35·4′N.

In the following questions (11–15) find the error and deviation of the compass from the information given, using the amplitude method.

11. Latitude 30°15′N. Declination of sun 22°56·3′S, compass bearing 110° at theoretical sunrise. Variation 12°20′W.

12. Latitude 50°10′N. Declination of sun 23°05·3′N, compass bearing 065° at theoretical sunrise. Variation 10°00′E.

13. Latitude 30°20′S. Declination of sun 12°27·3′S, compass bearing 240° at theoretical sunset. Variation 5°40′W.

14. Latitude 00°00′. Declination of sun 22°17·9′S, compass bearing 110° at theoretical sunrise. Variation 15°00′W.

15. Latitude 20°10′S. Declination of sun 00°00′, compass bearing 280° at theoretical sunset. Variation 7°20′W.

THE MARC ST. HILAIRE METHOD OF DETERMINING AN ASTRONOMICAL POSITION LINE

A position line for a given observer is, by definition, a line somewhere on which the observer is situated. An astronomical position line is one that is obtained by astronomical observation.

When finding the latitude by meridian altitude observation, the result obtained indicates that the observer is on a certain parallel of latitude. This is true, but the observer is, in fact, only at one particular point on the given parallel of latitude; namely, at that point where the parallel of latitude is cut by the meridian which passes through the geographical position of the heavenly body observed.

By referring to Fig. 99, it will be seen that the observer is at O, where the parallel of latitude *ll* is cut by the meridian *pOgq*. He is not at any other point on *ll*.

As explained in Chapter 8, if a circle is drawn on the earth with centre *g* and radius *gO* (the circle drawn round *g* in Fig. 99), then this circle is the circle of position, somewhere on the circumference of which the observer is situated. He is, in fact, at the point where this circumference is cut by the meridian of the body's geographical position at O, which is also the one point where the parallel of latitude through O cuts the same meridian.

If a small portion of the circumference of the position circle on either side of O (*hOk* in Fig. 99) is considered, then it will be seen that this forms a slightly curved line which is at right-angles to the true bearing of *g*, the geographical position of the body observed.

It is only when the distance from the observer to the geographical position of the body observed is small (i.e. when the altitude of the body is great and the zenith distance is small) that the curvature of the position line is at all pronounced. Except in these unusual circumstances, no harm is done in practice if it is assumed that the portion of the astronomical position line which passes through the observer's position is a straight line. In other words, the line *hOk* in Fig. 99 can be drawn on a chart as a straight line *at right-angles to the bearing of the body observed*. This is a fundamental concept of the astronomical position line. It must always be drawn at right-angles to the bearing or azimuth of the body observed, simply because any part of the circumference of a circle must be at right-angles to the radius of the circle.

In Fig. 99, *gO* is the radius of the circle, and *hOk* is that part of the circumference of the circle which passes through O.

When a heavenly body is observed on the meridian, its bearing is North or South, and the position line on which the observer is situated lies in an East–West direction, so that it approximates to the observer's parallel of latitude.

When a heavenly body is observed bearing South-East as in Example 8 of this chapter (Fig. 105(b)), then the observer's position line will lie on a NE/SW direction. Similarly, when the heavenly body bears 307°T, as in Example 9 of this chapter, the position line will lie in a direction 217°/037°T.

When a heavenly body is observed bearing East or West, i.e. when it is on the Prime Vertical (WZE in either of the above diagrams), then the observer's position line will lie in a North/South direction and will approximate to the observer's meridian of longitude. Thus, to obtain longitude accurately, a body must be observed when it bears East or West, for the same reason that a body must be observed bearing North or South when the observer wishes to find his latitude.

An astronomical position line, however, is useful, no matter in which direction it lies. There is no particular virtue in one that lies North/South or East/West, except that the former gives the observer his latitude and the latter gives him his longitude, without any further work.

A position line can be obtained by observation of a heavenly body bearing in *any* direction, and the observer will then know that he is situated *somewhere* on it. If he wishes to know exactly *where* he is on it, he will have to obtain a second position line which crosses the first one at a reasonable "angle of cut" (preferably more than 40°), and he will then know his exact position is at the point of intersection of the two position lines. The latitude and longitude of the point of intersection can then be taken off the chart.

The Marc St. Hilaire method of determining an astronomical position line, which is named after the French naval officer who discovered it, is based on the above fundamental concept that any astronomical position line is at right-angles to the bearing or azimuth of the body observed.

The procedure for obtaining a position line by the Marc St. Hilaire method is as follows:

(1) The sextant altitude of a heavenly body is observed, and the G.M.T. of the observation is noted by reference to a chronometer or chronometer-watch. The sextant altitude is converted to true altitude and this is subtracted from 90° to give the true zenith distance. This true zenith distance is the distance, in degrees and minutes, that the observer is distant from the geographical position of the body observed. It is, in fact, the radius of the position circle, with centre at the geographical position of the body observed, somewhere on the circumference of which the observer is situated. Every

1 min of this radius is 1 n. mile. This fact should be readily appreciated by considering the definitions of (i) a nautical mile and (ii) one minute of true altitude or true zenith distance.

(2)   By the use of information obtained from the observer's D.R. or estimated position, and by information obtained from the Nautical Almanac, the zenith distance and azimuth of the body observed can be calculated. The zenith distance so obtained is called the Calculated zenith distance, and this is the distance that the observer's zenith would be from the body, if the D.R. or estimated position used in the calculation were correct.

(3)   The difference between the True zenith distance and the Calculated zenith distance is now obtained, and this is called the "Intercept". The intercept is "towards" if the True zenith distance is less than the Calculated zenith distance, and it is "away" if the True zenith distance is greater than the Calculated zenith distance.

(4)   The position line is now plotted on the chart by making use of the D.R. or estimated position, the azimuth and the intercept.

Three worked examples to illustrate this procedure will now be given.

The first of these is based on Example 8 of this chapter, Let it be supposed that, in this example, the observer wished to plot a position line on the chart, instead of wishing to find the error and deviation of the compass. He would therefore observe the sun with his sextant, instead of taking a bearing of the sun by compass. Let it be supposed that the sextant altitude he obtained at $11^h 10^m 00^s$ G.M.T., when corrected, gave a true altitude of $32°12'$. This, subtracted from $90°$, gives a True zenith distance of $57°48'$.

The observer would then use the information at his disposal to find the Calculated zenith distance, exactly as in the working of Example 8, where ZX in Fig. 105(b) is the Calculated zenith distance of the sun for an observer in D.R. position $50°, 20'N, 25°15'W$ at $11^h 10^m 00^s$ G.M.T. on 20th September 1958. This Calculated zenith distance is found, by the working in Example 8, to be $57°54'$.

The observer would then calculate the azimuth of the sun from the same D.R. position, and this is found, by the working in Example 8, to be $136°T$, to the nearest whole degree.

The True zenith distance is $57°48'$. The Calculated zenith distance is $57°54'$. Therefore the intercept is $6'$ towards. This means that the observer is on a position line that is $6'$ nearer to the geographical position of the body than the position line passing through the D.R. position.

The method of plotting this position line on the chart is shown in Fig. 108.

The D.R. position is plotted on the chart in its correct latitude and longitude. From the D.R. position a line is drawn in the direction of the azimuth ($136°T$). Along this line, the intercept of 6 n. miles is marked off *towards* the body observed. The point so obtained is called the "Intercept Terminal

Point", and through this point the required position line *PL* is drawn at right angles to the azimuth.

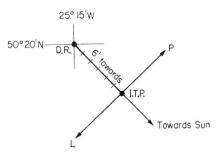

Fig. 108

It should be emphasized once again that the position line *PL* is part of the circumference of a position circle, of radius equal to the True zenith distance, which is drawn round the geographical position of the body observed at the time of observation. In this example, where the True zenith distance is 57°48', it follows that the geographical position of the body observed is 3468 n. miles distant from the I.T.P. on a bearing of 136°T.

The second example of this method of obtaining a position line is based on Example 9 of this chapter.

Let it be supposed that, in this case, instead of taking a compass bearing of the star Menkar in order to obtain the error of the compass, the observer obtains a sextant altitude of the star at $01^h20^m00^s$ G.M.T. The date and D.R. position are as in Example 9. Let it also be supposed that the sextant altitude when corrected gives a true altitude of 30°20'. This, subtracted from 90°, gives a True zenith distance of 59°40'.

From the working of Example 9, *ZX*, the Calculated zenith distance from the observer's D.R. position, is found to be 59°36', and the azimuth of the star is found to be 307°T to the nearest whole degree.

It follows, therefore, that the intercept in this case is 4' *away* because the True zenith distance is 4' greater than the Calculated zenith distance.

The plotting of the position line is shown in Fig. 109.

The latitude and longitude of the D.R. position is plotted on the chart. The bearing or azimuth of the star is laid off in its direction of 307°T, but because the intercept is away, this line of bearing is produced backwards, away from the star for 4 n. miles to the I.T.P., through which the position line, *PL*, is plotted.

Finally, a third, fully worked, example will now be given.

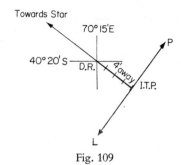

Fig. 109

EXAMPLE 11

At about 9 a.m. ship's time on 31st December 1958, on board a vessel in D.R. position 46°10′S, 157°30′E, a sextant altitude of the sun's lower limb was observed to be 47°10′. Index error was NIL, height of eye 50 ft. At the instant of observation, a chronometer, correct for G.M.T., showed 10ʰ32ᵐ20ˢ. Calculate the azimuth and intercept that must be used to plot the position line on which the vessel is situated.

The first step is to collect the necessary information with which to calculate ZX, the Calculated zenith distance, and angle Z, the azimuth.

$$\text{D.R. lat} = 46°10′\text{S} \quad \therefore \; PZ \text{ (from the South Pole)} = 43°50′.$$

In order to extract the correct declination and Hour Angle from the Nautical Almanac, the correct G.M.T. must be known.

In this example, however, a little care must be exercised at this point. It is about 9 a.m. on 31st December *at ship*; but the ship is on D.R. long 157°30′E, and therefore the approx. time at Greenwich must be 10ʰ30ᵐ *less* than the ship's time. If 10ʰ30ᵐ is subtracted from 0900 hr on 31st December, the result is 22ʰ30ᵐ G.M.T. on 30th December.

The chronometer, which has a 12 hr face like any other clock, reads 10ʰ32ᵐ20ˢ, but because we know that the approximate G.M.T. is 22ʰ30ᵐ on 30th December, we know that the G.M.T. given by the chronometer is, in fact, 22ʰ32ᵐ20ˢ on *30th December* 1958.

Declination for 22ʰ = 23°09·3′S	G.H.A. sun at 22ʰ	= 149°20·7′
Declination for 23ʰ = 23 09·2S	Increment for 32ᵐ20ˢ =	8 05·0
∴ Declination = 23°09·25′S	G.H.A. sun	= 157 25·7
	long E +	= 157 30
Since the latitude and declination	L.H.A. sun	= 314 55·7W
are both South, the polar distance		360 00
PX, measured from the South		
Celestial Pole,	L.H.A. sun	= 45°04·3′E
= 90° − 23°09·25′ = 66°50·75′		

The diagrams to illustrate this problem are shown in Fig. 110 (a) and (b).

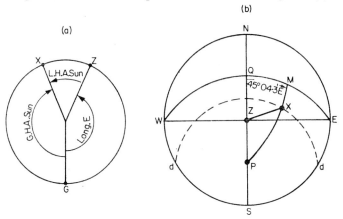

Fig. 110

To find ZX, the Calculated zenith distance

$PZ = 43°50'$ $PX = 66°50·75'$ Angle $P = 45°04·3'$E

$P, 45°04·3'$ natural Hav $= 0·1469$ log	$= \bar{1}·1671$
$PZ, 43°50'$ log sin	$= \bar{1}·8405$
$PX, 66°50·75'$ log sin	$= \bar{1}·9636$

$$\bar{2}·9712$$

Antilog	$= 0·0936$
$(PZ \sim PX)\ 23°00·7'$ natural Hav	$= 0·0399$

ZX natural Hav $= 0·1335$ $\therefore ZX = 42°52'$

To find the Intercept

Sextant altitude of sun's L.L. $= 47°10'$

Dip	$-6·9$	True altitude	$= 47°18·6'$
			$90\ 00$
	$47\ 03·1$		
Refraction	$-0·9$		
		True Z distance	$= 42\ 41·4$
	$47\ 02·2$	Calculated	
S.D.+	$16·3$	Z distance	$= 42\ 52·0$
	$47\ 18·5$	Intercept	$=\ 10·6'$
Px +	$0·1$		
			Towards
True altitude	$= 47°18·6'$		

The calculation of ZX by five-figure Nautical Tables is as follows:

$$P, 45°04·3' \log \text{Hav} = 9·16699$$
$$PZ, 43°50' \log \sin = 9·84046$$
$$PZ, 66°50·7' \log \sin = 9·96353$$

$$8·97098$$

$$\text{natural} = 0·09353$$
$$(PX \sim PZ)\ 23°00·7'\ \text{natural Hav} = 0·03979$$

$$ZX\ \text{natural Hav} = 0·13332$$
$$ZX = 42°50'$$

This gives an Intercept of 8·6 Towards.

To find Angle Z, the Azimuth

$$PX = 66°50·7' \quad PZ = 43°50' \quad ZX = 42°51'$$
$$PX, 66°50·7'\ \text{natural Hav} = 0·3034$$
$$(PZ \sim ZX)\ 0°59'\ \text{natural Hav} = 0·0001$$

$$0·3033 \qquad \log = \bar{1}·4818$$
$$PZ \log \text{cosec} = 0·1595$$
$$ZX \log \text{cosec} = 0·1673$$

$$\log \text{Hav } Z = \bar{1}·8086$$
$$\therefore \text{natural Hav } Z = 0·6436$$
$$\therefore Z = 106°42'$$

From diagram (Fig. 110(b)) Azimuth $= 073°18'$T

Check by A.B.C. Tables

H.A.	$= 45°04'$E	$A = 1·04$N
lat	$= 46°10'$S	$B = 0·60$S
Declination	$= 23°09'$S	$C = 0·44$N

$$\therefore \text{Azimuth} = \text{N73°E}$$

Answer: Intercept 9·6 Towards*.   Azimuth $= 073°$T.

The plotting of the position line is shown in Fig. 111.

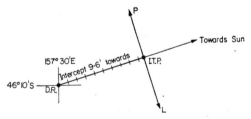

Fig. 111

* Mean of 8·6 and 10·6.

ASTRONOMICAL CALCULATIONS

From the information given in each question calculate the azimuth and intercept of the heavenly body observed, and state if the intercept is towards or away. Also give the direction in which the position line is to be drawn through the Intercept Terminal Point.

1. D.R. position 46°30′S 52°32′W. Sextant altitude of sun's lower limb 37°21′, index error +3′, height of eye 26 ft, declination of sun 21°37·7′S, G.H.A. sun 110°16·6′. Date, 12th January 1958.

2. D.R. position 20°42′S 50°10′W. Sextant altitude of star Menkar 51°28′, index error NIL, height of eye 35 ft, declination of star 3°55·7′N, G.H.A. Aries 64°40′. S.H.A. star 314°58·3′.

3. D.R. position 47°40′N 179°50′E. Sextant altitude of sun's L.L. 30°21′, index error NIL, height of eye 40 ft, declination of sun 2°12·2′N, G.H.A. sun 135°38·7′. Date, 18th September 1958.

4. D.R. position 46°50′N 151°30′E. Sextant altitude of sun's L.L. 14°05′, index error NIL, height of eye 30 ft, declination of sun 22°20·3′S, G.H.A. sun 173°58·9′. Date, 8th January 1958.

5. D.R. position 48°32′N 38°40′W. Sextant altitude of star Rasalhague 36°02′, index error NIL, height of eye 21 ft, declination of star 12°35·6′N, G.H.A. Aries 350°36·7′. S.H.A. star 96°44·8′.

6. D.R. position 46°43·3′N 150°44·1′E. Sextant altitude of sun's L.L. 19°02′, index error NIL, height of eye 30 ft, declination of sun 22°19·1′S, G.H.A. sun 227°09·3′. Date, 8th January 1958.

7. D.R. position 35°16′N 10°45′W. Sextant altitude of star Regulus 40°06′, index error −3′, height of eye 48 ft, declination of star 12°10·2′N, G.H.A. Aries 211°29·8′. S.H.A. star 208°27·6′.

8.* (a) D.R. position 46°46′S 33°40′E. Sextant altitude of sun's L.L. 39°36′, index error 3′ off the arc, height of eye 18 ft, declination of sun 23°15·6′S, G.H.A. sun 270°23·8′. Date, 29th December 1958.
    (b) Following the above observation, the vessel steamed 37 n. miles on a course of 233°T through a current which set 270°T drift 3·7 n. miles until noon, when a meridian altitude observation of the sun gave a latitude of 47°12′S. Find the vessel's longitude at noon.

9.* (a) D.R. position 45°05′N 35°00′W. Sextant altitude of sun's L.L. 26°33′, index error −2·5′, height of eye 38 ft, declination of sun 2°01·0′S, G.H.A. sun 82°19·3′. Date, 28th September 1958.
    (b) Following the above observation, the vessel steamed on a course of 243°T distance 33 n. miles until evening twilight. Then, when in D.R. position 44°50′N, 35°41·6′W, an observation of the star Altair was taken. Sextant altitude of star 50°01′. Index error and height of eye as in Question 9 (a) above, declination of star 8°45·8′N, G.H.A. Aries 313°17·6′. S.H.A. star 62°48·3′. Find the vessel's latitude and longitude at the time of the star observation.

★ Questions 8 and 9 should not be attempted until Chapter 11 has been studied.

Astronomical position lines

It has already been explained in Chapter 8 and Chapter 10 that an observation of a heavenly body places the observer somewhere on a line at right-angles to the azimuth of the body. If observations of two bodies are taken simultaneously, then the actual position of the observer can be fixed at the point of intersection of the two position lines. This point may be obtained by actually plotting the position lines on the chart, or by means of squared paper.

FIX BY SIMULTANEOUS ALTITUDES OF TWO BODIES

Example 1

A vessel in D.R. lat 45°15'N, long 28°13'W takes observations of two stars A and B. A, bearing 063°(T) gave an intercept of 6'A, and B, bearing 118°(T) gave an intercept of 3'T. Find the ship's position.

A point (X) on the squared paper is chosen to represent the D.R. position. The bearings of A and B, and their corresponding intercepts are then laid off from X.

The position of the ship is fixed at the point of intersection of the two position lines, which are drawn at right-angles to the two bearings.

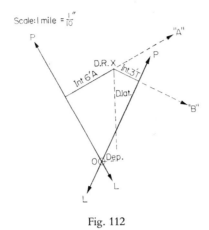

Fig. 112

Having fixed the ship's position at O, the d.lat and dep. between X and O can be measured directly and the position of O found.

				From traverse table:
X lat	45°15′N	long	28°13′W	dep. 1·6′W
d.lat	9·6′S	d.long	2·3′W	m.lat 45°10′N
				d.long 2·3′W
O lat	45°05·4′N	long	28°15·3′W	

DETERMINATION OF POSITION WITH A RUN BETWEEN OBSERVATIONS

The ship's position can be fixed by means of two observations of the same body, or of different bodies, with a run between observations in the same manner as described in Chapter 4 for the running fix. The following example illustrates the method.

EXAMPLE 2

A vessel in D.R. lat 25°23′S, long 136°18′E observes the sun bearing 042°(T) and obtains an intercept of 4′T. Later, after having steamed for 28 miles on a course of 256°(T) the sun is again observed, bearing 336°(T) and an intercept of 5′T is obtained. Find the ship's position at each observation.

Suppose that *A* is the first D.R. position, then the ship is placed somewhere along the position *PL*. *B* is the intercept terminal point and the course and distance are laid off from it. After steaming 256°(T) for 28 miles, the vessel's

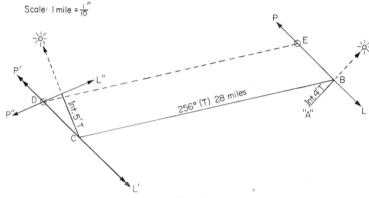

Fig. 113

D.R. position is at *C* and the transferred position line *P'L'* is drawn through this point. A second observation of the sun is then taken which places the vessel on the position line *P"L"*. The ship's position is now fixed at *D*, the point of intersection of the two position lines. The position at the first observation can then be found by laying the course back from *D* to cut the first position line in *E*.

In Fig. 113 the positions of *D* and *E* can be found by direct measurement from *A*.

To find *D*

A lat	25°23·0'S	long	136°18·0'E	dep.	28·5'W	
d.lat	0·3'S	d.long	31·5'W	d.long	31·5'W	
D lat	25°23·3'S	long	135°46·5'E	m.lat	25°23'S	

To find *E*

A lat	25°23·0'S	long	136°18·0'E	dep	1·3'W	
d.lat	6·5'N	d.long	1·4'W	m.lat	25°20'S	
E lat	25°16·5'S	long	136°16·6'E	d.long	1·4'W	

EXAMPLE 3

A vessel in D.R. lat 35°32'N, long 17°46'W observes the sun bearing 158°(T) and obtains an intercept of 6·5'A. The ship then steams on a course of 306°(T) at 12 kt for 2 hr through a current setting 207°(T) at 2 kt, at the end of which time a lighthouse in lat 35°56′N, long 18°18′W is observed bearing 008°(T). Find the position of the ship at both observations.

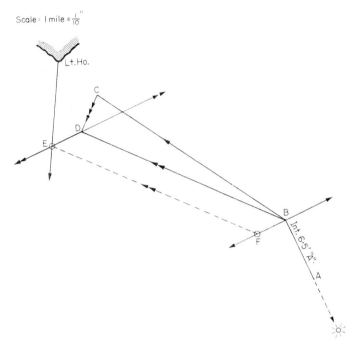

Fig. 114

In this example, the position is obtained by combining an astronomical observation with a terrestrial bearing, making allowance for the run of the ship between observations.

The original D.R., A, is plotted and the position of the lighthouse is plotted from A by measuring the d.lat and dep. between the two points.

The 1st position line is drawn in and the course laid off from the intercept terminal point, B. The line BC represents the run of the ship in two hours and from C the effect of the current (CD) is laid off. The transferred position line is then drawn through the end of the current at D, and combined with the bearing of the lighthouse to fix the ship at E. The position of the ship at the 1st observation is found by laying back the course made good (BD) from E to cut the 1st position line in F.

The position of E and F are then found in the same manner as before, by measuring the d.lat and dep. between them and A.

To find E

A lat	35°32′N	long	17°46′W	dep.	27·2′W
d.lat	15′N	d.long	33·4′W	mean lat	35°40′N
E lat	35°47′N	long	18°19·4′W	d.long	33·4′W

To find F

A lat	35°32·0′N	long	17°46·0′W	dep.	5·2′W
d.lat	4·4′N	d.long	6·4′W	mean lat	35°34′N
F lat	35°36·4′N	long	17°52·4′W	d.long	6·4′W

EXERCISE XI

1. In each of the following simultaneous observations, find the vessel's position.
   (a) D.R. lat 54°24′N long 36°18′E
      Vega bearing 312°. Intercept 3·6′A
      Procyon bearing 243°. Intercept 7′T.
   (b) D.R. lat 20°36′S long 173°12′W
      Sirius, bearing 072°. Intercept 2·5′A
      Canopus, bearing 147°. Intercept 3·2′T.
   (c) D.R. lat 35°12′N long 72°53′W
      Altair, bearing 292°. Intercept nil
      Betelgeuse, bearing 183°. Intercept 6′A.
2. A vessel in D.R. lat 44°32′N long 16°47′W observes the sun bearing 153°, intercept 3′T. After steaming for 24 miles on a course of 036°, the sun was again observed bearing 218°, intercept 4′A. Find the ship's position at each observation.
3. A vessel in D.R. lat 54°24′S long 06°10′E observes the sun bearing 043°, intercept 5·4′T. The vessel then steams 112° for 26 miles until noon when the lat by meridian altitude of the sun was 54°28′S. Find the vessel's position at noon.
4. A vessel in D.R. lat 20°18′N long 16°36′E observes a star at morning twilight bearing 067°, intercept nil. The vessel then steamed 218° at 10 kt for 2½ hr, through a current setting 290° at 3 kt, after which an observation of the sun on the prime vertical gave an intercept of 3′A. Find the position at the 2nd observation.
5. At 0900 hr, in D.R. lat 44°52′S long 18°35′E an observation of the sun, bearing 043°, gave an intercept of 5′T. The ship then steamed 306° at 12 kt until 1030 hr when a point of land in lat 44°44′S long 18°15′E was observed bearing 210°. Find the position of the ship at 0900 and at 1030.
6. A vessel in D.R. lat 10°15′N long 12°16′W observes the sun bearing 246° intercept 4·6′A. She then steams 038° for 2 hr at 11 kt through a current setting 158° at 2 kt when a lighthouse in lat 10°33′N long 11°50′W is observed 75° on the starboard bow. Find the position of the ship at each observation.

THE USE OF A SINGLE POSITION LINE

Although a single position line does not give much indication of the ship's position, it can be of considerable advantage to the navigator, as the following example shows (Fig. 115).

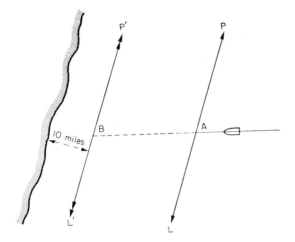

Fig. 115

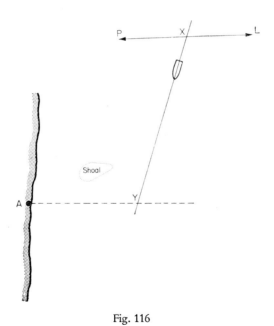

Fig. 116

Suppose a ship is approaching a coastline running, say, NNE–SSW, which she expects to reach after dark. Sometime in the late afternoon the sun is observed bearing WNW. This places the ship on the position line *PL*, and although the exact location of the ship along *PL* is uncertain, the distance of the ship from the coast is known, for the position line runs parallel to it.

Suppose that it is intended to steam along the coast at a distance of 10 miles off during the night, then by drawing *P'L'* parallel to *PL* at a distance of 10 miles from the coast, the navigator can tell how far he must steam before altering course, by measuring the distance *AB*.

Another example of a similar nature is shown in Fig. 116. In this a vessel is steering a southwesterly course and making for a port *A*. A dangerous shoal exists to the NE of *A* and the vessel wishes to ensure that, when she alters in for the port, she will be well to the southward of this shoal. From the chart the navigator can see that if he is to clear the shoal, he must approach *A* steering due West. The shoal, however, is a good distance off the shore, so that the land will not be visible when the alteration point is reached. To ensure that he is on the correct line when he alters, the navigator observes the sun at noon which places him on the position line *PL* running E–W. If this position line is now transferred through *A*, then the distance between the two position lines measured along the course (*XY*) will indicate the exact distance that the vessel has to steam before altering course.

CHAPTER 12 The rising and setting of heavenly bodies. The tides. The magnitude of stars

THEORETICAL AND VISIBLE SUNRISE AND SUNSET

IN Chapter 10 it was seen that when it is required to find the error and deviation of the compass by the amplitude method, the sun must be observed at the time of theoretical sunrise or sunset. It was also shown that, at this time, when the true altitude of the sun is zero, the sun's lower limb appears to be a semi-diameter above the visible horizon for an observer at sea level.

In the Nautical Almanac, however, the times of sunrise and sunset are tabulated against latitude. For example, on 20th September 1958, in latitude 50°N, sunrise is tabulated as occurring at 0542 and sunset at 1804. This date, 20th September, is the "middle day" of the page. Similar information is tabulated for 17th September and for 23rd September, which are the "middle days" of the two pages on either side of the one given in this book. Sunrise on 17th September, in lat 50°N, is given as occurring at 0538. Therefore, by interpolation, sunrise in this latitude on 19th September occurs at 0541 and on 18th it occurs at 0539. Similarly, sunset is given for lat 50°N on 23rd

199

September as occurring at 1757. Therefore, by interpolation, it occurs at 1802 on 21st September and at 1800 on 22nd.

The times of sunrise obtained in this manner are given in Local Mean Time, and they are the times of visible sunrise and sunset. This means that they represent the Local Mean Time when the upper limb of the sun just appears above the visible horizon, for an observer at sea level, at sunrise, or when the upper limb of the sun just disappears below the visible horizon at sunset.

This is another way of saying that the observed altitude of the sun's upper limb at visible sunrise or sunset is 0°0′. To this observed altitude, corrections for refraction and semi-diameter must be applied. The refraction for 0°0′ is 34′ to subtract, and the semi-diameter is 16′ to subtract. Therefore, at visible sunrise, the true altitude of the sun's centre is −0°50′, and the true zenith distance of the sun is 90°50′.

Again, it will be noted that the Local Mean Time of the sun's meridian passage on 20th September is given as 1154. This is 6h12m after sunrise for an observer in lat 50°N and 6h10m before sunset for an observer in the same latitude. The reason that these two intervals are not exactly equal are two: the changing declination of the sun and the changing value of the equation of time during the course of the day.

It is a useful exercise to calculate the L.M.T. of visible sunrise on a given day as follows. For example, find by calculation the L.M.T. of visible sunrise for an observer at sea level in lat 50°N on 20th September 1958.

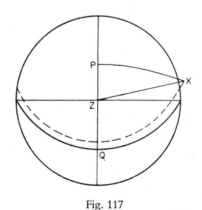

Fig. 117

Take the declination of the sun for the approximate G.M.T. of sunrise from the Nautical Almanac. This is 1°18′N at 0500 G.M.T. Then in the PZX triangle of Fig. 117, $PZ = 40°00′$, $PX = 88°42′$ and $ZX = 90°50′$.

Now calculate angle P by the Spherical Haversine Formula, because angle P is the easterly hour angle of the sun at sunrise, which, when expressed in time and subtracted from the L.M.T. of meridian passage, will give the L.M.T. of visible sunrise.

$$\text{Hav } P = \{\text{Hav } ZX - \text{Hav } (PZ \sim PX)\} \text{ cosec } PZ \text{ cosec } PX$$
$$ZX \; 90°50' \text{ natural Hav} = 0{\cdot}5073$$
$$(PZ \sim PX) \; 48°42' \text{ natural Hav} = 0{\cdot}1700$$

$$0{\cdot}3373 \text{ log} = \bar{1}{\cdot}5280$$
$$PZ \text{ log cosec} = 0{\cdot}1919$$
$$PX \text{ log cosec} = 0{\cdot}0001$$

$$P \text{ log Hav} = \bar{1}{\cdot}7200$$
$$P \text{ natural Hav} = 0{\cdot}5248$$
$$P = 92°51'$$
$$6^{\text{h}}11\tfrac{1}{2}^{\text{m}} \text{ in time}$$

L.M.T. of meridian passage from Almanac $= 11 \quad 54$
$$-6 \quad 11\tfrac{1}{2}$$

∴ L.M.T. of visible sunrise $\qquad\qquad 5 \quad 42\tfrac{1}{2}$

which agrees to within one minute with the time tabulated in the Nautical Almanac for visible sunrise in lat 50°N.

TWILIGHT

Twilight is the period of half light which precedes sunrise and follows sunset. The light which is visible during the twilight period is the reflection of sunlight from the upper layers of the earth's atmosphere.

There are three stages of twilight which overlap each other.

(1) Civil Twilight is the interval of time that elapses between visible sunrise or sunset and the time when the sun's centre is 6° below the rational horizon. It is the interval that elapses between the sun's centre having a true zenith distance of 90°50' and 96°00'.

(2) Nautical Twilight is the interval of time that elapses between visible sunrise or sunset and the time when the sun's centre is 12° below the rational horizon. It is the interval that elapses between the sun's centre having a true zenith distance of 90°50' and 102°00'.

(3) Astronomical Twilight is the interval of time that elapses between visible sunrise or sunset and the time when the sun's centre is 18° below the rational horizon. It is the interval that elapses between the sun's centre having a true zenith distance of 90°50' and 108°00'.

During the period of nautical twilight, the sea horizon can be seen at the same time as the stars, and it is during this period of time that stars can be observed with a marine sextant. When the sun's centre is more than 18° below the horizon, i.e. before the beginning of astronomical twilight in the morning and after the end of astronomical twilight in the evening, there is no reflected light from the sun at all.

The L.M.T. of the beginning and end of civil twilight and of nautical twilight is tabulated in the Nautical Almanac in exactly the same way as the L.M.T. of visible sunrise and sunset is tabulated.

If, in the previous calculation of the L.M.T. of sunrise in lat 50°N on 20th September 1958, zenith distances of 102° and 108° respectively are used instead of 90°50′, the L.M.T. of the beginning of civil twilight and the beginning of nautical twilight will be obtained, and will be found to be at 0510 and 0432 respectively, as given in the Almanac.

If the sunrise and twilight tables in the Nautical Almanac are inspected, it will be seen that the twilight period is of much longer duration in high latitudes than in low latitudes. For example, on 20th September 1958, in latitude 70°N, the interval between the beginning of nautical twilight (0305) and sunrise (0530) is 2ʰ 25ᵐ, whereas, in latitude 10°N, the corresponding interval is only 45 min (between 0504 and 0549).

The reason for this is illustrated in Figs. 118(a) and (b) which are diagrams of the celestial sphere drawn in the plane of the observer's meridian for lat 70°N and lat 10°N respectively. The shaded portion of each diagram is the nautical twilight zone, extending from the rational horizon to 12° below the horizon.

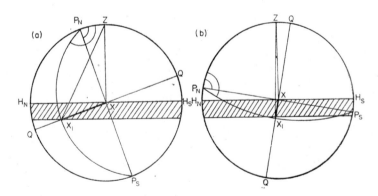

Fig. 118

In both of the above diagrams it is assumed, for simplicity, that the sun's declination is zero, so that its apparent path is along the equinoctial.

In each diagram, therefore, the duration of twilight is represented by the arc of the equinoctial XX_1 (or by the corresponding angle at the pole, $\angle ZP_NX_1 - \angle ZP_NX$). In Fig. 118(a) XX_1 is obviously greater than it is in Fig. 118(b), since the sun passes through the shaded twilight zone at a much more oblique angle in lat 70°N than it does in lat 10°N.

THE MOON'S PHASES AND THEIR EFFECT ON THE TIDES. SPRING AND NEAP TIDES

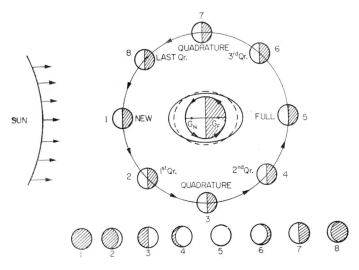

Fig. 119

Figure 119 is a diagram which shows the moon's motion round the earth and the eight successive positions of the moon, relative to the earth and the sun, that the moon occupies during the course of a "lunation". A lunation is the interval of time between two successive "New Moons", or between any other two successive similar phases of the moon. This period of time is approximately $29\frac{1}{2}$ days, and is the basis of the calendar month. The lower portion of the diagram shows the appearance of the moon from the earth at each of its eight phases.

The moon is in position 1 at New Moon, when the moon and the sun are "in conjunction". The dark side of the moon is facing the earth and the moon is on the observer's meridian at noon.

At position 2, the moon is in its 1st Quarter and the observer sees a crescent of light on that side of the moon which is nearer to the sun in the early evening.

At position 3, the moon and the sun are "in quadrature" and half the face of the moon is illuminated.

At position 4, about three-quarters of the moon's face is illuminated, the moon now being in its 2nd Quarter. It is now said to be "gibbous".

Position 5 is the position of Full Moon, when the full face of the moon is illuminated. The moon and the sun are now "in opposition" and the moon is on the observer's meridian at midnight.

During the $14\frac{3}{4}$ day period between position 1 and 5 the moon is said to be "waxing".

In position 6, the moon is in its 3rd Quarter and has begun to "wane". About three quarters of its face is illuminated.

In position 7, the moon and the sun are again in quadrature and half the moon's face is illuminated.

Finally, in position 8, the moon is in its Last Quarter and only a sickle of light is visible on its surface when it is seen in the morning.

The Tides

The moon and the sun both exert a gravitational pull on the waters of the earth, and since the moon is so much nearer to the earth than the sun, the moon's influence is the greater. The force of attraction between any two bodies varies directly as the mass of the bodies and inversely as the square of the distance between them. This is expressed mathematically as $F \propto m_1 m_2 / d^2$. Since the earth is of much greater mass than the moon, the common centre of gravity of the earth–moon system is inside the earth's surface on the lunar side of the earth's centre. At New Moon it is at G_N in Fig. 119 and at Full Moon it is at G_F.

At New Moon, when the moon and the sun are in conjunction, both act together in pulling up the waters of the earth towards them. At the same time, on the opposite side of the earth, the waters are thrown outward by centrifugal force because they are rotating round the common centre of gravity G_N, at a radius of gyration that is greater than that for the waters under the moon. At Full Moon, when the common centre of gravity is at G_F, the waters are pulled up under the moon and thrown out by centrifugal force under the sun as well as being pulled upwards by the sun. It follows, therefore, that on any given day there are two "high waters", one on each side of the earth, and at New Moon and Full Moon these high waters are higher than at any other time of the month. Since the increased height (or depth) of water must come from somewhere, it follows that, at places 90° of longitude to the East and West of the moon's meridian, the water must fall lower at New Moon and at Full Moon than it does at any other time. This phenomenon of "higher high waters" and "lower low waters", which occurs twice a month, is called "Spring Tides". The waters of the earth at Spring Tides are indicated by the firm line ellipse in Fig. 119.

When the moon and the sun are in quadrature at the end of the First and Third Quarters of the moon, the moon pulls the waters of the earth up beneath it and the sun does likewise. But these two forces act at right-angles to each other and the net result is that the high waters (under the moon) are not so high, and the lower waters (under the sun) are not so low, as the average. This phenomenon is known as "Neap Tides", and the waters of the earth at Neap Tides are indicated by the pecked line ellipse in Fig. 119.

THE USE OF TIDE TABLES.
REDUCTION OF SOUNDINGS TO CHART DATUM

The times and heights of high and low water at all the principal ports of the world are tabulated in Admiralty or other Tide Tables. An extract from the Admiralty Tide Tables for the port of Cardiff is given in the Appendix to this book, for the months of January, February, March and April, 1964. The times given are for the Time Zone of Greenwich, i.e. they are given in G.M.T. The times of high and low water at ports in other parts of the world are given in the time of the Time Zone in which each particular port is situated. The height of high or low water given in the Tide Tables is always the height of the water measured relative to "Chart Datum". This is a fixed level of water for the given locality, which, until recently, has always approximated to the level of Mean Low Water Spring Tides. The level of Chart Datum, however, is now in the process of being adjusted, as opportunity offers, to the level of the Lowest Astronomical Tide, i.e. the lowest level that the tide can be expected to reach due to any combination of purely astronomical conditions. This excludes the effects of meteorological conditions such as wind and atmospheric pressure, which also affect the height of the tide.

The soundings in fathoms, which are shown on Admiralty Charts, are the depths of water measured below Chart Datum. For example, if, at a certain position on a chart, a sounding of 10 fathoms is shown, it means that, at Mean Low Water Spring Tides, or, if the Chart Datum has been recently changed, at the Lowest Astronomical Tide, there is a depth of 10 fathoms of water in that position on the chart. At Spring Tides, when the water rises higher and falls lower than usual, the low water level may fall below Chart Datum. It will be seen, for instance, that this occurred at Cardiff on 28th, 29th February, and also on several days in March and April 1964.

205

When a sounding is taken at sea, the depth of water from the surface of the sea to the ocean bed is measured, either by means of an old-fashioned "cast of the lead" or by means of a modern echo-sounder. When using the latter instrument, allowance is made for the draught of the ship, i.e. for the vertical distance between the water line and the bottom of the ship, where the transmitter of the echometer is situated. The navigator on board the ship from which the sounding is taken can use the depth of water he obtains to help fix his position, by comparing it with the depth of water shown on the local chart. Or, alternatively, he may wish to take his ship across a "bar" at the entrance to an estuary, and he cannot do this until the water has risen to a given level. In either of these two cases he will need to apply the principle of the "Reduction of Soundings to Chart Datum".

The following examples are intended to explain this principle, and the procedure to be adopted in applying it.

EXAMPLE 1

The navigator of a ship approaching Cardiff observed that a depth of 15 fathoms was recorded on his echo-sounder at 0700 G.M.T. on 31st January 1964. Find (a) the correction that must be applied to this sounding before it can be compared with the soundings given on the chart and (b) the earliest G.M.T. on this date that the water level will be 10 ft above Chart Datum in this locality.

In Fig. 120, AB is a "tide-pole" drawn vertically upwards from the sea bed. The height of the pole from A to Chart Datum is not to scale, but above the level of Chart Datum, the pole is graduated from 0 to 40 ft to a suitable scale.

The reason 40 ft is chosen is, because, if the times and heights of high and low water at Cardiff on 31st January 1964 are examined (see page 223 of Appendix) it will be seen that, at 0700 G.M.T., the level of the tide lies somewhere between the previous Low Water at 0244 G.M.T. (height 0·4 ft) and the following High Water at 0842 G.M.T. (height 38·4 ft). Therefore, the tide-pole is made to extend to 40 ft so that the H.W. level of 38·4 ft can be marked on it. The L.W. level of 0·4 ft is also marked on it. The "Range" of the tide is the number of feet the water level rises or falls between Low Water and High Water on any given tide. In this example, the Range is 38 ft. The Mean Tide Level, also shown in Fig. 120, is the level of the tide midway between High Water and Low Water.

Since the time at which the sounding was taken is 0700 G.M.T., the "interval" between the time of the sounding and the following High Water is 1^h42^m. Since the duration of rise is 5^h58^m, it follows that the level of the tide at 0700 G.M.T. must be much nearer to the H.W. level than to the L.W. level.

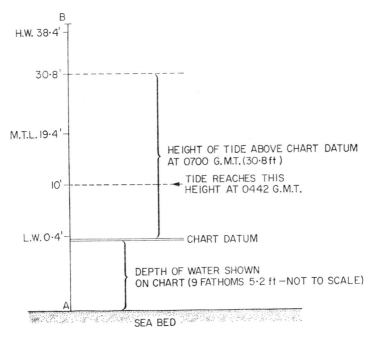

Fig. 120

The procedure for finding the level of the tide at 0700 G.M.T. is as follows:

(1) Write down the predicted heights of H.W. and L.W. and, by subtraction, deduce the predicted range. In this example the predicted range is 38 ft.

(2) Compare the predicted range with the mean ranges given on the tidal diagram (page 224 of Appendix) and select the appropriate curve. In this example the range is 38 ft, which is very close to the Mean Spring Range of 36·3 ft for which the upper of the two curves is drawn. Therefore, this upper curve is the one to use.

(3) Write down the predicted time of H.W. and the time for which the height of tide is required, and hence deduce the interval from H.W. In this example the interval is 1^{h}42^m.

(4) From the graph, read off the factor for the interval from H.W. In this example, the interval is 1^{h}42^m before H.W. Therefore, follow the vertical line of −1^{h}42^m downwards until it cuts the Spring Tide Curve, and read off the factor on the horizontal line which passed through the point of intersection. The factor is 0·8.

(5) Multiply this factor by the predicted range, and add the answer to the predicted height of L.W. to obtain the height of tide required.

In this example the working is as follows:

$$0{\cdot}8 \times 38 = 30{\cdot}4$$
$$\text{Height of L.W.} = 0{\cdot}4$$

$$\therefore \text{ Height of Tide at 0700 G.M.T.} = 30{\cdot}8 \text{ ft.}$$

This height of tide is marked on Fig. 120, and it will be seen that a correction of $-30{\cdot}8$ ft must be applied to the recorded depth of 15 fathoms. This means that the depth shown on the chart in the position at which the sounding was taken was 15 fathoms less 5 fathoms 0·8 ft, i.e. 9 fathoms 5·2 ft.

In order to find the time at which the tide will be at a given height above Chart Datum the method is as follows:

The "factor" used above, when multiplied by the range, gives the height of the tide above L.W. (The factor is 0 at L.W. and 1 at H.W.)

Therefore, if Factor $\times$ Range = Height above L.W.

$$\text{Factor} = \frac{\text{Height above L.W.}}{\text{Range}}$$

In part (b) of this example, it is required to find the earliest G.M.T. at which the water level will be 10 ft above Chart Datum. Since the L.W. height is 0·4 ft, the required level is 9·6 ft above L.W. The Range is 38 ft. Therefore:

$$\text{Factor} = \frac{9{\cdot}6}{38} = 0{\cdot}26$$

With this factor, enter the tidal graph on the left-hand side of the diagram and against the factor of 0·26 it will be found that the interval from H.W. (in this case before H.W.) is -4 hr. The G.M.T. of H.W. is 0842. Therefore, the water will be 10 ft above Chart Datum at 0442 G.M.T. This level is shown in Fig. 120.

EXAMPLE 2

Find (a) the correction that must be applied to a cast of the lead taken near Cardiff on Friday 7th February 1964 at 1500 G.M.T., and (b) the earliest G.M.T. in the afternoon of 7th February at which the water level would have fallen to 20 ft above Chart Datum.

In Fig. 121, *AB*, the total height of the tide-pole, is 27 ft, since the H.W. given in the Tide Tables at 1322 G.M.T. on 7th February is 26·3 ft. In this example the tide is falling, and L.W. occurs at 1919 G.M.T. when the height of the tide is 10·9 ft. It follows, therefore, that the Range of the tide is 15·4 ft.

Since the height of the tide is required at 1500 G.M.T., the interval after H.W. is 1ʰ38ᵐ and, since the Range of the tide is 15·4 ft, it follows that the tidal diagram for Neap Tides must be used. (The Mean Neap Range is given on the diagram as 18·4 ft.)

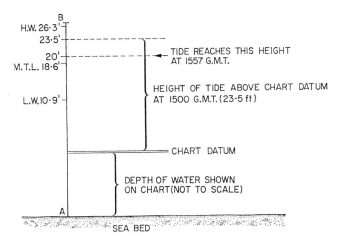

Fig. 121

Therefore, in this example, the lower of the two graphs must be used, and for an interval of +1ʰ38ᵐ a factor of 0·82 is obtained where the vertical line of +1ʰ38ᵐ intersects the curve.

Thus, the height of tide above L.W. at 1500 G.M.T. is found to be 0·82 × 15·4 ft, or 12·6 ft.

The height of the L.W. of the tide in question is given as 10·9 ft at 1919 G.M.T. Therefore, the height of the tide above Chart Datum at 1500 G.M.T. is 23·5 ft, and a correction of 23·5 ft must be subtracted from the depth obtained by the cast of the lead before it can be compared with the depth shown on the chart.

In order to find the earliest G.M.T. at which the water level will have fallen to 20 ft above Chart Datum on the afternoon in question, the procedure is as follows:

From the information used above it will be apparent that the Neap Tide graph is to be used.

$$\text{Factor} = \frac{\text{Height of Tide above L.W.}}{\text{Range}}$$

$$\therefore \text{Factor} = \frac{9 \cdot 1}{15 \cdot 4} = 0 \cdot 6.$$

N—H*

With this factor on the right-hand side of the lower graph, an interval of 2^h35^m after H.W. is obtained. Therefore the tide will have fallen to a height of 20 ft at $1322 + 2^h35^m = 1557$ G.M.T.

In the above two worked examples, the first was quite obviously a Spring Tide, and the second was obviously a Neap Tide. When the tide in question lies somewhere between Springs and Neaps, some interpolation is recommended to give accurate results.

For instance, consider the rising tide on the evening of Wednesday 4th March 1964. The Range of this tide is 27·3 ft, which is almost exactly midway between the Mean Spring Range and the Mean Neap Range, for which the two Cardiff graphs are drawn. Let it be supposed that we wish to find the factor appropriate to a G.M.T. of 1933 which is 3 hr before H.W. From the Spring Tide graph the factor is 0·48, and from the Neap Tide graph the factor is 0·56. Therefore, by interpolation, the factor to use is 0·52.

Again, let it be supposed that the G.M.T. of a given height of tide is required, and by using the formula

$$\text{Factor} = \frac{\text{Height of Tide above L.W.}}{\text{Range}}$$

a factor of 0·5 is obtained. On the Spring Range graph this would give an interval of 2^h50^m after H.W. On the Neap Range graph the interval for a factor of 0·5 is $3^h 00^m$. It follows, therefore, that, by visual interpolation, the required interval lies somewhere between 2^h50^m and 3^h00^m, depending on the actual Range of the tide. If the Range were 30 ft, the interval would be 2^h54^m. If it were 24 ft, the interval would be 2^h57^m and so on.

Mention has been made at the beginning of this section of the occasions when the L.W. level is below Chart Datum. When this occurs, some care must be taken in determining the Range of the tide. For instance, at 1411 G.M.T. on 13th April 1964 at Cardiff, the L.W. height is given as $-1·6$ ft. The following H.W. height is given as 39·9 ft. It follows, therefore, that the Range of this tide is $39·9 + 1·6 = 41·5$ ft. When the "factor", obtained from the graph, is multiplied by this predicted range, the result is the height of the tide above L.W. Suppose the factor to be 0·5. Then the height of the tide above L.W. at the given time would be 20·75 ft. Since, however, the L.W. level is $-1·6$ ft, it follows that the height of the tide at the time in question is $20·75 - 1·6 = 19·15$ ft above Chart Datum, and this would be the correction to apply to the cast of the lead.

The above examples deal only with the tidal phenomena of one of the "Standard Ports" in the British Isles. For other ports, other methods may need to be used, but these are fully explained in the appropriate volume of the Tide Tables.

THE MAGNITUDES OF STARS AND PLANETS

The magnitude of a star is a measure of its *relative* brightness.

A 6th Magnitude star is a star that can just be seen with the naked eye on a clear, dark night.

A 1st Magnitude star is 100 times brighter than a 6th Magnitude star.

There are thus five intermediate magnitudes between 6th Magnitude and 1st Magnitude.

But $100 = (2 \cdot 51)^5$.

This means that a 5th Magnitude star is 2·51 times brighter than a 6th Magnitude star, a 4th Magnitude star is 2·51 times brighter than a 5th Magnitude star, and so on.

Some stars are brighter than 1st Magnitude, such as Sirius, the brightest star in the sky, which has a magnitude of $-1 \cdot 6$.

The relative brightness of planets is also given in terms of their magnitudes, as if they were stars, but the magnitudes of planets vary, for two reasons.

(1) Planets have phases, very similar to the phases of the moon, i.e. at some times their fully illuminated faces are towards the earth, and at other times their faces are only partly illuminated.

(2) The distance of a planet from the earth varies.

There are a few stars whose magnitudes vary and these are known as "variables" by astronomers. The star Betelguese, in the constellation of Orion, is the only variable that is ordinarily used by navigators. Its magnitude is given in the Nautical Almanac as 0·1–1·2.

EXERCISE XII(a)

Use the extracts from the 1958 Nautical Almanac printed in this book to answer all the questions in this exercise.

1. Find the L.M.T. of sunrise and sunset of 20th September 1958 for an observer in lat 50°00′N.

2. Find the L.M.T. of the beginning of civil twilight on the morning of 20th September 1958 for an observer in lat 50°00′N.

3. Find the L.M.T. of sunrise and sunset on 20th September 1958 for an observer in latitude 15°00′S.

4. Find the L.M.T. of the beginning of nautical twilight on the morning of 20th September 1958 for an observer in lat 50°00′N.

5. Find the duration of nautical twilight in the evening of 20th September 1958 (a) for an observer in lat 60°00′N, (b) for an observer in lat 10°00′N.

EXERCISE XII(b)

Use the extracts from the Admiralty Tide Tables printed in this book to answer the questions in this exercise.

1. In a certain position on a chart of the British Channel, near Cardiff, the depth of water is shown as 5 fathoms. Find the actual depth of water that would be obtained by a cast of the lead in this position at 0600 G.M.T. on 2nd January 1964.

Also, find the G.M.T. at which the tide will have risen to a height of 10 ft above Chart Datum on the early morning of the same day.

2. At a certain position off Cardiff on 28th February 1964, the echo-sounder is used and shows a depth of water of 42 ft at 1200 G.M.T. What is the depth shown on the chart in this position? Also find the G.M.T. at which the tide will have fallen to a height of 6 ft above Chart Datum at about noon on the same day.

3. Find the correction to apply to the depth of water obtained by a cast of the lead before the depth can be compared with the sounding shown on the chart. The position is off Cardiff, the date is 7th March 1964, and the time is 0700 G.M.T. Also, find the G.M.T. at which the water level will have risen to a height of 20 ft before noon on the same day.

4. Find the correction to apply to the depth of water obtained by a cast of the lead off Cardiff at 1400 G.M.T. on 5th April 1964. Find also the G.M.T. at which the water level will have fallen to a height of 15 ft above Chart Datum during the afternoon of the same day.

5. Find the correction to apply to the depth of water obtained by the echo-sounder near Cardiff at 1300 G.M.T. on 12th January 1964. Also find the G.M.T. at which the water level will have risen to 25 ft above Chart Datum on the afternoon of the same day.

**Derivation
of the spherical
trigonometrical
formulae used in
this book**

(A) THE SPHERICAL HAVERSINE FORMULA

In the derivation of this formula, two basic trigonometrical formulae are used, which are commonly met with in plane trigonometry.

$$c^2 = a^2 + b^2 - 2ab \cos C. \tag{I}$$

This is derived as follows:

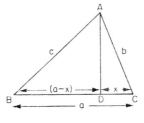

Fig. A.1

In the triangle ABC as shown above, a perpendicular is dropped from A on to BC, meeting BC in D.

Let $DC = x$. Then $BD = (a - x)$.

By Pythagoras:

$$AD^2 = c^2 - (a - x)^2$$

and
$$AD^2 = b^2 - x^2$$

$$\therefore \quad c^2 - (a - x)^2 = b^2 - x^2$$
$$\therefore \quad c^2 - (a^2 - 2ax + x^2) = b^2 - x^2$$
$$\therefore \quad c^2 - a^2 + 2ax - x^2 = b^2 - x^2$$
$$c^2 = a^2 + b^2 - 2ax.$$

But $x = b \cos C$.

$$\therefore \quad c^2 = a^2 + b^2 - 2ab \cos C. \tag{I}$$

The second basic trigonometrical formula used is the formula for expressing the cosine of the difference between two angles, viz:

$$\cos(A - B) = \cos A \cdot \cos B + \sin A \cdot \sin B. \tag{II}$$

This is derived as follows:

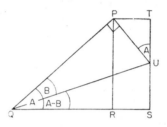

Fig. A.2

In the above diagram PU is perpendicular to QP and UT is perpendicular to QS. Therefore angle $PUT =$ angle PQS and both are called angle A. Angle PQU is angle B.

$$\text{Now } \cos (A - B) = \frac{QS}{UQ} = \frac{QR + PT}{UQ} = \frac{QR}{UQ} + \frac{PT}{UQ}.$$

Now multiply the numerator and the denominator of QR/UQ by QP and multiply the numerator and denominator of PT/UQ by UP. Then

$$\cos(A - B) = \frac{QR}{QP} \times \frac{QP}{UQ} + \frac{PT}{UP} \times \frac{UP}{UQ}$$

$$\therefore \quad \cos(A - B) = \cos A \cdot \cos B + \sin A \cdot \sin B. \tag{II}$$

The basis of the Spherical Haversine Formula is the Spherical Cosine Formula, and this is derived as follows:

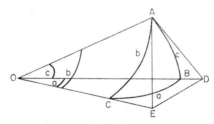

Fig. A.3

214

DERIVATION OF SPHERICAL TRIGONOMETRICAL FORMULAE

In the above diagram, ABC is a spherical triangle on the surface of a sphere. The dimensions of the sides of a spherical triangle are determined by the angles that the sides subtend at the centre of the sphere. In the diagram, O is the centre of the sphere on which ABC is drawn. Therefore, side AC (b) = angle AOC, side AB (c) = angle AOB, and side BC (a) = angle BOC.

Tangents are drawn to the great circle arcs AC and AB at A. These tangents, AE and AD respectively, are each at right angles to AO, since AO is a radius of the sphere. Therefore, OAE and OAD are each right-angled plane triangles, right-angled at A. D and E are on OB and OC produced, and AED and OED are "oblique" plane triangles.

Using the relationship established in (I) above, we have:

In $\triangle AED$: $\qquad\qquad DE^2 = AD^2 + AE^2 - 2AD \cdot AE \cos A.$ $\qquad\qquad$ (1)

In $\triangle OED$: $\qquad\qquad DE^2 = OD^2 + OE^2 - 2OD \cdot OE \cos a.$ $\qquad\qquad$ (2)

But $OD^2 = OA^2 + AD^2$ and $OE^2 = OA^2 + AE^2$.

Substitute for OD^2 and OE^2 in (2).

$$DE^2 = OA^2 + AD^2 + OA^2 + AE^2 - 2OD \cdot OE \cos a. \qquad\qquad (3)$$

Subtract (1) from (3)

$$0 = 2OA^2 + 2AD \cdot AE \cos A - 2OD \cdot OE \cos a.$$

$$\therefore 2\, OD \cdot OE \cos a = 2OA^2 + 2AD \cdot AE \cos A.$$

$$\therefore OD \cdot OE \cos a = OA^2 + AD \cdot AE \cos A.$$

$$\therefore \cos a = \frac{OA}{OD} \times \frac{OA}{OE} + \frac{AD}{OD} \times \frac{AE}{OE} \cos A.$$

$$\therefore \cos a = \cos c \cos b + \sin c \sin b \cos A.$$

$$\therefore \cos a = \cos b \cos c + \sin b \sin c \cos A. \qquad\qquad \text{(III)}$$

Similarly it may be proved that:

$$\cos b = \cos a \cos c + \sin a \sin c \cos B$$

and $\qquad\qquad \cos c = \cos a \cos b + \sin a \sin b \cos C.$

From this formula the Spherical Haversine Formula is directly derived as follows:

$$\text{Versine } A = 1 - \cos A \text{ and Haversine } A = \frac{1 - \cos A}{2}.$$

$$\therefore 1 - \cos A = 2 \text{ Hav } A.$$

$$\therefore \qquad \cos A = 1 - 2 \text{ Hav } A.$$

From (III) $\cos a = \cos b \cos c + \sin b \sin c \cos A.$

$$\cos a = \cos b \cos c + \sin b \sin c \,(1 - 2 \text{ Hav } A).$$

$$\cos a = \cos b \cos c + \sin b \sin c - \sin b \sin c \, 2 \text{ Hav } A.$$

But, from (II), $\cos b \cos c + \sin b \sin c = \cos (b \sim c).$

$$\therefore \cos a = \cos (b \sim c) - 2 \sin b \sin c \text{ Hav } A.$$

$$\therefore 1 - 2 \text{ Hav } a = 1 - 2 \text{ Hav } (b \sim c) - 2 \sin b \sin c \text{ Hav } A.$$

$$\therefore -2 \text{ Hav } a = -2 \text{ Hav } (b \sim c) - 2 \sin b \sin c \text{ Hav } A.$$

$$\therefore \text{ Hav } a = \text{ Hav } (b \sim c) + \sin b \sin c \text{ Hav } A.$$

Whence $\qquad\qquad\qquad \text{Hav } A = \dfrac{\text{Hav } a - \text{Hav } (b \sim c)}{\sin b \sin c} \qquad\qquad \text{(IV)}$

215

which is the form in which the formula is usually memorized. Similarly it may be proved that:

$$\text{Hav } B = \frac{\text{Hav } b - \text{Hav } (a \sim c)}{\sin a \sin c}$$

and

$$\text{Hav } C = \frac{\text{Hav } c - \text{Hav } (a \sim b)}{\sin a \sin b}.$$

(B) THE AMPLITUDE FORMULA

The amplitude of a heavenly body is the arc of the horizon, or the corresponding angle at the observer's zenith, contained between the Prime Vertical and the vertical circle passing through the body at theoretical rising or setting of the body, i.e. when the body's true altitude is 0° and its true zenith distance is 90°.

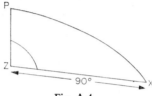

Fig. A.4

In the above diagram $ZX = 90°$, when the body X is observed at theoretical rising or setting.

Angle $Z = (90 \pm \text{amplitude})$

$\therefore \cos Z = \sin \text{amplitude}$.

$\cos ZX = \cos 90° = 0.$ $\sin ZX = \sin 90° = 1.$

$\cos PX = \sin \text{declination}.$ $\sin PZ = \cos \text{lat}.$

By formula (III) above:

$$\cos Z = \frac{\cos PX - \cos PZ \cos ZX}{\sin PZ \sin ZX}$$

i.e.

$$\sin \text{amplitude} = \frac{\sin \text{declination} - \cos PZ \times 0}{\cos \text{lat} \times 1}$$

$\therefore \sin \text{amplitude} = \dfrac{\sin \text{declination} - 0}{\cos \text{lat}}$

$\therefore \sin \text{amplitude} = \dfrac{\sin \text{declination}}{\cos \text{lat}}$

$\therefore \sin \text{amplitude} = \sin \text{declination} . \text{secant lat}$, which is the formula **required**.

APPENDIX II **Extracts from Nautical Almanac and tide tables**

APPENDIX II

1958. September 19, 20, 21 (Fri., Sat., Sun.)

G.M.T. d h	ARIES G.H.A.	VENUS −3·4 G.H.A.	Dec.	MARS −0·9 G.H.A.	Dec.
19 00	357 23·6	193 43·8 N 8	24·7	299 44·2 N18	05·6
01	12 26·0	208 43·3	23·5	314 45·9	05·8
02	27 28·5	223 42·9	22·4	329 47·7	06·0
03	42 31·0	238 42·5 ··	21·2	344 49·5 ··	06·2
04	57 33·4	253 42·0	20·1	359 51·2	06·4
05	72 35·9	268 41·6	18·9	14 53·0	06·6
06	87 38·4	283 41·1 N 8	17·8	29 54·8 N18	06·8
07	102 40·8	298 40·7	16·6	44 56·6	07·0
08	117 43·3	313 40·2	15·5	59 58·3	07·2
F 09	132 45·8	328 39·8 ··	14·3	75 00·1 ··	07·3
R 10	147 48·2	343 39·3	13·2	90 01·9	07·5
I 11	162 50·7	358 38·9	12·0	105 03·7	07·7
D 12	177 53·1	13 38·5 N 8	10·9	120 05·5 N18	07·9
A 13	192 55·6	28 38·0	09·7	135 07·2	08·1
Y 14	207 58·1	43 37·6	08·6	150 09·0	08·3
15	223 00·5	58 37·1 ··	07·4	165 10·8 ··	08·5
16	238 03·0	73 36·7	06·3	180 12·6	08·7
17	253 05·5	88 36·2	05·1	195 14·4	08·9
18	268 07·9	103 35·8 N 8	04·0	210 16·2 N18	09·1
19	283 10·4	118 35·4	02·8	225 18·0	09·3
20	298 12·9	133 34·9	01·6	240 19·7	09·5
21	313 15·3	148 34·5 8	00·5	255 21·5 ··	09·7
22	328 17·8	163 34·0 7	59·3	270 23·3	09·9
23	343 20·2	178 33·6	58·2	285 25·1	10·0
20 00	358 22·7	193 33·2 N 7	57·0	300 26·9 N18	10·2
01	13 25·2	203 32·7	55·9	315 28·7	10·4
02	28 27·6	223 32·3	54·7	330 30·5	10·6
03	43 30·1	238 31·8 ··	53·5	345 32·3 ··	10·8
04	58 32·6	253 31·4	52·4	0 34·1	11·0
05	73 35·0	268 31·0	51·2	15 35·9	11·2
06	88 37·5	283 30·5 N 7	50·1	30 37·7 N18	11·4
S 07	103 40·0	298 30·1	48·9	45 39·5	11·6
A 08	118 42·4	313 29·7	47·7	60 41·3	11·8
T 09	133 44·9	328 29·2 ··	46·6	75 43·1 ··	12·0
U 10	148 47·4	343 28·8	45·4	90 44·9	12·1
R 11	163 49·8	358 28·3	44·2	105 46·7	12·3
D 12	178 52·3	13 27·9 N 7	43·1	120 48·5 N18	12·5
A 13	193 54·7	28 27·5	41·9	135 50·3	12·7
Y 14	208 57·2	43 27·0	40·8	150 52·2	12·9
15	223 59·7	58 26·6 ··	39·6	165 54·0 ··	13·1
16	239 02·1	73 26·2	38·4	180 55·8	13·3
17	254 04·6	88 25·7	37·3	195 57·6	13·5
18	269 07·1	103 25·3 N 7	36·1	210 59·4 N18	13·6
19	284 09·5	118 24·9	34·9	226 01·2	13·8
20	299 12·0	133 24·4	33·8	241 03·0	14·0
21	314 14·5	148 24·0 ··	32·6	256 04·9 ··	14·2
22	329 16·9	163 23·5	31·4	271 06·7	14·4
23	344 19·4	178 23·1	30·3	286 08·5	14·6
21 00	359 21·8	193 22·7 N 7	29·1	301 10·3 N18	14·8
01	14 24·3	208 22·2	27·9	316 12·2	15·0
02	29 26·8	223 21·8	26·8	331 14·0	15·1
03	44 29·2	238 21·4 ··	25·6	346 15·8 ··	15·3
04	59 31·7	253 20·9	24·4	1 17·6	15·5
05	74 34·2	268 20·5	23·3	16 19·5	15·7
06	89 36·6	283 20·1 N 7	22·1	31 21·3 N18	15·9
07	104 39·1	298 19·6	20·9	46 23·1	16·1
08	119 41·6	313 19·2	19·7	61 25·0	16·3
S 09	134 44·0	328 18·8 ··	18·6	76 26·8 ··	16·4
U 10	149 46·5	343 18·4	17·4	91 28·6	16·6
N 11	164 49·0	358 17·9	16·2	106 30·5	16·8
D 12	179 51·4	13 17·5 N 7	15·1	121 32·3 N18	17·0
A 13	194 53·9	28 17·1	13·9	136 34·1	17·2
Y 14	209 56·3	43 16·6	12·7	151 36·0	17·4
15	224 58·8	58 16·2 ··	11·5	166 37·8 ··	17·5
16	240 01·3	73 15·8	10·4	181 39·7	17·7
17	255 03·7	88 15·3	09·2	196 41·5	17·9
18	270 06·2	103 14·9 N 7	08·0	211 43·3 N18	18·1
19	285 08·7	118 14·5	06·9	226 45·2	18·3
20	300 11·1	133 14·0	05·7	241 47·0	18·5
21	315 13·6	148 13·6 ··	04·5	256 48·9 ··	18·6
22	330 16·1	163 13·2	03·3	271 50·7	18·8
23	345 18·5	178 12·8	02·2	286 52·6	19·0
Mer. Pass.	0ʰ 06·5ᵐ	v −0·4	d 1·2	v 1·8	d 0·2

STARS

Name	S.H.A.	Dec.
Acamar	315 49·3	S 40 28·0
Achernar	335 56·9	S 57 26·6
Acrux	173 55·9	S 62 52·3
Adhara	255 45·0	S 28 54·8
Aldebaran	291 36·5	N 16 25·6
Alioth	166 57·4	N 56 11·1
Alkaid	153 31·7	N 49 31·3
Al Na'ir	28 35·0	S 47 09·6
Alnilam	276 28·1	S 1 13·6
Alphard	218 36·8	S 8 28·7
Alphecca	126 46·1	N 26 51·5
Alpheratz	358 25·7	N 28 51·9
Altair	62 48·2	N 8 45·8
Ankaa	353 55·9	S 42 31·6
Antares	113 16·9	S 26 20·4
Arcturus	146 33·6	N 19 24·0
Atria	108 55·8	S 68 57·4
Avior	234 35·2	S 59 22·4
Bellatrix	279 16·1	N 6 18·8
Betelgeuse	271 45·9	N 7 24·0
Canopus	264 14·5	S 52 40·2
Capella	281 35·2	N 45 57·2
Deneb	49 59·2	N 45 08·3
Denebola	183 15·9	N 14 48·2
Diphda	349 36·9	S 18 12·6
Dubhe	194 42·8	N 61 58·4
Elnath	279 04·6	N 28 34·3
Eltanin	91 05·3	N 51 30·0
Enif	34 27·2	N 9 41·4
Fomalhaut	16 09·0	S 29 50·3
Gacrux	172 47·3	S 56 52·9
Gienah	176 35·0	S 17 18·7
Hadar	149 46·8	S 60 10·5
Hamal	328 47·0	N 23 16·1
Kaus Aust.	84 38·3	S 34 24·3
Kochab	137 19·1	N 74 19·8
Markab	14 19·0	N 14 59·2
Menkar	314 57·9	N 3 55·8
Menkent	148 56·4	S 36 10·0
Miaplacidus	221 49·1	S 69 32·7
Mirfak	309 39·0	N 49 42·8
Nunki	76 49·2	S 26 20·9
Peacock	54 23·7	S 56 52·1
Pollux	244 18·2	N 28 07·5
Procyon	245 42·9	N 5 19·9
Rasalhague	96 44·7	N 12 35·6
Regulus	208 27·6	N 12 10·2
Rigel	281 51·6	S 8 14·8
Rigil Kent.	140 48·4	S 60 40·0
Sabik	102 59·8	S 15 40·4
Schedar	350 26·9	N 56 18·7
Shaula	97 17·8	S 37 04·5
Sirius	259 10·1	S 16 39·4
Spica	159 14·9	S 10 56·7
Suhail	223 23·0	S 43 15·8
Vega	81 06·7	N 38 45·1
Zuben'ubi	137 51·2	S 15 52·2

	S.H.A.	Mer. Pass.
Venus	195 10·5	11 06
Mars	302 04·2	3 58
Jupiter	149 27·4	14 07
Saturn	101 07·8	17 19

EXTRACTS FROM NAUTICAL ALMANAC

1958. September 19, 20, 21 (Fri., Sat., Sun.)

G.M.T. d h	SUN G.H.A.	SUN Dec.	MOON G.H.A.	v	Dec.	d	H.P.
19 00	181 28.6	N 1 46.1	107 22.5	6.9	S18 12.2	2.5	58.9
01	196 28.8	45.1	121 48.4	6.8	18 14.7	2.5	58.8
02	211 29.0	44.1	136 14.2	6.9	18 17.2	2.4	58.8
03	226 29.2	·· 43.2	150 40.1	6.9	18 19.6	2.2	58.8
04	241 29.5	42.2	165 06.0	7.0	18 21.8	2.1	58.7
05	256 29.7	41.2	179 32.0	7.0	18 23.9	2.0	58.7
06	271 29.9	N 1 40.3	193 58.0	7.0	S18 25.9	1.9	58.7
07	286 30.1	39.3	208 24.0	7.0	18 27.8	1.7	58.6
08	301 30.3	38.3	222 50.0	7.0	18 29.5	1.7	58.6
F 09	316 30.6	·· 37.4	237 16.0	7.1	18 31.2	1.5	58.6
R 10	331 30.8	36.4	251 42.1	7.2	18 32.7	1.4	58.5
I 11	346 31.0	35.4	266 08.3	7.1	18 34.1	1.3	58.5
D 12	1 31.2	N 1 34.4	280 34.4	7.2	S18 35.4	1.2	58.5
A 13	16 31.4	33.5	295 00.6	7.2	18 36.6	1.0	58.4
Y 14	31 31.7	32.5	309 26.8	7.3	18 37.6	1.0	58.4
15	46 31.9	·· 31.5	323 53.1	7.2	18 38.6	0.8	58.4
16	61 32.1	30.6	338 19.3	7.4	18 39.4	0.7	58.4
17	76 32.3	29.6	352 45.7	7.3	18 40.1	0.6	58.3
18	91 32.6	N 1 28.6	7 12.0	7.4	S18 40.7	0.5	58.3
19	106 32.8	27.7	21 38.4	7.5	18 41.2	0.3	58.3
20	121 33.0	26.7	36 04.9	7.4	18 41.5	0.3	58.2
21	136 33.2	·· 25.7	50 31.3	7.5	18 41.8	0.1	58.2
22	151 33.4	24.7	64 57.8	7.6	18 41.9	0.0	58.2
23	166 33.7	23.8	79 24.4	7.6	18 41.9	0.1	58.1
20 00	181 33.9	N 1 22.8	93 51.0	7.6	S18 41.8	0.2	56.1
01	196 34.1	21.8	108 17.6	7.7	18 41.6	0.3	58.1
02	211 34.3	20.9	122 44.3	7.7	18 41.3	0.5	58.0
03	226 34.6	·· 19.9	137 11.0	7.8	18 40.8	0.5	58.0
04	241 34.8	18.9	151 37.8	7.8	18 40.3	0.7	58.0
05	256 35.0	18.0	166 04.6	7.8	18 39.6	0.8	57.9
06	271 35.2	N 1 17.0	180 31.4	7.9	S18 38.8	0.8	57.9
07	286 35.4	16.0	194 58.3	8.0	18 38.0	1.0	57.9
S 08	301 35.7	15.0	209 25.3	8.0	18 37.0	1.1	57.8
A 09	316 35.9	·· 14.1	223 52.3	8.0	18 35.9	1.2	57.8
T 10	331 36.1	13.1	238 19.3	8.1	18 34.7	1.4	57.8
U 11	346 36.3	12.1	252 46.4	8.1	18 33.3	1.4	57.7
R 12	1 36.5	N 1 11.2	267 13.5	8.2	S18 31.9	1.5	57.7
D 13	16 36.8	10.2	281 40.7	8.2	18 30.4	1.7	57.7
A 14	31 37.0	09.2	296 07.9	8.3	18 28.7	1.7	57.6
Y 15	46 37.2	·· 08.2	310 35.2	8.3	18 27.0	1.9	57.6
16	61 37.4	07.3	325 02.5	8.4	18 25.1	1.9	57.6
17	76 37.7	06.3	339 29.9	8.4	18 23.2	2.1	57.5
18	91 37.9	N 1 05.3	353 57.3	8.5	S18 21.1	2.2	57.5
19	106 38.1	04.4	8 24.8	8.5	18 18.9	2.3	57.5
20	121 38.3	03.4	22 52.3	8.6	18 16.6	2.3	57.5
21	136 38.5	·· 02.4	37 19.9	8.6	18 14.3	2.5	57.4
22	151 38.8	01.4	51 47.5	8.7	18 11.8	2.6	57.4
23	166 39.0	1 00.5	66 15.2	8.8	18 09.2	2.7	57.4
21 00	181 39.2	N 0 59.5	80 43.0	8.8	S18 06.5	2.8	57.3
01	196 39.4	58.5	95 10.8	8.8	18 03.7	2.9	57.3
02	211 39.6	57.6	109 38.6	8.9	18 00.8	2.9	57.3
03	226 39.9	·· 56.6	124 06.5	9.0	17 57.9	3.1	57.2
04	241 40.1	55.6	138 34.5	9.0	17 54.8	3.2	57.2
05	256 40.3	54.6	153 02.5	9.1	17 51.6	3.3	57.2
06	271 40.5	N 0 53.7	167 30.6	9.1	S17 48.3	3.3	57.1
07	286 40.7	52.7	181 58.7	9.2	17 45.0	3.5	57.1
08	301 41.0	51.7	196 26.9	9.2	17 41.5	3.6	57.1
S 09	316 41.2	·· 50.8	210 55.1	9.3	17 37.9	3.6	57.1
U 10	331 41.4	49.8	225 23.4	9.4	17 34.3	3.8	57.0
N 11	346 41.6	48.8	239 51.8	9.4	17 30.5	3.8	57.0
D 12	1 41.8	N 0 47.8	254 20.2	9.5	S17 26.7	4.0	57.0
A 13	16 42.1	46.9	268 48.7	9.5	17 22.7	4.0	56.9
Y 14	31 42.3	45.9	283 17.2	9.6	17 18.7	4.1	56.9
15	46 42.5	·· 44.9	297 45.8	9.6	17 14.6	4.2	56.9
16	61 42.7	44.0	312 14.4	9.7	17 10.4	4.3	56.9
17	76 43.0	43.0	326 43.1	9.8	17 06.1	4.4	56.8
18	91 43.2	N 0 42.0	341 11.9	9.8	S17 01.7	4.5	56.8
19	106 43.4	41.0	355 40.7	9.9	16 57.2	4.6	56.8
20	121 43.6	40.1	10 09.6	9.9	16 52.6	4.6	56.7
21	136 43.8	·· 39.1	24 38.5	10.0	16 48.0	4.8	56.7
22	151 44.1	38.1	39 07.5	10.1	16 43.2	4.8	56.7
23	166 44.3	37.1	53 36.6	10.1	16 38.4	4.9	56.7
	S.D. 16.0	d 1.0	S.D. 15.9		15.7		15.5

Twilight / Sunrise

Lat.	Naut.	Civil	Sunrise
N 72	02 42	04 18	05 27
N 70	03 05	04 28	05 30
68	03 23	04 36	05 32
66	03 37	04 42	05 34
64	03 48	04 48	05 36
62	03 58	04 52	05 37
60	04 06	04 57	05 38
N 58	04 12	05 00	05 39
56	04 18	05 03	05 40
54	04 23	05 06	05 41
52	04 28	05 08	05 42
50	04 32	05 10	05 42
45	04 40	05 15	05 44
N 40	04 46	05 18	05 45
35	04 51	05 21	05 46
30	04 55	05 23	05 47
20	05 01	05 26	05 48
N 10	05 04	05 28	05 49
0	05 06	05 30	05 50
S 10	05 06	05 30	05 51
20	05 04	05 30	05 52
30	05 01	05 29	05 53
35	04 59	05 28	05 53
40	04 55	05 27	05 54
45	04 51	05 25	05 54
S 50	04 45	05 22	05 54
52	04 42	05 21	05 55
54	04 39	05 20	05 55
56	04 35	05 18	05 55
58	04 30	05 16	05 55
S 60	04 25	05 14	05 56

Sunset / Twilight

Lat.	Sunset	Civil	Naut.
N 72	18 18	19 27	21 00
N 70	18 15	19 17	20 38
68	18 13	19 09	20 21
66	18 11	19 03	20 08
64	18 10	18 58	19 57
62	18 09	18 53	19 48
60	18 08	18 50	19 40
N 58	18 07	18 46	19 33
56	18 06	18 43	19 28
54	18 05	18 40	19 23
52	18 04	18 38	19 18
50	18 04	18 36	19 14
45	18 03	18 32	19 06
N 40	18 01	18 28	19 00
35	18 00	18 26	18 55
30	18 00	18 24	18 52
20	17 59	18 21	18 46
N 10	17 58	18 19	18 43
0	17 57	18 18	18 42
S 10	17 56	18 17	18 41
20	17 56	18 18	18 43
30	17 55	18 19	18 46
35	17 55	18 20	18 49
40	17 54	18 21	18 53
45	17 54	18 23	18 58
S 50	17 54	18 26	19 04
52	17 53	18 27	19 07
54	17 53	18 29	19 11
56	17 53	18 30	19 14
58	17 53	18 32	19 19
S 60	17 53	18 34	19 24

SUN

Day	Eqn. of Time 00h	Eqn. of Time 12h	Mer. Pass.
19	05 54	06 04	11 54
20	06 15	06 26	11 54
21	06 36	06 47	11 53

Moon. Upper Mer. Passage

Day	
19	17h 30m
20	18h 25m
21	19h 18m

June 1958

G.M.T. d h	SUN G.H.A. ° '	Dec. °
6 00	180 24·2	N22 34·5
01	195 24·1	34·8
02	210 24·0	35·0
03	225 23·9 ··	35·3
04	240 23·8	35·6
05	255 23·7	35·9
06	270 23·6	N22 36·1
07	285 23·4	36·4
08	300 23·3	36·7
F 09	315 23·2 ··	36·9
R 10	330 23·1	37·2
I 11	345 23·0	37·4
D 12	0 22·9	N22 37·7
A 13	15 22·8	38·0
Y 14	30 22·7	38·2
15	45 22·6 ··	38·5
16	60 22·4	38·7
17	75 22·3	39·0
18	90 22·2	N22 39·3
19	105 22·1	39·5
20	120 22·0	39·8
21	135 21·9 ··	40·0
22	150 21·8	40·3
23	165 21·7	40·5
7 00	180 21·5	N22 40·8
01	195 21·4	41·1
02	210 21·3	41·3
03	225 21·2 ··	41·6
04	240 21·1	41·8
05	255 21·0	42·1
06	270 20·9	N22 42·3
07	285 20·7	42·6
S 08	300 20·6	42·8
A 09	315 20·5 ··	43·1
T 10	330 20·4	43·3
U 11	345 20·3	43·6
R 12	0 20·2	N22 43·8
D 13	15 20·1	44·0
A 14	30 19·9	44·3
Y 15	45 19·8 ··	44·5
16	60 19·7	44·8
17	75 19·6	45·0
18	90 19·5	N22 45·3
19	105 19·4	45·5
20	120 19·2	45·7
21	135 19·1 ··	46·0
22	150 19·0	46·2
23	165 18·9	46·5

Day	SUN Eqn. of Time 00ʰ	12ʰ	Mer. Pass.
6	01 37	01 32	11 58
7	01 26	01 21	11 59
8	01 15	01 10	11 59

S.D. 15·8′

October 1958

G.M.T. d h	SUN G.H.A. ° '	Dec. °
25 00	183 56·5	S11 50·9
01	198 56·6	51·7
02	213 56·7	52·6
03	228 56·8 ··	53·5
04	243 56·8	54·3
05	258 56·9	55·2
06	273 57·0	S11 56·1
07	288 57·1	56·9
S 08	303 57·1	57·8
A 09	318 57·2 ··	58·7
T 10	333 57·3	11 59·5
U 11	348 57·4	12 00·4
R 12	3 57·4	S12 01·3
D 13	18 57·5	02·1
A 14	33 57·6	03·0
Y 15	48 57·7 ··	03·9
16	63 57·7	04·7
17	78 57·8	05·6
18	93 57·9	S12 06·4
19	108 57·9	07·3
20	123 58·0	08·2
21	138 58·1 ··	09·0
22	153 58·2	09·9
23	168 58·2	10·7
26 00	183 58·3	S12 11·6
01	198 58·4	12·5
02	213 58·4	13·3
03	228 58·5 ··	14·2
04	243 58·6	15·0
05	258 58·7	15·9
06	273 58·7	S12 16·8
07	288 58·8	17·6
08	303 58·9	18·5
S 09	318 58·9 ··	19·3
U 10	333 59·0	20·2
N 11	348 59·1	21·0
D 12	3 59·1	S12 21·9
A 13	18 59·2	22·7
Y 14	33 59·3	23·6
15	48 59·3 ··	24·5
16	63 59·4	25·3
17	78 59·5	26·2
18	93 59·5	S12 27·0
19	108 59·6	27·9
20	123 59·7	28·7
21	138 59·7 ··	29·6
22	153 59·8	30·4
23	168 59·9	31·3

Day	SUN Eqn. of Time 00ʰ	12ʰ	Mer. Pass.
25	15 46	15 50	11 44
26	15 53	15 56	11 44
27	16 00	16 02	11 44

S.D. 16·1′

December 1958

G.M.T. d h	SUN G.H.A. ° '	Dec. °
30 00	179 27·3	S23 12·8
01	194 27·0	12·7
02	209 26·7	12·5
03	224 26·4 ··	12·4
04	239 26·1	12·2
05	254 25·8	12·1
06	269 25·5	S23 11·9
07	284 25·2	11·7
T 08	299 24·9	11·6
U 09	314 24·6 ··	11·4
E 10	329 24·3	11·3
S 11	344 24·0	11·1
D 12	359 23·7	S23 11·0
A 13	14 23·4	10·8
Y 14	29 23·1	10·6
15	44 22·8 ··	10·5
16	59 22·5	10·3
17	74 22·2	10·2
18	89 21·9	S23 10·0
19	104 21·6	09·8
20	119 21·3	09·7
21	134 21·0 ··	09·5
22	149 20·7	09·3
23	164 20·4	09·2
31 00	179 20·1	S23 09·0
01	194 19·8	08·8
02	209 19·5	08·7
03	224 19·2 ··	08·5
04	239 18·9	08·3
05	254 18·6	08·1
06	269 18·3	S23 08·0
W 07	284 18·0	07·8
E 08	299 17·7	07·6
D 09	314 17·4 ··	07·5
N 10	329 17·1	07·3
E 11	344 16·8	07·1
S 12	359 16·5	S23 06·9
D 13	14 16·2	06·7
A 14	29 15·9	06·6
Y 15	44 15·6 ··	06·4
16	59 15·3	06·2
17	74 15·0	06·0
18	89 14·7	S23 05·8
19	104 14·4	05·7
20	119 14·1	05·5
21	134 13·8 ··	05·3
22	149 13·5	05·1
23	164 13·2	04·9

Day	SUN Eqn. of Time 00ʰ	12ʰ	Mer. Pass.
30	02 10	02 25	12 02
31	02 39	02 53	12 03
1	03 08	03 22	12 03

S.D. 16·3′

WALES—CARDIFF

Lat. 51°27'N. Long. 3°09'W.

TIME ZONE: Greenwich. TIMES AND HEIGHTS OF HIGH AND LOW WATERS YEAR: 1964

JANUARY

Day	TIME	Ht. Ft.	Day	TIME	Ht. Ft.
1 W	0215	0·6	16 Th	0149	2·0
	0810	38·5		0802	36·4
	1440	0·7		1412	1·7
	2037	38·3		2019	36·0
2 Th	0256	1·0	17 F	0229	2·1
	0855	38·2		0837	36·4
	1522	1·2		1453	1·9
	2122	37·2		2055	35·9
3 F	0336	1·8	18 Sa	0308	2·4
	0938	37·1		0914	36·1
	1559	2·3		1533	2·4
	2205	35·7		2133	35·4
4 Sa	0413	3·2	19 Su	0345	2·8
	1019	35·6		0950	35·6
	1638	3·8		1609	2·9
	2246	33·7		2210	34·5

FEBRUARY

Day	TIME	Ht. Ft.	Day	TIME	Ht. Ft.
1 Sa	0321	0·7	16 Su	0305	0·5
	0919	37·8		0901	38·3
	1544	1·1		1531	0·2
	2143	36·0		2115	36·9
2 Su	0354	1·5	17 M	0344	0·6
	0955	36·8		0938	37·8
	1616	2·4		1606	0·7
	2217	35·0		2156	36·9
3 M	0424	2·6	18 Tu	0417	1·3
	1028	34·9		1012	36·7
	1642	3·9		1637	1·7
	2248	32·9		2232	35·5
4 Tu	0448	4·2	19 W	0442	2·5
	1057	32·7		1047	34·8
	1704	5·8		1701	3·4
	2319	30·6		2308	33·3

MARCH

Day	TIME	Ht. Ft.	Day	TIME	Ht. Ft.
1 Su	0259	−0·2	16 M	0253	−1·1
	0855	38·0		0843	39·8
	1521	0·3		1518	−1·4
	2115	36·9		2100	39·5
2 M	0328	0·5	17 Tu	0332	−1·0
	0926	37·0		0920	39·4
	1546	1·4		1554	−0·8
	2144	35·8		2138	38·5
3 Tu	0352	1·5	18 W	0403	0·0
	0952	35·5		0956	37·9
	1604	2·7		1620	0·6
	2209	33·9		2213	36·7
4 W	0408	2·8	19 Th	0427	1·5
	1016	33·3		1031	35·6
	1616	4·4		1642	2·7
	2233	31·7		2248	34·1

APRIL

Day	TIME	Ht. Ft.	Day	TIME	Ht. Ft.
1 W	0318	1·0	16 Th	0346	−0·2
	0918	35·3		0940	38·0
	1526	2·2		1603	0·8
	2132	34·2		2156	36·9
2 Th	0332	2·3	17 F	0415	1·7
	0941	33·4		1020	35·5
	1535	3·7		1631	3·1
	2154	32·4		2237	34·2
3 F	0342	4·1	18 Sa	0442	4·0
	1004	31·2		1104	32·4
	1545	5·3		1702	5·4
	2222	30·2		2323	31·3
4 Sa	0359	6·2	19 Su	0525	6·5
	1038	28·8		1206	29·6
	1607	7·3		1759	7·7
	2258	28·1			

(Continued on page 222)

N—I

WALES—CARDIFF (continued)

Lat. 51°27'N. Long. 3°09'W.

YEAR: 1964

TIME ZONE: Greenwich.

TIMES AND HEIGHTS OF HIGH AND LOW WATERS

JANUARY

Day	TIME	Ht. Ft.	Day	TIME	Ht. Ft.
5 Su	0448	4.5	20 M	0420	3.5
	1059	33.6		1027	34.5
	1713	5.5		1643	3.8
	2327	31.5		2248	33.3
6 M	0525	6.0	21 Tu	0455	4.5
	1141	31.4		1106	33.2
	1755	7.3		1719	4.8
				2332	31.8
7 Tu	0013	29.5	22 W	0534	5.6
	0610	7.7		1158	31.5
	1232	29.5		1810	6.3
	1843	8.8			
8 W	0110	27.9	23 Th	0030	30.6
	0706	9.1		0633	6.9
	1333	28.0		1305	30.5
	1943	9.9		1918	7.1
9 Th	0216	27.4	24 F	0145	30.1
	0810	9.6		0753	7.5
	1443	27.9		1428	30.6
	2051	9.6		2042	6.9

FEBRUARY

Day	TIME	Ht. Ft.	Day	TIME	Ht. Ft.
5 W	0512	6.0	20 Th	0509	4.4
	1131	30.2		1130	32.4
	1728	7.7		1734	5.4
	2359	28.5		2357	30.9
6 Th	0547	8.2	21 F	0551	6.5
	1218	27.9		1230	30.2
	1812	9.7		1834	7.3
7 F	0054	26.7	22 Sa	0107	29.3
	0642	10.0		0710	8.1
	1322	26.3		1358	29.1
	1919	10.9		2003	8.1
8 Sa	0208	26.2	23 Su	0241	29.3
	0800	10.7		0854	7.8
	1444	26.2		1536	30.3
	2043	10.6		2144	6.8
9 Su	0331	27.3	24 M	0412	31.1
	0927	9.7		1029	5.6
	1605	27.9		1655	32.6
	2206	8.7		2303	4.5

MARCH

Day	TIME	Ht. Ft.	Day	TIME	Ht. Ft.
5 Th	0422	4.8	20 F	0450	3.8
	1043	30.8		1112	32.5
	1629	6.4		1711	5.2
	2302	29.4		2334	31.1
6 F	0442	7.0	21 Sa	0527	6.3
	1119	28.3		1211	29.7
	1656	8.5		1807	7.5
	2349	27.2			
7 Sa	0524	9.3	22 Su	0044	28.9
	1213	26.2		0646	8.3
	1755	10.5		1341	28.2
				1941	8.6
8 Su	0054	25.8	23 M	0225	28.5
	0644	10.9		0840	8.1
	1337	25.3		1526	29.3
	1932	11.1		2127	7.2
9 M	0231	25.9	24 Tu	0401	30.5
	0832	10.8		1017	5.5
	1518	26.3		1645	32.0
	2119	9.9		2249	4.6

APRIL

Day	TIME	Ht. Ft.	Day	TIME	Ht. Ft.
5 Su	0434	8.2	20 M	0034	29.0
	1125	26.8		0644	8.2
	1700	9.3		1332	28.1
	2334	31.1		1930	8.5
6 M	0001	26.4	21 Tu	0210	28.7
	0548	10.1		0830	7.7
	1242	25.5		1508	29.3
	1837	10.7		2110	7.1
7 Tu	0133	25.9	22 W	0341	30.4
	0743	10.5		1022	5.3
	1429	26.2		1623	31.6
	2034	10.1		2227	4.7
8 W	0319	27.6	23 Th	0448	33.0
	0934	8.5		1107	2.9
	1559	28.8		1717	34.0
	2209	7.4		2327	2.6
9 Th	0435	30.6	24 F	0538	35.1
	1049	5.3		1202	1.4
	1702	32.1		1803	35.6
	2317	4.4			

Day		Time Ht	Time Ht	Time Ht	Time Ht
25	Sa	0018 1·3	0620 36·2	1244 0·6	1840 36·4
26	Su	0057 0·6	0655 36·8	1319 0·4	1914 36·7
27	M	0130 0·3	0728 36·8	1349 0·5	1945 36·7
28	Tu	0158 0·3	0757 36·5	1414 0·8	2015 36·4
29	W	0224 0·6	0825 35·8	1436 1·7	2040 35·5
30	Th	0246 1·5	0849 34·5	1454 2·6	2103 34·2

Day		Time Ht	Time Ht	Time Ht	Time Ht
10	F	0529 33·8	1150 2·5	1752 35·1	
11	Sa	0012 2·0	0613 36·3	1239 0·6	1835 37·1
12	Su	0059 0·3	0655 38·2	1326 -0·9	1917 38·8
13	M	0146 -0·9	0737 39·5	1411 -1·6	1958 39·8
14	Tu	0232 -1·4	0820 40·2	1456 -1·6	2039 39·9
15	W	0312 -1·2	0900 39·6	1533 -0·9	2119 38·8

Day		Time Ht	Time Ht	Time Ht	Time Ht
25	W	0511 33·3	1132 2·8	1743 34·6	2356 2·2
26	Th	0604 35·6	1230 0·9	1830 36·2	
27	F	0047 0·8	0646 36·9	1316 -0·2	1908 37·0
28	Sa	0128 0·1	0723 37·5	1353 -0·5	1942 37·4
29	Su	0201 -0·3	0756 37·7	1423 -0·4	2015 37·4
30	M	0231 -0·4	0828 37·5	1450 0·3	2045 36·9
31	Tu	0257 0·2	0854 36·6	1511 1·1	2111 35·9

Day		Time Ht	Time Ht	Time Ht	Time Ht
10	Tu	0403 28·0	1008 8·3	1639 29·2	2241 7·1
11	W	0512 31·1	1119 5·2	1737 32·2	2346 4·2
12	Th	0603 34·0	1217 2·5	1823 34·8	
13	F	0038 1·9	0645 36·1	1304 0·6	1903 36·9
14	Sa	0125 0·4	0724 37·9	1349 -0·7	1944 38·4
15	Su	0209 -0·7	0803 39·3	1434 -1·3	2023 39·5

Day		Time Ht	Time Ht	Time Ht	Time Ht
25	Tu	0524 33·8	1145 3·1	1757 35·1	
26	W	0012 2·3	0619 36·0	1246 1·2	1848 36·7
27	Th	0106 1·0	0705 37·4	1335 0·1	1928 37·6
28	F	0150 0·1	0745 38·0	1416 -0·5	2007 37·9
29	Sa	0227 -0·2	0822 38·4	1450 -0·4	2042 37·7

Day		Time Ht	Time Ht	Time Ht	Time Ht
10	M	0443 29·6	1040 7·4	1711 30·3	2310 6·3
11	Tu	0542 32·0	1144 4·8	1804 32·6	
12	W	0008 3·9	0629 34·2	1234 2·7	1847 34·6
13	Th	0054 2·2	0708 35·9	1321 1·3	1926 36·2
14	F	0140 1·2	0746 37·1	1405 0·5	2005 37·2
15	Sa	0223 0·5	0824 37·9	1449 0·1	2043 37·8

Day		Time Ht	Time Ht	Time Ht	Time Ht
25	Sa	0308 30·9	0922 6·8	1552 32·1	2206 5·5
26	Su	0425 32·8	1041 4·8	1704 34·2	2317 3·7
27	M	0531 35·0	1152 2·9	1804 36·0	
28	Tu	0021 2·0	0628 36·7	1253 1·5	1856 37·2
29	W	0117 1·1	0716 37·7	1346 0·5	1942 37·9
30	Th	0203 0·5	0800 38·4	1431 0·1	2026 38·0
31	F	0244 0·4	0842 38·4	1509 0·3	2105 37·6

Day		Time Ht	Time Ht	Time Ht	Time Ht
10	F	0324 28·1	0919 8·9	1551 28·8	2153 8·4
11	Sa	0426 29·7	1021 7·4	1651 30·5	2250 6·7
12	Su	0521 31·6	1117 5·5	1742 32·2	2343 4·7
13	M	0608 33·4	1206 3·8	1827 33·6	
14	Tu	0028 3·4	0648 34·8	1249 2·6	1905 34·8
15	W	0109 2·4	0726 35·8	1332 1·8	1942 35·5

TIDAL DIAGRAM

CARDIFF

Mean spring and Neap curves

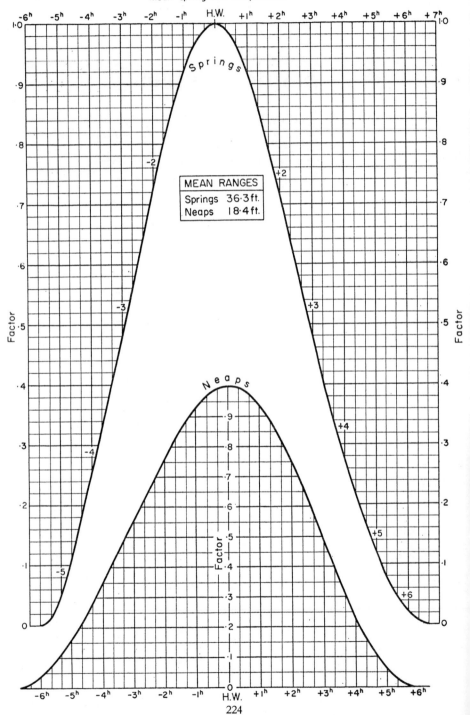

MEAN RANGES

Springs	36·3 ft.
Neaps	18·4 ft.

Abridged nautical tables

Traverse table.
Meridional parts for the
terrestrial spheroid table.
Mean latitude to middle
latitude conversion table.
Altitude correction tables.
Natural haversines table.

ABRIDGED NAUTICAL TABLES
TRAVERSE TABLE

0°   9°

D. long	Dep.		D. long	Dep.		D. long	Dep.		D. long	Dep.	
Dist.	D. lat	Dep.	Dist.	D. lat	Dep.	Dist.	D. lat	Dep.	Dist.	D. lat	Dep.
1	01·0	00·0	51	51·0	00·0	1	01·0	00·2	51	50·4	08·0
2	02·0	00·0	52	52·0	00·0	2	02·0	00·3	52	51·4	08·1
3	03·0	00·0	53	53·0	00·0	3	03·0	00·5	53	52·3	08·3
4	04·0	00·0	54	54·0	00·0	4	04·0	00·6	54	53·3	08·4
5	05·0	00·0	55	55·0	00·0	5	04·9	00·8	55	54·3	08·6
6	06·0	00·0	56	56·0	00·0	6	05·9	00·9	56	55·3	08·8
7	07·0	00·0	57	57·0	00·0	7	06·9	01·1	57	56·3	08·9
8	08·0	00·0	58	58·0	00·0	8	07·9	01·3	58	57·3	09·1
9	09·0	00·0	59	59·0	00·0	9	08·9	01·4	59	58·3	09·2
10	10·0	00·0	60	60·0	00·0	10	09·9	01·6	60	59·3	09·4
11	11·0	00·0	61	61·0	00·0	11	10·9	01·7	61	60·2	09·5
12	12·0	00·0	62	62·0	00·0	12	11·9	01·9	62	61·2	09·7
13	13·0	00·0	63	63·0	00·0	13	12·8	02·0	63	62·2	09·9
14	14·0	00·0	64	64·0	00·0	14	13·8	02·2	64	63·2	10·0
15	15·0	00·0	65	65·0	00·0	15	14·8	02·3	65	64·2	10·2
16	16·0	00·0	66	66·0	00·0	16	15·8	02·5	66	65·2	10·3
17	17·0	00·0	67	67·0	00·0	17	16·8	02·7	67	66·2	10·5
18	18·0	00·0	68	68·0	00·0	18	17·8	02·8	68	67·2	10·6
19	19·0	00·0	69	69·0	00·0	19	18·8	03·0	69	68·2	10·8
20	20·0	00·0	70	70·0	00·0	20	19·8	03·1	70	69·1	11·0
21	21·0	00·0	71	71·0	00·0	21	20·7	03·3	71	70·1	11·1
22	22·0	00·0	72	72·0	00·0	22	21·7	03·4	72	71·1	11·3
23	23·0	00·0	73	73·0	00·0	23	22·7	03·6	73	72·1	11·4
24	24·0	00·0	74	74·0	00·0	24	23·7	03·8	74	73·1	11·6
25	25·0	00·0	75	75·0	00·0	25	24·7	03·9	75	74·1	11·7
26	26·0	00·0	76	76·0	00·0	26	25·7	04·1	76	75·1	11·9
27	27·0	00·0	77	77·0	00·0	27	26·7	04·2	77	76·1	12·0
28	28·0	00·0	78	78·0	00·0	28	27·7	04·4	78	77·0	12·2
29	29·0	00·0	79	79·0	00·0	29	28·6	04·5	79	78·0	12·4
30	30·0	00·0	80	80·0	00·0	30	29·6	04·7	80	79·0	12·5
31	31·0	00·0	81	81·0	00·0	31	30·6	04·8	81	80·0	12·7
32	32·0	00·0	82	82·0	00·0	32	31·6	05·0	82	81·0	12·8
33	33·0	00·0	83	83·0	00·0	33	32·6	05·2	83	82·0	13·0
34	34·0	00·0	84	84·0	00·0	34	33·6	05·3	84	83·0	13·1
35	35·0	00·0	85	85·0	00·0	35	34·6	05·5	85	84·0	13·3
36	36·0	00·0	86	86·0	00·0	36	35·6	05·6	86	84·9	13·5
37	37·0	00·0	87	87·0	00·0	37	36·5	05·8	87	85·9	13·6
38	38·0	00·0	88	88·0	00·0	38	37·5	05·9	88	86·9	13·8
39	39·0	00·0	89	89·0	00·0	39	38·5	06·1	89	87·9	13·9
40	40·0	00·0	90	90·0	00·0	40	39·5	06·3	90	88·9	14·1
41	41·0	00·0	91	91·0	00·0	41	40·5	06·4	91	89·0	14·2
42	42·0	00·0	92	92·0	00·0	42	41·5	06·6	92	90·9	14·4
43	43·0	00·0	93	93·0	00·0	43	42·5	06·7	93	91·9	14·5
44	44·0	00·0	94	94·0	00·0	44	43·5	06·9	94	92·8	14·7
45	45·0	00·0	95	95·0	00·0	45	44·4	07·0	95	93·8	14·9
46	46·0	00·0	96	96·0	00·0	46	45·4	07·2	96	94·8	15·0
47	47·0	00·0	97	97·0	00·0	47	46·4	07·4	97	95·8	15·2
48	48·0	00·0	98	98·0	00·0	48	47·4	07·5	98	96·8	15·3
49	49·0	00·0	99	99·0	00·0	49	48·4	07·7	99	97·8	15·5
50	50·0	00·0	100	100·0	00·0	50	49·4	07·8	100	98·8	15·6
Dist.	D. lat	Dep.	Dist.	D. lat	Dep.	Dist.	Dep.	D. lat	Dist.	Dep.	D. lat
D. long		Dep.	D. long		Dep.	D. long		Dep.	D. long		Dep.

90°   81°

TRAVERSE TABLE

10° 11°

Dist.	D. lat	Dep.	Dist.	D. lat	Dep.	Dist.	D. lat	Dep.	Dist.	D. lat	Dep.
1	01·0	00·2	51	50·2	08·9	1	01·0	00·2	51	50·1	09·7
2	02·0	00·3	52	51·2	09·0	2	02·0	00·4	52	51·0	09·9
3	03·0	00·5	53	52·2	09·2	3	02·9	00·6	53	52·0	10·1
4	03·9	00·7	54	53·2	09·4	4	03·9	00·8	54	53·0	10·3
5	04·9	00·9	55	54·2	09·6	5	04·9	01·0	55	54·0	10·5
6	05·9	01·0	56	55·1	09·7	6	05·9	01·1	56	55·0	10·7
7	06·9	01·2	57	56·1	09·9	7	06·9	01·3	57	56·0	10·9
8	07·9	01·4	58	57·1	10·1	8	07·9	01·5	58	56·9	11·1
9	08·9	01·6	59	58·1	10·2	9	08·9	01·7	59	57·9	11·3
10	09·8	01·7	60	59·1	10·4	10	09·8	01·9	60	58·9	11·4
11	10·8	01·9	61	60·1	10·6	11	10·8	02·1	61	59·9	11·6
12	11·8	02·1	62	61·1	10·8	12	11·8	02·3	62	60·9	11·8
13	12·8	02·3	63	62·0	10·9	13	12·8	02·5	63	61·8	12·0
14	13·8	02·4	64	63·0	11·1	14	13·7	02·7	64	62·8	12·2
15	14·8	02·6	65	64·0	11·3	15	14·7	02·9	65	63·8	12·4
16	15·8	02·8	66	65·0	11·5	16	15·7	03·1	66	64·8	12·6
17	16·7	03·0	67	66·0	11·6	17	16·7	03·2	67	65·8	12·8
18	17·7	03·1	68	67·0	11·8	18	17·7	03·4	68	66·8	13·0
19	18·7	03·3	69	68·0	12·0	19	18·7	03·6	69	67·7	13·2
20	19·7	03·5	70	68·9	12·2	20	19·6	03·8	70	68·7	13·4
21	20·7	03·6	71	69·9	12·3	21	20·6	04·0	71	69·7	13·5
22	21·7	03·8	72	70·9	12·5	22	21·6	04·2	72	70·7	13·7
23	22·7	04·0	73	71·9	12·7	23	22·6	04·4	73	71·7	13·9
24	23·6	04·2	74	72·9	12·8	24	23·6	04·6	74	72·6	14·1
25	24·6	04·3	75	73·9	13·0	25	24·5	04·8	75	73·6	14·3
26	25·6	04·5	76	74·8	13·2	26	25·5	05·0	76	74·6	14·5
27	26·6	04·7	77	75·8	13·4	27	26·5	05·2	77	75·6	14·7
28	27·6	04·9	78	76·8	13·5	28	27·5	05·3	78	76·6	14·9
29	28·6	05·0	79	77·8	13·7	29	28·5	05·5	79	77·5	15·1
30	29·5	05·2	80	78·8	13·9	30	29·4	05·7	80	78·5	15·3
31	30·5	05·4	81	79·8	14·1	31	30·4	05·9	81	79·5	15·5
32	31·5	05·6	82	80·8	14·2	32	31·4	06·1	82	80·5	15·6
33	32·5	05·7	83	81·7	14·4	33	32·4	06·3	83	81·5	15·8
34	33·5	05·9	84	82·7	14·6	34	33·4	06·5	84	82·5	16·0
35	34·5	06·1	85	83·7	14·8	35	34·4	06·7	85	83·4	16·2
36	35·5	06·3	86	84·7	14·9	36	35·3	06·9	86	84·4	16·4
37	36·4	06·4	87	85·7	15·1	37	36·3	07·1	87	85·4	16·6
38	37·4	06·6	88	86·7	15·3	38	37·3	07·3	88	86·4	16·8
39	38·4	06·8	89	87·6	15·5	39	38·3	07·4	89	87·4	17·0
40	39·4	06·9	90	88·6	15·6	40	39·3	07·6	90	88·3	17·2
41	40·4	07·1	91	89·6	15·8	41	40·2	07·8	91	89·3	17·4
42	41·4	07·3	92	90·6	16·0	42	41·2	08·0	92	90·3	17·6
43	42·3	07·5	93	91·6	16·1	43	42·2	08·2	93	91·3	17·7
44	43·3	07·6	94	92·6	16·3	44	43·2	08·4	94	92·3	17·9
45	44·3	07·8	95	93·6	16·5	45	44·2	08·6	95	93·3	18·1
46	45·3	08·0	96	94·5	16·7	46	45·2	08·8	96	94·2	18·3
47	46·3	08·2	97	95·5	16·8	47	46·1	09·0	97	95·2	18·5
48	47·3	08·3	98	96·5	17·0	48	47·1	09·2	98	96·2	18·7
49	48·3	08·5	99	97·5	17·2	49	48·1	09·3	99	97·2	18·9
50	49·2	08·7	100	98·5	17·4	50	49·1	09·5	100	98·2	19·1
Dist.	Dep.	D. lat	Dist.	Dep.	D. lat	Dist.	Dep.	D. lat	Dist.	Dep.	D. lat
D. long		Dep.	D. long		Dep.	D. long		Dep.	D. long		Dep

80° 79°

TRAVERSE TABLE

20°

D. long	Dep.		D. long	Dep.	
Dist.	D. lat	Dep.	Dist.	D. lat	Dep.
1	00·9	00·3	51	47·9	17·4
2	01·9	00·7	52	48·9	17·8
3	02·8	01·0	53	49·8	18·1
4	03·8	01·4	54	50·7	18·5
5	04·7	01·7	55	51·7	18·8
6	05·6	02·1	56	52·6	19·2
7	06·6	02·4	57	53·6	19·5
8	07·5	02·7	58	54·5	19·8
9	08·5	03·1	59	55·4	20·2
10	09·4	03·4	60	56·4	20·5
11	10·3	03·8	61	57·3	20·9
12	11·3	04·1	62	58·3	21·2
13	12·2	04·4	63	59·2	21·5
14	13·2	04·8	64	60·1	21·9
15	14·1	05·1	65	61·1	22·2
16	15·0	05·5	66	62·0	22·6
17	16·0	05·8	67	63·0	22·9
18	16·9	06·2	68	63·9	23·3
19	17·9	06·5	69	64·8	23·6
20	18·8	06·8	70	65·8	23·9
21	19·7	07·2	71	66·7	24·2
22	20·7	07·5	72	67·7	24·6
23	21·6	07·9	73	68·6	25·0
24	22·6	08·2	74	69·5	25·3
25	23·5	08·6	75	70·5	25·7
26	24·4	08·9	76	71·4	26·0
27	25·4	09·2	77	72·4	26·3
28	26·3	09·6	78	73·3	26·7
29	27·3	09·9	79	74·2	27·0
30	28·2	10·3	80	75·2	27·4
31	29·1	10·6	81	76·1	27·7
32	30·1	10·9	82	77·1	28·0
33	31·0	11·3	83	78·0	28·4
34	31·9	11·6	84	78·9	28·7
35	32·9	12·0	85	79·9	29·1
36	33·8	12·3	86	80·8	29·4
37	34·8	12·7	87	81·8	29·8
38	35·7	13·0	88	82·7	30·1
39	36·6	13·3	89	83·6	30·4
40	37·6	13·7	90	84·6	30·8
41	38·5	14·0	91	85·5	31·1
42	39·5	14·4	92	86·5	31·5
43	40·4	14·7	93	87·4	31·8
44	41·3	15·0	94	88·3	32·1
45	42·3	15·4	95	89·3	32·5
46	43·2	15·7	96	90·2	32·8
47	44·2	16·1	97	91·2	33·2
48	45·1	16·4	98	92·1	33·5
49	46·0	16·8	99	93·0	33·9
50	47·0	17·1	100	94·0	34·2
Dist.	Dep.	D. lat	Dist.	Dep.	D. lat
D. long		Dep.	D. long		Dep.

21°

D. long	Dep.		D. long	Dep.	
Dist.	D. lat	Dep.	Dist.	D. lat	Dep.
1	00·9	00·4	51	47·6	18·3
2	01·9	00·7	52	48·5	18·6
3	02·8	01·1	53	49·5	19·0
4	03·7	01·4	54	50·4	19·4
5	04·7	01·8	55	51·3	19·7
6	05·6	02·2	56	52·3	20·1
7	06·5	02·5	57	53·2	20·4
8	07·5	02·9	58	54·1	20·8
9	08·4	03·2	59	55·1	21·1
10	09·3	03·6	60	56·0	21·5
11	10·3	03·9	61	56·9	21·9
12	11·2	04·3	62	57·9	22·2
13	12·1	04·7	63	58·8	22·6
14	13·1	05·0	64	59·7	22·9
15	14·0	05·4	65	60·7	23·3
16	14·9	05·7	66	61·6	23·7
17	15·9	06·1	67	62·5	24·0
18	16·8	06·5	68	63·5	24·4
19	17·7	06·8	69	64·4	24·7
20	18·7	07·2	70	65·4	25·1
21	19·6	07·5	71	66·3	25·4
22	20·5	07·9	72	67·2	25·8
23	21·5	08·2	73	68·2	26·2
24	22·4	08·6	74	69·1	26·5
25	23·3	09·0	75	70·0	26·9
26	24·3	09·3	76	71·0	27·2
27	25·2	09·7	77	71·9	27·6
28	26·1	10·0	78	72·8	28·0
29	27·1	10·4	79	73·8	28·3
30	28·0	10·8	80	74·7	28·7
31	28·9	11·1	81	75·6	29·0
32	29·9	11·5	82	76·6	29·4
33	30·8	11·8	83	77·5	29·7
34	31·7	12·2	84	78·4	30·1
35	32·7	12·5	85	79·4	30·5
36	33·6	12·9	86	80·3	30·8
37	34·5	13·3	87	81·2	31·2
38	35·5	13·6	88	82·2	31·5
39	36·4	14·0	89	83·1	31·9
40	37·3	14·3	90	84·0	32·3
41	38·3	14·7	91	85·0	32·6
42	39·2	15·1	92	85·9	33·0
43	40·1	15·4	93	86·8	33·3
44	41·1	15·8	94	87·8	33·7
45	42·0	16·1	95	88·7	34·0
46	42·9	16·5	96	89·6	34·4
47	43·9	16·8	97	90·6	34·8
49	44·8	17·2	98	91·5	35·1
49	45·7	17·6	99	92·4	35·5
50	46·7	17·9	100	93·4	35·8
Dist.	Dep.	D. lat	Dist.	Dep.	D. lat
D. long		Dep.	D. long		Dep.

70°   69°

TRAVERSE TABLE

			25°						26°		
D. long	Dep.		D. long	Dep.		D. long	Dep.		D. long	Dep.	
Dist.	D. lat	Dep.	Dist.	D. lat	Dep.	Dist.	D. lat	Dep.	Dist.	D. lat	Dep.
1	00·9	00·4	51	46·2	21·6	1	00·9	00·4	51	45·8	22·4
2	01·8	00·8	52	47·1	22·0	2	01·8	00·9	52	46·7	22·8
3	02·7	01·3	53	48·0	22·4	3	02·7	01·3	53	47·6	23·2
4	03·6	01·7	54	48·9	22·8	4	03·6	01·8	54	48·5	23·7
5	04·5	02·1	55	49·8	23·2	5	04·5	02·2	55	49·4	24·1
6	05·4	02·5	56	50·8	23·7	6	05·4	02·6	56	50·3	24·5
7	06·3	03·0	57	51·7	24·1	7	06·3	03·1	57	51·2	25·0
8	07·3	03·4	58	52·6	24·5	8	07·2	03·5	58	52·1	25·4
9	08·2	03·8	59	53·5	24·9	9	08·1	03·9	59	53·0	25·9
10	09·1	04·2	60	54·5	25·4	10	09·0	04·4	60	53·9	26·3
11	10·0	04·6	61	55·3	25·8	11	09·9	04·8	61	54·8	26·7
12	10·9	05·1	62	56·2	26·2	12	10·8	05·3	62	55·7	27·2
13	11·8	05·5	63	57·1	26·6	13	11·7	05·7	63	56·6	27·6
14	12·7	05·9	64	58·0	27·0	14	12·6	06·1	64	57·5	28·1
15	13·6	06·3	65	58·9	27·5	15	13·5	06·6	65	58·4	28·5
16	14·5	06·8	66	59·8	27·9	16	14·4	07·0	66	59·3	28·9
17	15·4	07·2	67	60·7	28·3	17	15·3	07·5	67	60·2	29·4
18	16·3	07·6	68	61·6	28·7	18	16·2	07·9	68	61·1	29·8
19	17·2	08·0	69	62·5	29·2	19	17·1	08·3	69	62·0	30·2
20	18·1	08·5	70	63·4	29·6	20	18·0	08·8	70	62·9	30·7
21	19·0	08·9	71	64·3	30·0	21	18·9	09·2	71	63·8	31·1
22	19·9	09·3	72	65·3	30·4	22	19·8	09·6	72	64·7	31·6
23	20·8	09·7	73	66·2	30·9	23	20·7	10·1	73	65·6	32·0
24	21·8	10·1	74	67·1	31·3	24	21·6	10·5	74	66·5	32·4
25	22·7	10·6	75	68·0	31·7	25	22·5	11·0	75	67·4	32·9
26	23·6	11·0	76	68·9	32·1	26	23·4	11·4	76	68·3	33·3
27	24·5	11·4	77	69·8	32·5	27	24·3	11·8	77	69·2	33·8
28	25·4	11·8	78	70·7	33·0	28	25·2	12·3	78	70·1	34·2
29	26·3	12·3	79	71·6	33·4	29	26·1	12·7	79	71·0	34·6
30	27·2	12·7	80	72·5	33·8	30	27·0	13·2	80	71·9	35·1
31	28·1	13·1	81	73·4	34·2	31	27·9	13·6	81	72·8	35·5
32	29·0	13·5	82	74·3	34·7	32	28·8	14·0	82	73·7	35·9
33	29·9	13·9	83	75·2	35·1	33	29·7	14·5	83	74·6	36·4
34	30·8	14·4	84	76·1	35·5	34	30·6	14·9	84	75·5	36·8
35	31·7	14·8	85	77·0	35·9	35	31·5	15·3	85	76·4	37·3
36	32·6	15·2	86	77·9	36·3	36	32·4	15·8	86	77·3	37·7
37	33·5	15·6	87	78·8	36·8	37	33·3	16·2	87	78·2	38·1
38	34·4	16·1	88	79·8	37·2	38	34·2	16·7	88	79·1	38·6
39	35·3	16·5	89	80·7	37·6	39	35·1	17·1	89	80·0	39·0
40	36·3	16·9	90	81·6	38·0	40	36·0	17·5	90	80·9	39·5
41	37·2	17·3	91	82·5	38·5	41	36·9	18·0	91	81·8	39·9
42	38·1	17·7	92	83·4	38·9	42	37·7	18·4	92	82·7	40·3
43	39·0	18·2	93	84·3	39·3	43	38·6	18·8	93	83·6	40·8
44	39·9	18·6	94	85·2	39·7	44	39·5	19·3	94	84·5	41·2
45	40·8	19·0	95	86·1	40·1	45	40·4	19·7	95	85·4	41·6
46	41·7	19·4	96	87·0	40·6	46	41·3	20·2	96	86·3	42·1
47	42·6	19·9	97	87·9	41·0	47	42·2	20·6	97	87·2	42·5
48	43·5	20·3	98	88·8	41·4	48	43·1	21·0	98	88·1	43·0
49	44·4	20·7	99	89·7	41·8	49	44·0	21·5	99	89·0	43·4
50	45·3	21·1	100	90·6	42·3	50	44·9	21·9	100	89·9	43·8
Dist.	Dep.	D. lat	Dist.	Dep.	D. lat	Dist.	Dep.	D. lat	Dist.	Dep.	D. lat
D. long		Dep.	D. long		Dep.	D. long		Dep.	D. long		Dep.

65°	64°

TRAVERSE TABLE

				35°							36°	
D. long	Dep.		D. long	Dep.			D. long	Dep.		D. long	Dep.	
Dist.	D. lat	Dep.	Dist.	D. lat	Dep.		Dist.	D. lat	Dep.	Dist.	D. lat	Dep.
1	00·8	00·6	51	41·8	29·3		1	00·6	00·6	51	41·3	30·0
2	01·6	01·1	52	42·6	29·8		2	01·6	01·2	52	42·1	30·6
3	02·5	01·7	53	43·4	30·4		3	02·4	01·8	53	42·9	31·2
4	03·3	02·3	54	44·2	31·0		4	03·2	02·4	54	43·7	31·7
5	04·1	02·9	55	4·51	31·5		5	04·0	02·9	55	44·5	32·3
6	04·9	03·4	56	45·9	32·1		6	04·9	03·5	56	45·3	32·9
7	05·7	04·0	57	46·7	32·7		7	05·7	04·1	57	46·1	33·5
8	06·6	04·6	58	47·5	33·3		8	06·5	04·7	58	46·9	34·1
9	07·4	05·2	59	48·3	33·8		9	07·3	05·3	59	47·7	34·7
10	08·2	05·7	60	49·1	34·4		10	08·1	05·9	60	48·5	35·3
11	09·0	06·3	61	50·0	35·0		11	08·9	06·5	61	49·4	35·9
12	09·8	06·9	62	50·8	35·6		12	09·7	07·1	62	50·2	36·4
13	10·6	07·5	63	51·6	36·1		13	10·5	07·6	63	51·0	37·0
14	11·5	08·0	64	52·4	36·7		14	11·3	08·2	64	51·8	37·6
15	12·3	08·6	65	53·2	37·3		15	12·1	08·8	65	52·6	38·2
16	13·1	09·2	66	54·1	37·9		16	12·9	09·4	66	53·4	38·8
17	13·9	09·8	67	54·9	38·4		17	13·8	10·0	67	54·2	39·4
18	14·7	10·3	68	55·7	39·0		18	14·6	10·6	68	55·0	40·0
19	15·6	10·9	69	56·5	39·6		19	15·4	11·2	69	55·8	40·6
20	16·4	11·5	70	57·3	40·2		20	16·2	11·8	70	56·6	41·1
21	17·2	12·0	71	58·2	40·7		21	17·0	12·3	71	57·4	41·7
22	18·0	12·6	72	59·0	41·3		22	17·8	12·9	72	58·2	42·3
23	18·8	13·2	73	59·8	41·9		23	18·6	13·5	73	59·1	42·9
24	19·7	13·8	74	60·6	42·4		24	19·4	14·1	74	59·9	43·5
25	20·5	14·3	75	61·4	43·0		25	20·2	14·7	75	60·7	44·1
25	21·3	14·9	76	62·3	43·6		26	21·0	15·3	76	61·5	44·7
27	22·1	15·5	77	63·1	44·2		27	21·8	15·9	77	62·3	45·3
28	22·9	16·1	78	63·9	44·7		28	22·7	16·5	78	63·1	45·8
29	23·8	16·6	79	64·7	45·3		29	23·5	17·0	79	63·9	46·4
30	24·6	17·2	80	65·5	45·9		30	24·3	17·6	80	64·7	47·0
31	25·4	17·8	81	66·4	46·5		31	25·1	18·2	81	65·5	47·6
32	26·2	18·4	82	67·2	47·0		32	25·9	18·8	82	66·3	48·2
33	27·0	18·9	83	68·0	47·6		33	26·7	19·4	83	67·1	48·8
34	27·9	19·5	84	68·8	48·2		34	27·5	20·0	84	68·0	49·4
35	28·7	20·1	85	69·6	48·8		35	28·3	20·6	85	68·8	50·0
36	29·5	20·6	86	70·4	49·3		36	29·1	21·2	86	69·6	50·5
37	30·3	21·2	87	71·3	49·9		37	29·9	21·7	87	70·4	51·1
38	31·1	21·8	88	72·1	50·5		38	30·7	22·3	88	71·2	51·7
39	31·9	22·4	89	72·9	51·0		39	31·6	22·9	89	72·0	52·3
40	32·8	22·9	90	73·7	51·6		40	32·4	23·5	90	72·8	52·9
41	33·6	23·5	91	74·5	52·2		41	33·2	24·1	91	73·6	53·5
42	34·4	24·1	92	75·4	52·8		42	34·0	24·7	92	74·4	54·1
43	35·2	24·7	93	76·2	53·3		43	34·8	25·3	93	75·2	54·7
44	36·0	25·2	94	77·0	53·9		44	35·6	25·9	94	76·0	55·3
45	36·9	25·8	95	77·8	54·5		45	36·4	26·5	95	76·9	55·8
46	37·7	26·4	96	78·6	55·1		46	37·2	27·0	96	77·7	56·4
47	38·5	27·0	97	79·5	55·6		47	38·0	27·6	97	78·5	57·0
48	39·3	27·5	98	80·3	56·2		48	38·8	28·2	98	79·3	57·6
49	40·1	28·1	99	81·1	56·8		49	39·6	28·8	99	80·1	58·2
50	41·0	28·7	100	81·9	57·4		50	40·5	29·4	100	80·9	58·8
Dist.	Dep.	D. lat	Dist.	Dep.	D. lat		Dist.	Dep.	D. lat	Dist.	Dep.	D. lat
D. long		Dep.	D. long		Dep.		D. long		Dep.	D. long		Dep.

| 55° | | | | | | | 54° | | | | | |

TRAVERSE TABLE

44°　　　　　　　　　　　　　　　　　　　45°

D. long	Dep.		D. long	Dep.		D. long	Dep.		D. long	Dep.	
Dist.	D. lat	Dep.	Dist.	D. lat	Dep.	Dist.	D. lat	Dep.	Dist.	D. lat	Dep.
1	00·7	00·7	51	36·7	35·4	1	00·7	00·7	51	36·1	36·1
2	01·4	01·4	52	36·4	36·1	2	01·4	01·4	52	36·8	36·8
3	02·2	02·1	53	38·1	36·8	3	02·1	02·1	53	37·5	37·5
4	02·9	02·8	54	38·8	37·5	4	02·8	02·8	54	38·2	38·2
5	03·6	03·5	55	39·6	38·2	5	03·5	03·5	55	38·9	38·9
6	04·3	04·2	56	40·3	38·9	6	04·2	04·2	56	39·6	39·6
7	05·0	04·9	57	41·0	39·6	7	04·9	04·9	57	40·3	40·3
8	05·8	05·6	58	41·7	40·3	8	05·7	05·7	58	41·0	41·0
9	06·5	06·3	59	42·4	41·0	9	06·4	06·4	59	41·7	41·7
10	07·2	06·9	60	43·2	41·7	10	07·1	07·1	60	42·4	42·4
11	07·9	07·6	61	43·9	42·4	11	07·8	07·8	61	43·1	43·1
12	08·6	08·3	62	44·6	43·1	12	08·5	08·5	62	43·8	43·8
13	09·4	09·0	63	45·3	43·8	13	09·2	09·2	63	44·5	44·5
14	10·1	09·7	64	46·0	44·5	14	09·9	09·9	64	45·3	45·3
15	10·8	10·4	65	46·8	45·2	15	10·6	10·6	65	46·0	46·0
16	11·5	11·1	66	47·5	45·8	16	11·3	11·3	66	46·7	46·7
17	12·2	11·8	67	48·2	46·5	17	12·0	12·0	67	46·4	47·4
18	12·9	12·5	68	48·9	47·2	18	12·7	12·7	68	48·1	48·1
19	13·7	13·2	69	49·6	47·9	19	13·4	13·4	69	48·8	48·8
20	14·4	13·9	70	50·4	48·6	20	14·1	14·1	70	49·5	49·5
21	15·1	14·6	71	51·1	49·3	21	14·8	14·8	71	50·2	50·2
22	15·8	15·3	72	51·8	50·0	22	15·6	15·6	72	50·9	50·9
23	16·5	16·0	73	52·5	50·7	23	16·3	16·3	73	51·6	51·6
24	17·3	16·7	74	53·2	51·4	24	17·0	17·0	74	52·3	52·3
25	18·0	17·4	75	54·0	52·1	25	17·7	17·7	75	53·0	53·0
26	18·7	18·1	76	54·7	52·8	26	18·4	18·4	76	53·7	53·7
27	19·4	18·8	77	55·4	53·5	27	19·1	19·1	77	54·4	54·4
28	20·1	19·5	78	56·1	54·2	28	19·8	19·6	78	55·2	55·2
29	20·9	20·1	79	56·8	54·9	29	20·5	20·5	79	55·9	55·9
30	21·6	20·8	80	57·5	55·6	30	21·2	21·2	80	56·6	56·6
31	22·3	21·5	81	58·3	56·3	31	21·9	21·9	81	57·3	57·3
32	23·0	22·2	82	59·0	57·0	32	22·6	22·6	82	58·0	58·0
33	23·7	22·9	83	59·7	57·7	33	23·3	23·3	83	58·7	58·7
34	24·5	23·6	84	60·4	58·4	34	24·0	24·0	84	59·4	59·4
35	25·2	24·3	85	61·1	59·0	35	24·7	24·7	85	60·1	60·1
36	25·9	25·0	86	61·9	59·7	36	25·6	25·6	86	60·8	60·8
37	26·6	25·7	87	62·6	60·4	37	26·2	26·2	87	61·5	61·5
38	27·3	26·4	88	63·3	61·1	38	26·9	26·9	88	62·2	62·2
39	28·1	27·1	89	64·0	61·8	39	27·6	27·6	89	62·9	62·9
40	28·8	27·8	90	64·7	62·5	40	28·3	28·3	90	63·6	63·6
41	29·5	28·5	91	65·5	63·2	41	29·0	29·0	91	64·3	64·3
42	30·2	29·2	92	66·2	63·9	42	29·7	29·7	92	65·1	65·1
43	30·9	29·9	93	66·9	64·6	43	30·4	30·4	93	65·8	65·8
44	31·7	30·6	94	67·6	65·3	44	31·1	31·1	94	66·5	66·5
45	32·4	31·3	95	68·3	66·0	45	31·8	31·8	95	67·2	67·2
46	33·1	32·0	96	69·1	66·7	46	32·5	32·5	96	67·9	67·9
47	33·8	32·6	97	69·8	67·4	47	33·2	33·2	97	68·6	68·6
48	34·5	33·3	98	70·5	68·1	48	33·9	33·9	98	69·3	69·3
49	35·2	34·0	99	71·2	68·8	49	34·6	34·6	99	70·0	70·0
50	36·0	34·7	100	71·9	69·5	50	35·4	35·4	100	70·7	70·7
Dist.	Dep.	D. lat	Dist.	Dep.	D. lat	Dist.	Dep.	D. lat	Dist.	Dep.	D. lat
D. long		Dep.	D. long		Dep.	D. long		Dep.	D. long		Dep.

46°　　　　　　　　　　　　　　　　　　　45°

MERIDIONAL PARTS FOR THE TERRESTRIAL SPHEROID

Lat.	0′	10′	20′	30′	40′	50′	1′	2′	3′	4′	5′	6′	7′	8′	9′
0°	0·00	9·93	19·86	29·80	39·73	49·66	0·99	1·99	2·98	3·97	4·97	5·96	6·95	7·95	8·94
1°	59·60	69·53	79·46	89·40	99·33	109·3	0·99	1·99	2·98	3·97	4·97	5·96	6·95	7·94	8·94
2°	119·2	129·2	139·1	149·0	159·0	168·9	1·0	2·0	3·0	4·0	5·0	6·0	7·0	8·0	9·0
3°	178·9	188·8	198·8	208·7	218·7	228·6	1·0	2·0	3·0	4·0	5·0	6·0	7·0	8·0	9·0
4°	238·6	248·5	258·5	268·4	278·4	288·4	1·0	2·0	3·0	4·0	5·0	6·0	7·0	8·0	9·0
5°	298·3	308·3	318·3	328·3	338·3	348·2	1·0	2·0	3·0	4·0	5·0	6·0	7·0	8·0	9·0
6°	358·2	368·2	378·2	388·2	398·2	408·2	1·0	2·0	3·0	4·0	5·0	6·0	7·0	8·0	9·0
7°	418·2	428·2	438·2	448·2	458·3	468·3	1·0	2·0	3·0	4·0	5·0	6·0	7·0	8·0	9·0
8°	478·3	488·3	498·4	508·4	518·5	528·5	1·0	2·0	3·0	4·0	5·0	6·0	7·1	8·1	9·1
9°	538·6	548·6	558·7	568·7	578·8	588·9	1·0	2·0	3·0	4·0	5·1	6·1	7·1	8·1	9·1
10°	599·0	609·1	619·2	629·3	639·4	649·5	1·0	2·0	3·0	4·0	5·1	6·1	7·1	8·1	9·1
11°	659·6	669·8	679·9	690·0	700·2	710·3	1·0	2·0	3·0	4·0	5·1	6·1	7·1	8·1	9·2
12°	720·5	730·6	740·8	751·0	761·1	771·3	1·0	2·0	3·1	4·1	5·1	6·1	7·2	8·2	9·2
13°	781·5	791·7	801·9	812·1	822·4	832·6	1·0	2·1	3·1	4·1	5·1	6·2	7·2	8·2	9·2
14°	842·8	853·1	863·3	873·6	883·9	894·1	1·0	2·1	3·1	4·1	5·2	6·2	7·2	8·2	9·3
15°	904·4	914·7	925·0	935·3	945·6	955·9	1·0	2·1	3·1	4·1	5·2	6·2	7·3	8·3	9·3
16°	966·3	976·6	987·0	997·3	1007·7	1018·1	1·0	2·1	3·1	4·1	5·2	6·3	7·3	8·3	9·3
17°	1028·5	1038·9	1049·3	1059·7	1070·1	1080·5	1·0	2·1	3·1	4·2	5·2	6·3	7·3	8·3	9·3
18°	1091·0	1101·4	1111·9	1122·4	1132·9	1143·4	1·0	2·1	3·2	4·2	5·3	6·3	7·4	8·4	9·5
19°	1153·9	1164·4	1174·9	1185·5	1196·0	1206·6	1·1	2·1	3·2	4·2	5·3	6·4	7·4	8·5	9·6
20°	1217·1	1227·7	1238·3	1248·9	1259·5	1270·2	1·1	2·1	3·2	4·2	5·3	6·4	7·5	8·5	9·6
21°	1280·8	1291·5	1302·1	1312·8	1323·5	1334·2	1·1	2·2	3·2	4·3	5·4	6·5	7·5	8·6	9·7
22°	1344·9	1355·7	1366·4	1377·1	1387·9	1398·7	1·1	2·2	3·3	4·3	5·4	6·5	7·6	8·7	9·8
23°	1409·5	1420·3	1431·1	1442·0	1452·8	1463·7	1·1	2·2	3·3	4·3	5·5	6·6	7·7	8·7	9·8
24°	1474·5	1485·4	1496·3	1507·3	1518·2	1529·1	1·1	2·2	3·3	4·4	5·5	6·6	7·7	8·8	9·9
25°	1540·1	1551·1	1562·1	1573·1	1584·1	1595·2	1·1	2·2	3·3	4·4	5·6	6·7	7·8	8·9	10·0
26°	1606·2	1617·3	1628·4	1639·5	1650·6	1661·7	1·1	2·2	3·4	4·5	5·6	6·7	7·9	9·0	10·1
27°	1672·9	1684·1	1695·3	1706·5	1717·7	1728·9	1·1	2·3	3·4	4·5	5·7	6·8	7·9	9·1	10·2
28°	1740·2	1751·5	1762·7	1774·1	1785·4	1796·7	1·1	2·3	3·4	4·6	5·7	6·9	8·0	9·1	10·3
29°	1808·1	1819·5	1830·9	1842·3	1853·7	1865·2									

MERIDIONAL PARTS FOR THE TERRESTRIAL SPHEROID

9'	8'	7'	6'	5'	4'	3'	2'	1'	50'	40'	30'	20'	10'	0'	Lat.
10.4	9.2	8.1	6.9	5.8	4.6	3.5	2.3	1.2	1934.4	1922.8	1911.2	1899.7	1888.2	1876.7	30°
10.5	9.3	8.2	7.0	5.8	4.7	3.5	2.3	1.2	2004.3	1992.6	1980.9	1969.2	1957.6	1946.0	31°
10.6	9.4	8.3	7.1	5.9	4.7	3.6	2.4	1.2	2074.9	2063.1	2051.3	2039.5	2027.7	2016.0	32°
10.7	9.6	8.4	7.2	6.0	4.8	3.6	2.4	1.2	2146.4	2134.4	2122.5	2110.6	2098.7	2086.8	33°
10.9	9.7	8.5	7.3	6.1	4.8	3.6	2.4	1.2	2218.7	2206.6	2194.5	2182.5	2170.4	2158.4	34°
11.0	9.8	8.5	7.3	6.1	4.9	3.7	2.4	1.2	2291.9	2279.7	2267.4	2255.2	2243.0	2230.9	35°
11.2	9.9	8.7	7.4	6.2	5.0	3.7	2.5	1.2	2366.1	2353.7	2341.3	2328.9	2316.6	2304.2	36°
11.3	10.0	8.8	7.5	6.3	5.0	3.8	2.5	1.3	2441.2	2428.6	2416.1	2403.5	2391.0	2378.5	37°
11.5	10.2	8.9	7.6	6.4	5.1	3.8	2.5	1.3	2517.4	2504.6	2491.9	2479.2	2466.5	2453.9	38°
11.6	10.3	9.0	7.7	6.5	5.2	3.9	2.6	1.3	2594.7	2581.7	2568.8	2555.9	2543.0	2530.2	39°
11.8	10.5	9.2	7.9	6.6	5.2	3.9	2.6	1.3	2673.1	2659.9	2646.8	2633.7	2620.7	2607.6	40°
12.0	10.6	9.3	8.0	6.7	5.3	4.0	2.7	1.3	2752.7	2739.3	2726.0	2712.7	2699.5	2686.2	41°
12.2	10.8	9.5	8.1	6.8	5.4	4.1	2.7	1.4	2833.5	2820.0	2806.4	2792.9	2779.5	2766.1	42°
12.3	11.0	9.6	8.2	6.9	5.5	4.1	2.7	1.4	2915.7	2901.9	2888.2	2874.5	2860.8	2847.1	43°
12.6	11.2	9.8	8.4	7.0	5.6	4.2	2.8	1.4	2999.3	2985.3	2971.3	2957.3	2943.4	2929.6	44°
12.8	11.4	9.9	8.5	7.1	5.7	4.3	2.8	1.4	3084.4	3070.1	3055.9	3041.7	3027.5	3013.4	45°
13.0	11.6	10.1	8.7	7.2	5.8	4.3	2.9	1.4	3171.0	3156.5	3141.9	3127.5	3113.1	3098.7	46°
13.3	11.8	10.3	8.9	7.3	5.9	4.4	3.0	1.5	3259.3	3244.4	3229.6	3214.9	3200.2	3185.6	47°
13.5	12.0	10.5	9.0	7.5	6.0	4.5	3.0	1.5	3349.2	3334.1	3319.0	3304.0	3289.1	3274.1	48°
13.8	12.3	10.7	9.2	7.7	6.1	4.6	3.1	1.5	3441.1	3425.6	3410.2	3394.9	3379.6	3364.4	49°
14.0	12.6	11.0	9.4	7.9	6.3	4.7	3.1	1.6	3534.8	3519.0	3503.3	3487.7	3472.1	3456.5	50°
14.1	12.8	11.2	9.6	8.0	6.4	4.8	3.2	1.6	3630.6	3614.5	3598.4	3582.4	3566.5	3550.6	51°
14.0	13.1	11.5	9.8	8.2	6.6	4.9	3.3	1.6	3728.5	3712.0	3695.6	3679.3	3663.0	3647.7	52°
15.0	13.4	11.8	10.1	8.4	6.7	5.0	3.4	1.7	3828.8	3811.9	3795.1	3778.3	3761.7	3745.1	53°
15.0	13.8	12.0	10.3	8.6	6.9	5.2	3.4	1.7	3931.4	3914.1	3896.9	3879.8	3862.7	3845.7	54°
15.0	14.1	12.3	10.6	8.8	7.0	5.3	3.5	1.8	4036.7	4019.0	4001.3	3983.7	3966.2	3948.8	55°
16.0	14.5	12.7	10.8	9.0	7.2	5.4	3.6	1.8	4144.7	4126.5	4108.4	4090.3	4072.4	4054.5	56°
16.0	14.9	13.0	11.1	9.3	7.4	5.6	3.7	1.9	4255.6	4236.9	4218.3	4199.8	4181.3	4163.0	57°
17.0	15.3	13.4	11.5	9.5	7.6	5.7	3.8	1.9	4369.7	4350.5	4331.3	4312.3	4293.3	4274.4	58°
17.0	15.8	13.8	11.8	9.8	7.9	5.9	3.9	2.0	4487.2	4467.4	4447.6	4428.0	4408.5	4389.1	59°
18.0	16.2	14.2	12.2	10.1	8.1	6.1	4.1	2.0	4608.2	4587.8	4567.4	4547.2	4527.1	4507.1	60°

MEAN LATITUDE TO MIDDLE LATITUDE

SUBTRACT / ADD

DIFFERENCE OF LATITUDE

Mean Lat.	20°	19°	18°	17°	16°	15°	14°	13°	12°	11°	10°	9°	8°	7°	6°	5°	4°	3°	2°	Mean Lat.
14	9	16	24	31	38	45	51	57	62	67	72	76	80	83	86	89	90	92	93	14
15	6	13	21	27	34	40	46	51	56	61	65	69	73	76	79	81	83	84	85	15
16	4	10	17	24	30	36	41	46	51	56	60	63	66	70	72	74	76	77	79	16
17	2	8	15	21	27	32	37	42	47	51	55	58	61	64	66	68	70	71	72	17
18	1	6	12	18	24	29	34	38	43	46	50	53	56	59	61	63	65	66	67	18
19	3	3	9	15	21	25	30	35	39	43	46	49	52	55	57	59	60	61	62	19
20	5	1	7	13	18	22	27	31	35	39	42	45	48	51	53	54	56	57	58	20
22	9	3	3	8	13	17	22	25	29	33	36	39	41	44	45	47	48	49	50	22
24	12	6	1	4	8	13	17	21	24	28	31	33	36	38	40	41	42	43	44	24
26	15	10	5	0	5	9	13	16	20	23	26	28	31	33	35	36	37	38	39	26
28	18	13	8	3	1	5	9	12	16	19	22	24	26	28	30	31	32	33	34	28
30	21	16	11	6	2	2	6	9	12	15	18	20	22	24	26	28	29	29	30	30
35	28	23	18	14	10	6	2	1	5	7	10	12	15	17	18	19	21	21	22	35
40	34	29	25	20	16	12	8	5	2	1	4	6	8	10	12	13	14	15	16	40
45	41	36	31	27	22	18	14	11	7	4	1	1	3	5	7	8	10	11	11	45
50	49	44	38	33	28	24	20	16	12	9	6	3	1	1	3	5	6	7	8	50
55	58	52	46	40	35	30	25	21	17	14	10	7	5	2	0	2	3	4	5	55
60	69	62	55	49	43	37	32	27	22	18	14	11	8	5	3	1	1	2	3	60
	20°	19°	18°	17°	16°	15°	14°	13°	12°	11°	10°	9°	8°	7°	6°	5°	4°	3°	2°	

ABRIDGED NAUTICAL TABLES

MEAN REFRACTION
Barometer 29·6 in. Thermometer (Fahr.) 50°

App. Alt.	Refr.	App. Alt.	Refr.	App. Alt.	Refr.	App. Alt.	Refr.
° ′	′	° ′	′	° ′	′	° ′	′
0 00	33·00	4 00	11·85	16 00	3·28	42 00	1·05
0 15	30·58	5 00	9·90	18 00	2·90	46 00	0·92
0 30	28·38	6 00	8·47	20 00	2·58	50 00	0·80
0 45	26·33	7 00	7·33	22 00	2·33	55 00	0·67
1 00	24·48	8 00	6·48	24 00	2·13	60 00	0·55
1 30	21·25	9 00	5·80	26 00	1·93	65 00	0·43
2 00	18·58	10 00	5·25	28 00	1·78	70 00	0·35
2 30	16·40	11 00	4·78	30 00	1·63	75 00	0·25
3 00	14·60	12 00	4·38	34 00	1·40	80 00	0·17
3 30	13·10	14 00	3·75	38 00	1·22	90 00	0·00

DIP OF THE SEA HORIZON
Subtractive

H.E.	Dip	H.E.	Dip	H.E.	Dip	H.E.	Dip
Feet	′	Feet	′	Feet	′	Feet	′
1	0·98	19	4·27	37	5·96	54	7.20
2	1·39	20	4·38	38	6·04	55	7·27
3	1·70	21	4·49	39	6·12	56	7·33
4	1·96	22	4·60	40	6·20	57	7·40
5	2·19	23	4·70	41	6·28	58	7·46
6	2·40	24	4·80	42	6·35	59	7·53
7	2·59	25	4·90	43	6·43	60	7·59
8	2·77	26	5·00	44	6·50	61	7·65
9	2·94	27	5·09	45	6·57	62	7·72
10	3·10	28	5·19	46	6·65	63	7·78
11	3·25	29	5·28	47	6·72	64	7.84
12	3·40	30	5·37	48	6·79	65	7·90
13	3·53	31	5·46	49	6·86	66	7·96
14	3·67	32	5·54	50	6·93	67	8·02
15	3·80	33	5·63	51	7·00	68	8·08
16	3·92	34	5·71	52	7·08	69	8·14
17	4·04	35	5·80	53	7·14	70	8·20
18	4·16	36	5·88				

Sun's Parallax in Altitude Additive				Sun's Semi-diameter on the 1st Day of Each Month			
Alt.	Parlx.	Alt.	Parlx.	Month	S.D.	Month	S.D.
°	′	°	′		′		′
0	0·15	45	0·11	Jan.	16·29	July	15·76
5	0·15	50	0·10	Feb.	16·26	Aug.	15·78
10	0·15	55	0·09	Mar.	16·16	Sept.	15·88
15	0·14	60	0·08	April	16·03	Oct.	16·01
20	0·14	65	0·06	May	15·89	Nov.	16·14
25	0·14	70	0·05	June	15·78	Dec.	16·25
30	0·13	75	0·04				
35	0·12	80	0·03				
40	0·12	85	0·01				

NATURAL HAVERSINES

	0′	10′	20′	30′	40′	50′	1′	2′	3′	4′	5′	6′	7′	8′	9′
0°	·0000	·0000	·0000	·0000	·0000	·0001	0	0	0	0	0	0	0	0	0
1	·0001	·0001	·0001	·0002	·0002	·0003	0	0	0	0	0	0	0	0	0
2	·0003	·0004	·0004	·0005	·0005	·0006	0	0	0	0	0	0	0	0	0
3	·0007	·0008	·0009	·0009	·0010	·0011	0	0	0	0	0	0	0	1	1
4	·0012	·0013	·0014	·0015	·0017	·0018	0	0	0	0	0	0	1	1	1
5	·0019	·0020	·0022	·0023	·0024	·0026	0	0	0	0	1	1	1	1	1
6	·0027	·0029	·0030	·0032	·0034	·0036	0	0	0	1	1	1	1	1	1
7	·0037	·0039	·0041	·0043	·0045	·0047	0	0	1	1	1	1	1	1	2
8	·0049	·0051	·0053	·0055	·0057	·0059	0	0	1	1	1	1	1	2	2
9	·0062	·0064	·0066	·0069	·0071	·0074	0	0	1	1	1	1	1	2	2
10	·0076	·0079	·0081	·0084	·0086	·0089	0	0	1	1	1	1	2	2	2
11	·0092	·0095	·0098	·0100	·0103	·0106	0	1	1	1	1	2	2	2	2
12	·0109	·0112	·0115	·0118	·0121	·0125	0	1	1	1	1	2	2	2	3
13	·0128	·0131	·0135	·0138	·0142	·0145	0	1	1	1	2	2	2	3	3
14	·0149	·0152	·0156	·0159	·0163	·0167	0	1	1	1	2	2	2	3	3
15	·0170	·0174	·0178	·0182	·0186	·0190	0	1	1	1	2	2	2	3	3
16	·0194	·0198	·0202	·0206	·0210	·0214	0	1	1	2	2	2	3	3	4
17	·0219	·0223	·0227	·0231	·0236	·0240	0	1	1	2	2	2	3	3	4
18	·0245	·0249	·0254	·0258	·0263	·0268	0	1	1	2	2	2	3	3	4
19	·0272	·0277	·0282	·0287	·0292	·0297	0	1	1	2	2	3	3	4	4
20	·0302	·0307	·0312	·0317	·0322	·0327	1	1	2	2	3	3	3	4	5
21	·0332	·0337	·0343	·0348	·0353	·0359	1	1	2	2	3	3	4	4	5
22	·0364	·0370	·0375	·0381	·0386	·0392	1	1	2	2	3	3	4	4	5
23	·0398	·0403	·0409	·0415	·0421	·0426	1	1	2	2	3	3	4	4	5
24	·0432	·0438	·0444	·0450	·0456	·0462	1	1	2	2	3	3	4	4	5
25	·0469	·0475	·0481	·0487	·0493	·0500	1	1	2	2	3	3	4	5	6
26	·0506	·0512	·0519	·0525	·0532	·0538	1	1	2	2	3	3	4	5	6
27	·0545	·0552	·0558	·0565	·0572	·0579	1	1	2	3	3	4	5	5	6
28	·0585	·0592	·0599	·0606	·0613	·0620	1	1	2	3	3	4	5	5	6
29	·0627	·0634	·0641	·0648	·0655	·0663	1	1	2	3	4	4	5	6	6
30	·0670	·0677	·0685	·0692	·0699	·0707	1	1	2	3	4	4	5	6	6
31	·0714	·0722	·0729	·0737	·0744	·0752	1	1	2	3	4	4	5	6	6
32	·0760	·0768	·0775	·0783	·0791	·0799	1	2	2	3	4	5	5	6	7
33	·0807	·0815	·0823	·0831	·0839	·0847	1	2	2	3	4	5	5	6	7
34	·0855	·0863	·0871	·0879	·0888	·0896	1	2	2	3	4	5	6	6	7
35	·0904	·0913	·0921	·0929	·0938	·0946	1	2	2	3	4	5	6	7	7
36	·0955	·0964	·0972	·0981	·0989	·0998	1	2	3	3	4	5	6	7	8
37	·1007	·1016	·1024	·1033	·1042	·1051	1	2	3	3	4	5	6	7	8
38	·1060	·1069	·1078	·1087	·1096	·1105	1	2	3	4	4	5	6	7	8
39	·1114	·1123	·1133	·1142	·1151	·1160	1	2	3	4	5	5	6	7	8
40	·1170	·1179	·1189	·1198	·1207	·1217	1	2	3	4	5	6	7	7	8
41	·1227	·1236	·1246	·1255	·1265	·1275	1	2	3	4	5	6	7	8	9
42	·1284	·1294	·1304	·1314	·1324	·1333	1	2	3	4	5	6	7	8	9
43	·1343	·1353	·1363	·1373	·1383	·1393	1	2	3	4	5	6	7	8	9
44	·1403	·1413	·1424	·1434	·1444	·1454	1	2	3	4	5	6	7	8	9
45	·1465	·1475	·1485	·1496	·1506	·1516	1	2	3	4	5	6	7	8	9
	0′	10′	20′	30′	40′	50′	1′	2′	3′	4′	5′	6′	7′	8′	9′

NATURAL HAVERSINES

	0′	10′	20′	30′	40′	50′	1′	2′	3′	4′	5′	6′	7′	8′	9′
46°	·1527	·1537	·1548	·1558	·1569	·1579	1	2	3	4	5	6	7	8	9
47	·1590	·1601	·1611	·1622	·1633	·1644	1	2	3	4	5	6	7	8	10
48	·1654	·1665	·1676	·1689	·1698	·1709	1	2	3	4	6	7	8	9	10
49	·1720	·1731	·1742	·1753	·1764	·1775	1	2	3	4	6	7	8	9	10
50	·1786	·1797	·1808	·1820	·1831	·1842	1	2	3	4	6	7	8	9	10
51	·1853	·1865	·1876	·1887	·1899	·1910	1	2	3	4	6	7	8	9	10
52	·1922	·1933	·1945	·1956	·1968	·1979	1	2	3	5	6	7	8	9	10
53	·1991	·2003	·2014	·2026	·2038	·2049	1	2	3	5	6	7	8	9	11
54	·2061	·2073	·2085	·2097	·2108	·2120	1	2	4	5	6	7	8	9	11
55	·2132	·2144	·2156	·2168	·2180	·2192	1	2	4	5	6	7	8	10	11
56	·2204	·2216	·2228	·2240	·2253	·2265	1	2	4	5	6	7	9	10	11
57	·2277	·2289	·2301	·2314	·2326	·2338	1	2	4	5	6	7	9	10	11
58	·2350	·2363	·2375	·2388	·2400	·2412	1	3	4	5	6	8	9	10	11
59	·2425	·2437	·2450	·2462	·2475	·2487	1	3	4	5	6	8	9	10	11
60	·2500	·2513	·2525	·2538	·2551	·2563	1	3	4	5	6	8	9	10	11
61	·2576	·2589	·2601	·2614	·2627	·2640	1	3	4	5	6	8	9	10	12
62	·2653	·2666	·2678	·2691	·2704	·2717	1	3	4	5	6	8	9	10	12
63	·2730	·2743	·2756	·2769	·2782	·2795	1	3	4	5	6	8	9	10	12
64	·2808	·2821	·2834	·2847	·2860	·2874	1	3	4	5	7	8	9	10	12
65	·2887	·2900	·2913	·2936	·2940	·2953	1	3	4	5	7	8	9	10	12
66	·2966	·2980	·2993	·3006	·3020	·3033	1	3	4	5	7	8	9	11	12
67	·3046	·3060	·3073	·3087	·3100	·3114	1	3	4	5	7	8	9	11	12
68	·3127	·3140	·3154	·3168	·3181	·3195	1	3	4	5	7	8	9	11	12
69	·3208	·3222	·3235	·3249	·3263	·3276	1	3	4	5	7	8	10	11	12
70	·3290	·3304	·3317	·3331	·3348	·3358	1	3	4	5	7	8	10	11	12
71	·3372	·3386	·3400	·3414	·3427	·3441	1	3	4	5	7	8	10	11	12
72	·3455	·3469	·3483	·3497	·3510	·3524	1	3	4	5	7	8	10	11	12
73	·3538	·3552	·3566	·3580	·3594	·3608	1	3	4	6	7	8	10	11	12
74	·3622	·3636	·3650	·3664	·3678	·3692	1	3	4	6	7	8	10	11	13
75	·3706	·3720	·3734	·3748	·3762	·3776	1	3	4	6	7	8	10	11	13
76	·3790	·3805	·3819	·3833	·3847	·3861	1	3	4	6	7	8	10	11	13
77	·3875	·3889	·3904	·3918	·3932	·3946	1	3	4	6	7	8	10	11	13
78	·3960	·3975	·3989	·4003	·4017	·4032	1	3	4	6	7	9	10	11	13
79	·4046	·4060	·4075	·4089	·4103	·4117	1	3	4	6	7	9	10	11	13
80	·4132	·4146	·4160	·4175	·4189	·4204	1	3	4	6	7	9	10	11	13
81	·4218	·4232	·4247	·4261	·4275	·4290	1	3	4	6	7	9	10	11	13
82	·4304	·4319	·4334	·4347	·4362	·4376	1	3	4	6	7	9	10	12	13
83	·4391	·4405	·4420	·4434	·4448	·4463	1	3	4	6	7	9	10	12	13
84	·4477	·4492	·4506	·4521	·4535	·4550	1	3	4	6	7	9	10	12	13
85	·4564	·4579	·4593	·4608	·4622	·4637	1	3	4	6	7	9	10	12	13
86	·4651	·4666	·4680	·4695	·4709	·4724	1	3	4	6	7	9	10	12	13
87	·4738	·4753	·4767	·4782	·4796	·4811	1	3	4	6	7	9	10	12	13
88	·4826	·4840	·4855	·4869	·4884	·4898	1	3	4	6	7	9	10	12	13
89	·4913	·4927	·4942	·4956	·4971	·4986	1	3	4	6	7	9	10	12	13
90	·5000	·5015	·5029	·5044	·5058	·5073	1	3	4	6	7	9	10	12	13
	0′	10′	20′	30′	40′	50′	1′	2′	3′	4′	5′	6′	7′	8′	9′

NATURAL HAVERSINES

	0′	10′	20′	30′	40′	50′	1′	2′	3′	4′	5′	6′	7′	8′	9′
91°	·5087	·5102	·5116	·5131	·5145	·5160	1	3	4	6	7	9	10	12	13
92	·5175	·5189	·5204	·5218	·5233	·5247	1	3	4	6	7	9	10	12	13
93	·5262	·5276	·5291	·5305	·5320	·5334	1	3	4	6	7	9	10	12	13
94	·5349	·5363	·5378	·5392	·5407	·5421	1	3	4	6	7	9	10	12	13
95	·5436	·5450	·5465	·5479	·5494	·5508	1	3	4	6	7	9	10	12	13
96	·5523	·5537	·5520	·5566	·5580	·5595	1	3	4	6	7	9	10	11	13
97	·5609	·5624	·5638	·5653	·5667	·5682	1	3	4	6	7	9	10	11	13
98	·5696	·5710	·5725	·5739	·5753	·5768	1	3	4	6	7	9	10	11	13
99	·5782	·5797	·5811	·5825	·5840	·5854	1	3	4	6	7	9	10	11	13
100	·5868	·5883	·5897	·5911	·5926	·5940	1	3	4	6	7	9	10	11	13
101	·5954	·5968	·5983	·5997	·6011	·6025	1	3	4	6	7	9	10	11	13
102	·6040	·6054	·6068	·6082	·6096	·6111	1	3	4	6	7	8	10	11	13
103	·6125	·6139	·6153	·6167	·6181	·6196	1	3	4	6	7	8	10	11	13
104	·6210	·6224	·6238	·6252	·6266	·6280	1	3	4	6	7	8	10	11	13
105	·6294	·6308	·6322	·6336	·6350	·6364	1	3	4	6	7	8	10	11	13
106	·6378	·6392	·6406	·6420	·6434	·6448	1	3	4	6	7	8	10	11	13
107	·6462	·6476	·6490	·6504	·6517	·6531	1	3	4	6	7	8	10	11	12
108	·6545	·6559	·6573	·6587	·6600	·6614	1	3	4	6	7	8	10	11	12
109	·6628	·6642	·6655	·6669	·6683	·6696	1	3	4	5	7	8	10	11	12
110	·6710	·6724	·6737	·6751	·6765	·6778	1	3	4	5	7	8	10	11	12
111	·6792	·6805	·6819	·6833	·6846	·6860	1	3	4	5	7	8	9	11	12
112	·6873	·6887	·6900	·6913	·6927	·6940	1	3	4	5	7	8	9	11	12
113	·6954	·6969	·6980	·6994	·7007	·7020	1	3	4	5	7	8	9	11	12
114	·7034	·7047	·7060	·7074	·7087	·7100	1	3	4	5	7	8	9	11	12
115	·7113	·7126	·7140	·7153	·7166	·7179	1	3	4	5	7	8	9	11	12
116	·7192	·7205	·7218	·7231	·7244	·7257	1	3	4	5	7	8	9	10	12
117	·7270	·7283	·7296	·7309	·7322	·7335	1	3	4	5	6	8	9	10	12
118	·7347	·7360	·7373	·7386	·7399	·7411	1	3	4	5	6	8	9	10	12
119	·7424	·7437	·7449	·7462	·7475	·7487	1	3	4	5	6	8	9	10	11
120	·7500	·7513	·7525	·7538	·7550	·7563	1	3	4	5	6	8	9	10	11
121	·7575	·7588	·7600	·7613	·7625	·7637	1	3	4	5	6	8	9	10	11
122	·7650	·7662	·7674	·7687	·7699	·7711	1	2	4	5	6	7	9	10	11
123	·7723	·7735	·7748	·7760	·7772	·7784	1	2	4	5	6	7	9	10	11
124	·7796	·7808	·7820	·7832	·7844	·7856	1	2	4	5	6	7	8	10	11
125	·7868	·7880	·7892	·7904	·7915	·7927	1	2	4	5	6	7	8	9	11
126	·7939	·7951	·7962	·7974	·7986	·7998	1	2	3	5	6	7	8	9	10
127	·8009	·8021	·8032	·8044	·8055	·8067	1	2	3	5	6	7	8	9	10
128	·8078	·8090	·8101	·8113	·8124	·8135	1	2	3	5	6	7	8	9	10
129	·8147	·8158	·8169	·8180	·8192	·8203	1	2	3	4	6	7	8	9	10
130	·8214	·8225	·8236	·8247	·8258	·8269	1	2	3	4	6	7	8	9	10
131	·8280	·8291	·8302	·8313	·8324	·8335	1	2	3	4	6	7	8	9	10
132	·8346	·8356	·8367	·8378	·8389	·8399	1	2	3	4	5	6	7	9	10
133	·8410	·8421	·8431	·8442	·8452	·8463	1	2	3	4	5	6	7	8	9
134	·8473	·8484	·8494	·8505	·8515	·8525	1	2	3	4	5	6	7	8	9
135	·8536	·8546	·8556	·8566	·8576	·8587	1	2	3	4	5	6	7	8	9
	0′	10′	20′	30′	40′	50′	1′	2′	3′	4′	5′	6′	7′	8′	9′

NATURAL HAVERSINES

	0′	10′	20′	30′	40′	50′	1′	2′	3′	4′	5′	6′	7′	8′	9′
136°	·8597	·8607	·8617	·8627	·8637	·8647	1	2	3	4	5	6	7	8	9
137	·8657	·8667	·8677	·8687	·8696	·8706	1	2	3	4	5	6	7	8	9
138	·8716	·8725	·8735	·8745	·8754	·8764	1	2	3	4	5	6	7	8	9
139	·8774	·8783	·8793	·8802	·8812	·8821	1	2	3	4	5	6	7	7	8
140	·8830	·8840	·8849	·8858	·8867	·8877	1	2	3	4	5	6	7	7	8
141	·8886	·8895	·8904	·8913	·8922	·8931	1	2	3	4	5	5	6	7	8
142	·8940	·8949	·8958	·8967	·8976	·8984	1	2	3	4	4	5	6	7	8
143	·8993	·9002	·9011	·9019	·9028	·9037	1	2	3	3	4	5	6	7	8
144	·9045	·9054	·9062	·9071	·9079	·9087	1	2	3	3	4	5	6	7	8
145	·9096	·9104	·9112	·9121	·9129	·9137	1	2	2	3	4	5	6	7	7
146	·9145	·9153	·9161	·9169	·9177	·9185	1	2	2	3	4	5	6	6	7
147	·9193	·9201	·9209	·9217	·9225	·9233	1	2	2	3	4	5	5	6	7
148	·9240	·9248	·9256	·9263	·9271	·9278	1	2	2	3	4	5	5	6	7
149	·9286	·9293	·9301	·9308	·9316	·9323	1	1	2	3	4	4	5	6	7
150	·9330	·9337	·9345	·9352	·9359	·9366	1	1	2	3	4	4	5	6	6
151	·9373	·9380	·9387	·9394	·9401	·9408	1	1	2	3	4	4	5	6	6
152	·9415	·9422	·9428	·9435	·9442	·9448	1	1	2	3	3	4	5	5	6
153	·9455	·9462	·9468	·9475	·9481	·9488	1	1	2	3	3	4	5	5	6
154	·9494	·9500	·9507	·9513	·9519	·9525	1	1	2	3	3	4	4	5	6
155	·9532	·9538	·9544	·9550	·9556	·9562	1	1	2	2	3	4	4	5	5
156	·9568	·9574	·9580	·9585	·9591	·9597	1	1	2	2	3	3	4	5	5
157	·9603	·9608	·9613	·9619	·9625	·9631	1	1	2	2	3	3	4	4	5
158	·9636	·9641	·9647	·9652	·9657	·9663	1	1	2	2	3	3	4	4	5
159	·9668	·9673	·9678	·9683	·9688	·9694	1	1	2	2	3	3	4	4	5
160	·9699	·9703	·9708	·9713	·9718	·9723	0	1	1	2	2	3	3	4	4
161	·9728	·9732	·9737	·9742	·9746	·9751	0	1	1	2	2	3	3	4	4
162	·9755	·9760	·9764	·9769	·9773	·9777	0	1	1	2	2	3	3	4	4
163	·9782	·9786	·9790	·9794	·9798	·9802	0	1	1	2	2	2	3	3	4
164	·9806	·9810	·9814	·9818	·9822	·9826	0	1	1	2	2	2	3	3	4
165	·9830	·9833	·9837	·9841	·9844	·9848	0	1	1	1	2	2	3	3	3
166	·9852	·9855	·9858	·9862	·9865	·9869	0	1	1	1	2	2	2	3	3
167	·9872	·9875	·9878	·9882	·9885	·9888	0	1	1	1	2	2	2	3	3
168	·9891	·9894	·9897	·9900	·9903	·9905	0	1	1	1	1	2	2	2	3
169	·9908	·9911	·9914	·9916	·9919	·9922	0	1	1	1	1	2	2	2	2
170	·9924	·9927	·9929	·9931	·9934	·9936	0	0	1	1	1	1	2	2	2
171	·9938	·9941	·9943	·9945	·9947	·9949	0	0	1	1	1	1	2	2	2
172	·9951	·9953	·9955	·9957	·9959	·9961	0	0	1	1	1	1	1	2	2
173	·9963	·9965	·9966	·9968	·9970	·9971	0	0	0	1	1	1	1	1	1
174	·9973	·9974	·9976	·9977	·9978	·9980	0	0	0	1	1	1	1	1	1
175	·9981	·9982	·9983	·9985	·9986	·9987	0	0	0	0	1	1	1	1	1
176	·9988	·9989	·9990	·9991	·9992	·9992	0	0	0	0	0	0	1	1	1
177	·9993	·9994	·9995	·9995	·9996	·9996	0	0	0	0	0	0	0	1	1
178	·9997	·9997	·9998	·9998	·9999	·9999	0	0	0	0	0	0	0	0	0
179	·9999	1·0000	1·0000	1·0000	1·0000	1·0000	0	0	0	0	0	0	0	0	0
180	1·0000	1·0000	1·0000	1·0000	1·0000	1·0000	0	0	0	0	0	0	0	0	0
	0′	10′	20′	30′	40′	50′	1′	2′	3′	4′	5′	6′	7′	8′	9′

Answers

EXERCISE I(a)

(1) d.lat 12°36′N d.long 41°39′W
(2) d.lat 29°23′S d.long 50°37′E
(3) d.lat 17°10′N d.long 18°08′W
(4) d.lat 23°41′N d.long 36°45′E
(5) d.lat 25°08′S d.long 44°19′E
(6) d.lat 13°31′N d.long 47°56′W
(7) d.lat 59°34′S d.long 37°58′E.

EXERCISE I(b)

(1) 2407 n. miles
(2) lat 34°56′S
(3) lat 22°39′S
(4) (a) 115·2 st. miles
(b) 86·8 n. miles
(c) 185·3 km
  (d) 161 km
(e) 62·1 st. miles
(f) 54 n. miles
(5) (a) 31·7 ft
(b) 20·6 ft.

EXERCISE II(a)

(1a) (a) 056°15′   (b) 073°07½′   (c) 101°15′   (d) 151°52½′
  (e) 213°45′   (f) 253°07½′   (g) 292°30′   (h) 331°52½′.
(1b) (a) N56°15′E   (b) N73°07½′E   (c) S78°45′E   (d) S28°07½′E
  (e) S33°45′W   (f) S73°07½′W   (g) N67°30′W   (h) N28°07½′W.

(2a) (a) NE × N   (b) E × N½N   (c) SE × E   (d) S½E
  (e) SSW   (f) SW½W   (g) NW × W½W   (h) N × W.
(2b) (a) N33°45′E   (b) N73°07½′E   (c) S56°15′E   (d) S5°37½′E
  (e) S22°30′W   (f) S50°37½′W   (g) N61°52½′W   (h) N11°15′W.

(3a) (a) N × E   (b) E × N½N   (c) E × S   (d) SSE
  (e) SW × S   (f) SW × W½W   (g) NW½W   (h) N½W.
(3b) (a) 011°15′   (b) 073°07½′   (c) 101°15′   (d) 157°30′
  (e) 213°45′   (f) 241°52½′   (g) 309°22½′   (h) 354°22½′.

ANSWERS

Exercise II(b)

(1) (a) 035°M (b) 137°M (c) 219°M (d) 005°M
     (e) 145°M (f) 214°M (g) 298°M (h) 355°M.
(2) (a) 055°C (b) 127°C (c) 231°C (d) 005°C
     (e) 155°C (f) 206°C (g) 298°C (h) 355°C.
(3) (a) 015°T (b) 175°T (c) 238°T (d) 004°T
     (e) 356°T (f) 270°T (g) 302°T (h) 003°T.
(4) (a) 035°M (b) 155°M (c) 252°M (d) 004°M
     (e) 004°M (f) 250°M (g) 318°M (h) 003°M.
(5) (a) 060°C (b) 137°C (c) 260°C (d) 010°C
     (e) 157°C (f) 354°C.
(6) (a) 030°T. (b) 167°T (c) 234°T (d) 010°T
     (e) 137°T (f) 354°T.

(7) Table A

     (1) dev. 6°E   var. 20°W   (7) 346°C   348°M
     (2) 217°C   var. 5°E   (8) 280°M   275°T
     (3) 284°C   262°T   (9) dev. 3°E   var. 25°W
     (4) dev. 5°W   var. 15°E   (10) 201°C   175°T
     (5) 245°C   230°T   (11) dev. NIL   var. 42°E
     (6) 172°M   var. 12°E   (12) dev. 2°W   var. NIL.

     Table B

     (1) error 20°W   026°T   (4) error 4°E   307°T
     (2) dev. 5°W   error 20°E   (5) 338°C   var. 2°E
     (3) 183°C   var. 5°W   (6) dev. 12°W   error 20°W.

Exercise III(a)

(1) 6°33·1′E   (2) 380·6 miles   (3) 158°09·1′W
(4) 338·9 miles   (5) lat 23°30′N, distance apart 364·1 miles
(6) distance steamed 974 miles, distance apart 199·9 miles
(7) lat 39°10′N, distance steamed 3206 miles
(8) 602·2 kt   (9) lat 00°00′N, long 38°56′W.

Exercise III(b)

(1) (a) course 053°55′, distance 147·6 miles
    (b) course 191°51′, distance 234·1 miles
    (c) course 329°09′, distance 286·5 miles
(2) (a) course 272°20′, distance 6371·5miles
    (b) course 123°23′, distance 1387 miles
    (c) course 261°16′, distance 2501 miles
(3) lat 42°51·1′N, long 32°28·8′E
(4) course 241°44′, distance 2091 miles
(5) distance 1436 miles, long 86°58·5′E
(6) parallels 34°28′ and 30°02′ Nor.S. course 141°03′.
(7) course 099°58′, distance 2797 miles. E.T.A. 11th May at 0100 hr G.M.T.
(8) alteration position lat 46°23′N, long 38°04′W
    2nd course 112°38′, distance 1600 miles
    E.T.A. 17th August at 0200 hr G.M.T.

Exercise III(c)

(1) (a) d.lat 40·3N, dep. 38.9E
    (c) d.lat 86·8S, dep. 31·6E
    (e) d.lat 49·8N, dep. 00·00
    (b) d.lat 2·87N, dep. 16·3W
    (d) d.lat 47·8S, dep. 47·8W
    (f) d.lat 84·1S, dep 15·6W

(2) (a) course 205°, distance 51 miles
    (c) course 144¼°, distance 49·7 miles
    (e) course 315½°, distance 93·2 miles
    (b) course 011°, distance 86·5 miles
    (d) course 305¼°, distance 49·7 miles
    (f) course 260½, distance 99·2 miles

(3) (a) dep. 67·9W   (b) dep. 17·55′E   (c) 37·3′E   (d) dep. 9·0′E

(4) (a) d.long 22·9′E
    (c) d.long 70·5′W
    (b) d.long 31·65′E
    (d) d.long 91·5′E

(5) course 339¾°, distance 40·5 miles

(6) 1st ship: lat 20°32·9′N, long 72°37·6E
    2nd ship: lat 20°43′N, long 73°09·4′E

(7) lighthouse lat 25°23·6′S, long 39°01·5′W

(8) lat 46°07·3′N, long 178°53·9′W.

Exercise III(d)

(1) (a) course 099°, distance 80·6 miles   (b) course 224¾°, distance 85½ miles
    (c) course 064¾°, distance 66·3 miles

(2) course 215¾°, distance 81·4 miles
    lat 35°09′N, long 80°13·7′W

(3) course 339½°, distance 65·5 miles
    lat 20°14·5′N, long 137°53·5′E

(4) course 170½°, distance 88·2 miles
    lat 65°44·8′S, long 179°40·3′W

(5) course 305½°, distance 75·6 miles
    lat 20°44·9′N, long 59°19·8′W

(6) course 045°, distance 86·4 miles
    lat 45°27·2′N, long 120°36·8′E

(7) lat 20°21·2′S, long 19°42·1′W

(8) course 225½°, distance 78·3 miles
    lat 54°22′N, long 15°47·4′W
    bearing 315°, distance 29·7 miles.

Exercise III(e)

(1) (a) course 068°50·5′, distance 1543·2 miles
    (b) course 317°11·6′, distance 1300·3 miles
    (c) course 287°08·2′, distance 1109·5 miles

(2) lat 59°04·3′N, long 35°01′E

(3) lat 31°12·2′N, long 155°26·8′W

(4) lat 21°43·2′N, distance 1565·6 miles

(5) course 085°23·7′, long 106°29·8′E.

Exercise III(f)

(1) initial course 091°20·7′, distance 3126 miles (G.C. sailing)
    course 111°25′, distance 3194 miles (Mercator sailing)

(2) initial course 274°47′, final course 302°48′, distance 3711 miles

(3) initial course 243°36′, final course 224°42′, distance 6746 miles

(4) by great circle sailing lat 15°37·3′S, long 34°17·7′W
    by parallel sailing lat 24°46′S, long 36°39·9′W

(5) lat 51°27·3′N, long 22°57·1′E

(6) by great circle E.T.A. 27th March at 0804 hr
by rhumb line E.T.A. 27th March at 1124 hr.

EXERCISE III(g)

(2) (a) lat 67°58·5′N or S (b) 0·617x
(3) course 236°51′, distance 830·3 miles (mid. lat sailing)
course 236°45′, distance 827·9 miles (plane sailing)
(4) course 086° 51·7′, distance 2247·2 miles (Mercator sailing)
course 086°52′, distance 2247·5 miles (mid. lat sailing)
(5) height 43·837 in., breadth 69·48 in.
(6) parallels 59°43′ and 45°59′
(7) A 13°27·6′N or 25°14·4′S
B 25°14·4′N or 13°27·6′S
(8) distance 14·7 miles
(9) d.long 41·17′, nat. scale 1/319, 100.

EXERCISE IV(a)

(1) lat 45°07·2′N, long 13°43·4′W
(2) lat 54°20·2′S, long 79°50·8′E, distance off 5·4 miles
(3) A 011°, B 079°
(4) lat 35°40·5′N, long 85°23·8′E
(5) lat 44°42·2′S, long 65°32·3′E
(6) lat 64°33·6′N, long 168°02·7′W.

EXERCISE IV(b)

(1) 1st bearing lat 35°10·8′S, long 02°10·6′E
2nd bearing lat 35°04·5′S, long 02°39·8′E
(2) 1st bearing lat 45°26·5′N, long 23°28·8′W
2nd bearing lat 45°53·0′N, long 23°17·5′W
(3) 1st bearing lat 44°33·8′N, long 15°59′W
2nd bearing lat 44°01·7′N, long 16°29·2′W
(4) 1st bearing lat 49°38·5′N, long 06°13·6′W
2nd bearing lat 49°44·5′N, long 05°20·9′W
(5) lat 49°51½′N, long 05°05′W
(6) 1st bearing lat 50°22′N, long 01°07′W
2nd bearing lat 49°46′N, long 04°00′W.

EXERCISE IV(c)

(1) bearing 208°06′
(2) bearing 117°07′ (from ship)
(3) bearing 237°20′
(4) 048°46′.

EXERCISE VI(a)

(1) long 81°E
(2) G.H.A. 221°45′
(3) G.H.A. ♈ 256°
(4) G.H.A. 322°
(5) long 21°E
(6) R.A. 55°.

EXERCISE VI(b)

(1) declination 20°N, G.H.A. 052°
(2) lat 12°18′S, long 47°13′E
(3) lat 36°N, long 89°14′E
(4) G.H.A. 75°, lat 42°N, long 135°W

EXERCISE VII

(1) 17ʰ 52ᵐ 08ˢ G.M.T.
(2) 2140 L.M.T.
(3) 54 min
(4) L.A.T. 1401. G.A.T. 1301.

(5) Eq. T −12 min

(6) Eq. T +11 min

(7) (a) 1208   (b) 1145

(8) G.H.A. sun = 002°30′

(9) Zone + 3. G.M.T. 1500

(10) Zone −8. Zone time 2000 hr

(11) Eq. T +4 min

(12) L.A.T. 1456

(13) April 4th at 1900 standard time. April 4th at 1904 L.M.T.

(14) March 10th at 2300 standard time

(15) March 12th at 0300 standard time

(16) (a) declination 1°33·7′N G.H.A. 12°01·2′
    (b) declination 1°00·2′N G.H.A. 171°39′
    (c) declination 22°39·1′N G.H.A. 82°52·3′
    (d) declination 12°15·3′S G.H.A. 248°58·6′
    (e) declination 23°10·1′S G.H.A. 82°22·2′

(17) (a) 1356 G.M.T. on 19th September   (b) 0833 G.M.T. on 20th September
    (c) 1839 G.M.T. on 7th June   (d) 2346 G.M.T. on 26th October
    (e) 0002 G.M.T. on 1st January 1959

(18) (a) long 53°36½′W   (b) long 34°16′E

(19) G.H.A. sun 341°28′

(20) G.M.T. 17ʰ32ᵐ55ˢ

(21) (a) 3ʰ50ᵐ14ˢ   (b) 2ʰ10ᵐ14ˢ

(22) (a) 15ʰ52ᵐ12ˢ   (b) 21ʰ12ᵐ12ˢ.

EXERCISE VIII

(4) index error 04′30″ "on", May or August

(5) index error 0° 33′ "on", distance off 6·48 miles

(6) (a) 46°30·7′   (b) 37°56·9′   (c) 65°00·6′
    (d) 18°37·5′   (e) 65°13·2′

(7) (a) 53°49·9′   (b) 31°35·5′   (c) 11°26·6′
    (d) 59°07·1′   (e) 26°22·3′.

EXERCISE IX

(1) (a) altitude 36½°, azimuth 259°   (b) altitude 20°, azimuth 072½°
    (c) altitude 18°, azimuth 140°   (d) altitude 26°, azimuth 015°

(2) (a) altitude 9°, L.H.A. 321°   (b) altitude 43°, L.H.A. 332°
    (c) altitude 31°, L.H.A. 64°   (d) altitude 58°, L.H.A. 014°

(3) L.H.A. 289° and 071° G.M.T. 0539 and 1507

(4) azimuth 088°, G.M.T. 0424

(5) L.H.A. 325°, declination 18°N

EXERCISE X(a)

(1) 51°11·4′N	(2) 31°39·5′S	(3) 39°12·7′S
(4) 1°39·2′S	(5) 5°05·6′N	(6) 38°06·6′N
(7) 29°46·8′S	(8) 21°43·9′N	(9) 69°54·5′S
(10) 68°02·1′S	(11) 27°10·9′S	(12) 6°07·2′S
(13) 50°12·6′N	(14) 10°28·8′S	(15) 62°13·3′N
(16) 56°39·1′S	(17) 58°04·7′N	(18) 26°14′N
(19) 39°40·9′N	(20) 26°40·5′N	(21) 45°32′S
(22) 12°15·0′N	(23) 76°48·7′S	(24) 68°57·9′S
(25) 7°07·7′N.		

ANSWERS

(Figures in brackets are those obtained by the use of five-figure Nautical Tables. If the true azimuths have been found by A.B.C. Tables, the errors and deviations obtained should be within 0·25° or 0°15′ of the figures given here.)

	PZ	PX	P	ZX	Z	True azimuth	Error	Deviation
(1)	35°50′	89°17·3′	57°28′W	68°29′ (68°29·3′)	121°32′ (121°33·5′)	238°28′ (238°26·5)	8°28′E	35°28′E
(2)	51°20′	106°25·6′	14°44·2′W	56°47′ (56°48′)	163°10′ (163°02′)	343°10′ (343°02′)	26°50′W	10°30′E
(3)	50°20′	67°20·1′	31°48′E	31°50′ (31°49·4′)	112°44′ (112°44′)	112°44′ (112°45·6′)	22°44′E	7°44′E
(4)	54°45′	98°28·7′	61°19·8′E	72°24′ (72°24′)	114°26′ (114°26′)	114°26′ (114°26′)	15°34′W	6°56′E
(5)	42°50′	66°47·8′	39°56′W	39°48′ (39°49′)	112°55′ (112°53′)	292°55′ (292°53′)	2°55′E	14°35′W
(6)	32°25′	51°15·3′	37°26·9′E	30°40′ (30°39·1′)	111°31′ (111°34′)	111°31′ (111°34′)	8°29′W	—
(7)	42°55′	66°43·2′	74°59′E	63°10′ (63°09·5′)	83°52′ (83°54′)	083°52′ (083°54′)	8°54′E	—
(8)	39°30′	29°49·5′	100°49·2′E	52°24′ (52°24·5′)	38°06′ (38°04′)	141°54′ (141°56′)	6°54′E	—
(9)	42°10′	110°34·8′	30°35·1′E	73°43·5′ (73°42·7′)	150°10′ (150°15′)	029°50′ (029°45′)	10°10′W	—
(10)	56°27′	77°24·6′	84°13·9′E	78°21′ (78°20·3′)	82°34′ (82°31′)	082°34′ (082°31′)	7°31′E	—

	True amplitude	True bearing	Error	Deviation
(11)	E26°46·5′S (26°49·5′)	116°49′	6°49′E	19°09′E
(12)	E37°44′N (37°45′)	052°16′	12°44′W	22°44′W
(13)	W14°28′S (14°28·5′)	255°32′	15°32′E	21°12′E
(14)	E22°17·9′S	112°17·9′S	2°17·9′E	17°17·9′E
(15)	00°00′	270°00′	10°00′W	2°40′W

245

Exercise X(c)

(The figures given in brackets are those obtained by the use of five-figure Nautical Tables. The azimuths and position lines are given to the nearest whole degree.)

	PZ	PX	P	TZD	CZD	Int.	Azimuth	P. Line
(1)	43°30'	68°22·3'	57°44·6'(W)	52°25·9'	52°29' (52°29·5')	3·1 towards (3·6 towards)	278°	008°/188°
(2)	69°18'	93°55·7'	30°31·7'(E)	38°38·5'	38°46' (38°46·3')	7·5 towards (7·8 towards)	054°	324°/144°
(3)	42°20'	87°47·8'	44°31·3'(E)	59°30·7'	59°27' (59°27·2')	3·7 away (3·5 away)	126°	216°/036°
(4)	43°10'	112°20·3'	34°31·1'(E)	75°47·8'	75°52' (75°52')	4·2 towards (4·2 towards)	147°	057°/237°
(5)	41°28'	77°24·4'	48°41·5'(W)	54°03·7'	53°50' (53°50·7')	13·7 away (13·0 away)	245°	335°/155°
(6)	43°16·7'	112°19·1'	17°53·4'(W)	70°49·8'	70°54·5' (70°54·6')	4·7 towards (4·8 towards)	198°	288°/108°
(7)	54°44'	77°49·8'	49°12·4'(W)	50°04·9'	49°58' (49°58·2')	6·9 away (6·7 away)	255°	345°/165°
(8a)	43°14'	66°44·4'	55°56·2'(E)	50°10'	50°12' (50°11·8')	2·0 towards (1·8 towards)	082°	172°/352°
(8b)	longitude at noon 32°53·5'E							
(9a)	44°55'	92°01'	47°19·3'(W)	63°21·4'	63°02' (63°02·2')	19·4 away (19·2 away)	236°	146°/326°
(9b)	45°10'	81°14·2'	19°35·7'(E)	40°08·3'	39°51' (39°51·2')	17·3 away (17·1 away)	149°	059°/239°

latitude and longitude at time of star observation = 45°14'N, 35°32'W.

ANSWERS

(1) (a) lat 54°21·8′N, long 36°06·3′E   (b) lat 20°40·6′S, long 173°13·2′W
    (c) lat 35°18·2′N, long 72°49·9′E

(2) 1st position lat 44°31·4′N, long 16°39·3′W
    2nd position lat 44°50·6′N, long 16°19·4′W

(3) lat 54°28′S, long 06°54·2′E

(4) lat 20°08′N, long 16°09·4′E

(5) 0900 lat 44°49·4′S, long 18°41·2′E
    1030 lat 44°38·9′S, long 18°20·9′E

(6) 1st position lat 10°23′N, long 12°14·5′W
    2nd position lat 10°36·7′N, long 11°59·1′W.

Exercise XII(a)

(1) sunrise 0542 L.M.T. sunset 1804 L.M.T.

(2) 0510 L.M.T.

(3) sunrise 0551½ L.M.T. sunset 1755½ L.M.T.

(4) 0432 L.M.T.

(5) (a) 1^h32^m (b) 0^h45^m.

Exercise XII(b)

(1) (a) 49·7 ft   (b) 0455 G.M.T.

(2) (a) 33·4 ft   (b) 1225 G.M.T.

(3) (a) −11·3 ft   (b) 0927 G.M.T.

(4) (a) −19·3 ft   (b) 1458 G.M.T.

(5) (a) −9·3 ft   (b) 1537 G.M.T.

index